EAA
AVIATI
FOUNDA

First printed 1997— Second printing (revised) 1980— Third printing (revised) 1992— Fourth printing (revised) 1996— Fifth printing (revised) 1999.

Printed by Action Printing Company
Fond du Lac, WI

THE
SPORTPLANE BUILDER

Aviation Foundation

THE SPORTPLANE BUILDER

Aircraft Construction Methods

tony bingelis

EDITOR
David A. Rivers

COVER DESIGN
Joan N. Rivers

Illustrated by the Author

**DEDICATED TO
MY WIFE MORINE**

acknowledgements

This book was written at the request and with the the encouragement of many builders, friends and correspondents who share my interest in building and flying airplanes for the sport of it.

Through the years many people have contributed to this book by giving advice, making comments and suggestions, or by providing useful information or references. I wish to express my appreciation to them.

There is always the risk of inadvertently overlooking some who deserve recognition, but after more than two decades of involvement in building, flying and writing about airplanes, how can one really do justice in this respect? Certainly, I must single out the following: Rollin C. Caller, Jim Carter, Donald Childs, Harold "Pop" Emigh, Chris Falconar, Bill Fleming, Seth Hancock, Frank Luft, James C. McCausland, Jr., Jay Miller, Luke Nall, Jim Newman, Bill Phy, H. Probyan, John Selgrath, Bob Serack, and Dr. Ronald O. Stearman.

My special thanks to my editor, David A. Rivers, for his encouragement and courage in undertaking the editing of this book, whereby its readability was increased while its bulk was decreased, and to Joan N. Rivers for her handsome cover design.

Tony Bingelis

forward

Like most beginning pilots, I made my first solo flight in a mass-produced, look-alike, 2-seat trainer. Nothing exotic. Still, that solo was fantastic — almost a religious experience. Immediately I wanted to get one of those little birds and spend the rest of my life transcending worldly cares. The price tag jolted me back to earth. That modestly equipped Cessna 150 cost nearly as much as my house.

Now you can understand why I was among the excited spectators at the airport last summer who watched Tony take his latest hand-built airplane, a 2-place Piel Emeraude, on its maiden flight. It seemed the perfect solution for people like me who want to fly but have been priced out of the market.

The French-designed Emeraude is the sixth plane Tony has built. It's made of wood, and its total construction cost was one-third that of the cheapest 2-seat, store-bought airplane. As Tony turned onto the runway and started his takeoff roll, the grin on his face was wing tip to wing tip. And when he pointed his nose skyward, my spirits lifted with him. Suddenly I understood what makes him and thousands like him spend 300 to 3,000 manhours each putting together one of these aerodynamic jigsaw puzzles. It's more than just good financial common sense. There is also an unmatched feeling of accomplishment when you challenge the elements in a machine you have constructed.

This manual will help you to successfully mount that challenge. Its contents represent the knowledge and experience gained in nearly a lifetime of interest in aviation. Tony's first "airplane" was a primary glider, which he built at age 17. His next project was an Emeraude, followed by a Scooter, a Volksplane, a Turner T-40, and the present airplane, an improved Emeraude. He has also built boats, bows, furniture and other gadgets in an effort to satisfy what he calls "a driving obsession to build."

To fill time between obsessions, he has resorted to regular jobs, as pilot and glider pilot, flight instructor, weather instructor, navigation instructor, helicopter theory-of-flight instructor, aircraft mechanic, aircraft inspector, aircraft maintenance officer and airport program administrator.

He has been a regular contributor of technical articles on aircraft construction to the Experimental Aircraft Association's SPORT AVIATION magazine. The first appeared in February 1972, and the column has been a regular feature ever since. Tony has become internationally known for his expertise in aircraft construction, and for his ability to bring light-hearted wit and easy comprehension to complex technical data.

This book contains the kind of information about aircraft construction methods and techniques that only the old pros know. With this manual and some manual labor, you too can fight the high cost of flying . . . . and have a beautiful little bird to show for your efforts.

February 1979   David A. Rivers

contents

(Photo by Lee Fray)

INTRODUCTION TO HOMEBUILTS

What Airplane Shall I Build ?

Perhaps you think that's an easy question to answer. I assure you it isn't. There are a number of factors to consider.

Some people have built a particular airplane simply because someone gave them the plans, or because they bought them cheaply or on a whim.

I know several people who are building because some friend talked them into building, either on a partnership basis or as an opportunity to build a second airplane sharing the same plans. I don't think much of this plans sharing bit, however. . . . too much can go wrong. I believe that each builder should buy his own set of plans and keep them as long as he owns the airplane.

Then there is the builder who happens to have an engine and only one design he is familiar with can handle such an engine.

Another situation that is common is the one in which a builder obtains a partially completed project that has been abandoned and given away or sold by someone else.

You can see that, so far, none of these conditions require great mental effort . . . . it is just a matter of backing into a project. No selection is involved other than permitting yourself to say yes or no. However, if you do not have a project to back into and you do want to build, how do you change that vague longing into a specific design?

There are so many nice designs that it's too bad everyone couldn't have at least two airplanes, one for weekdays and the other for weekends.

To make a satisfactory selection while retaining at least a modicum of objectivity, you must ask yourself some direct questions and answer them truthfully.

WHAT ABOUT A SINGLE–SEATER?

Should you build a single-seater rather than a 2-4 seater? Well, do you like to fly alone? Are you essentially a loner at heart? Are you most intrigued with the tiny airplanes? Are you in a hurry to get something built and flying? Is cost more important to you than being able to carry a passenger? Do you intend to use a VW or a 65 hp engine no matter what design you select? Is your workshop very small with no chance to expand the work area? Do you think that, as a rule, the small homebuilts are faster than the bigger jobs? Is a single-place easier to hangar and handle on the ground? Do you think single-seaters more attractive than the bigger aircraft?

HOW ABOUT A ROOMY 2–4 PLACE PLANE?

Now, just to establish your impartiality, why not ask yourself these questions? Do you like to have company when you fly? Would you let somebody else fly your airplane? How about your mate? Your youngsters may just be wild about flying. Do you

Would you like a nice, roomy 2-seat touring machine? (Emeraude)

think it would be just as easy to build a bigger airplane? Are you prepared to go the costs of a larger engine? Are you a pretty big individual physically? Do you like plenty of elbow room? Would a multi-seater job be more practical and useful to you than a single-placer? Can a 2-placer or 4-placer be just as much fun as a single-seat bird? Are the 2-4 place planes more sophisticated looking? Do you like to take long trips by air over the weekend? Does it seem to you that there is a better selection to choose from among the multi-seater aircraft? Do you think it more prestigious to own a 2-seater? Do you believe that most 2-place and 4-place homebuilts are often just as fast as most single-seat types? You can always sell a multi-seater easier than a single-seater, right?

WHAT'S THE VERDICT, DOC?

These questions are mostly rhetorical of course, but just think back over your responses. Which of the two categories of aircraft had the most positive answers in your own personal survey? Did you hedge on some of the questions?

If you had equally positive responses to both the single-place and the multi-seat questions, you need an impartial arbitrator.

I'll volunteer to act as tie-breaker for you. My conclusion is this. If you are so equally divided in your own mind, I recommend that you build a 2-place airplane and fly alone. Otherwise, I'm sure you already know your preference.

WHAT TYPE OF CONSTRUCTION TO CHOOSE

Your basic choices include all-metal, all-wood, composites (foam and fiberglass or dynel), or mixed construction (steel tube and fabric). Actually each of these classifications is somewhat misleading because aluminum, steel sheet, tubing and wood are to be found in practically any project. The descriptive grouping is one of convenience and only serves to identify the material that is used in the greatest quantity in that particular project.

I think most people who have piddled around a workshop of their own have had, as a rule, more experience working with wood than with metal. Many who build boats and birdhouses, and those who like to build airplane models, will probably want to build in wood or work with composite materials. Anyone who has grown up as a hot rod fancier has probably tinkered a lot with engines and welding. These areas of experience are very useful assets to an airplane builder even though welding on heavy structural steel is not the same as welding thin-walled aircraft tubing. But at least the basic skill is there.

It may be that, by occupation, you would be ideally suited to undertaking an all-metal project.

How about a roomy, rugged, all-metal single-seater?
(Pazmany PL-4)

Maybe you'd like to design your own one-of-a-kind airplane? (Ray Hegy's Chuporosa)

Maybe a simple, ultra-light week-end putt-putt would interest you? (Flaglor Scooter)

Don't think that working in aluminum requires super skills and some very expensive equipment. It does not. The few bends needed for long pieces can often be farmed out to the local tin shop and done under your anxious supervision. Most other functions can be handled by you. If you don't know how to weld, don't let that deter you from selecting a tube and fabric design, if the design appeals to you. You can easily learn to weld as you go along, using plenty of metal scraps for practice. If you really intend to be open minded about all of this, consider these general assumptions:

Anyone handy with hand tools could probably work just as well with metal as with wood unless he has had considerable experience with woodworking tools and woodworking methods. Actually, anyone not handy with tools can probably do a better job with an all-metal project. When working in metal, all you need to learn is how to cut it, bend it, file it, drill it, and rivet or bolt it together. Working with a wood project, on the other hand, requires that you learn how to select acceptable pieces of wood; know how to use a variety of cutting tools (and how to keep them sharp); how to steam or soak and bend wood; how to laminate, glue and prepare the wood surfaces; how to cover and protect the wood with fabric coverings; how to guard against improperly drained areas; develop techniques for drilling, filing, sanding, and then bolting the numerous wood pieces together. Wood structures are always more complicated and require more steps to complete than metal components. An aircraft with mixed construction contains both the desirable and undesirable features of both metal and wood construction.

Interest in the use of composite materials and structures is growing at an astonishing rate. It is an exciting and relatively easy medium for building an aircraft quickly. There is one word of caution, however. The epoxy resins utilized in composite-type construction can be absorbed through the skin, causing severe skin reactions in some people. You may be one of them so check it out first.

The type of construction you select does not matter too much if you are a relatively inexperienced workshop newcomer. Conversely, if you are a skilled woodworker, wood will likely be your preference unless you want to expand your experience into other skills.

The same holds true of metal work. Pick the type of construction with which you feel you will be most comfortable. It could be that the deciding factor will be the type of workshop equipment you have at your disposal.

Don't think for one moment that you have to

Ah! A seaplane?　　　　　(Baby Ace on floats)

Why not an advanced-concept, fast 3-seater?
　　　　　　　　　　　　　(Dyke Delta)

. . . . And then there is some new design that catches your eye, right?　　　　(Taylor Bird)

(Photo by Dick Stouffer)

buy a whole passel of machines to build an airplane.
You do not. Don't buy a bench saw, for example,
just to rip out a couple of spars and a few strips of
wood. This is not good economy. That saw might sit
for months before you ever find use for it again.

DECIDE ON THE CONFIGURATION

We are now to a point where we can isolate different types of aircraft. The basic choices, of course
are biplanes, low-wing types, mid-wing types, and
high-wingers. These come in open and closed cockpit
versions and that, unfortunately, does not make your
choice any easier. The options, quite naturally, are
yours for the making.

Those who really want to build a biplane, would
never settle for anything else. They like biplanes,
they like the open cockpit, and no doubt, they have
the secret aspiration of becoming another aerobatics
ace. What most of them blissfully choose to ignore
is the extra work and expense in building extra wings.
A biplane has four sets of wing sections to build (give
or take one), right? If you can overlook this handicap
then the biplane is for you . . . . so look no further.

All of the mid-wingers seem to be either aerobatic or racer-like in their characteristics (single-place
to boot). This makes it easy to determine if mid-wing
suits your fancy. The mid-wingers lend themselves
very nicely to speed and streamlining but require
agility in mounting and are pretty poor birds for sight
seeing.

The high-wingers and the low-wingers each have
their disciples and it just about comes down to which
seems best in your mind. A high-wing aircraft is a bit
more efficient, you can sit in the shade of its wing,
have things nice for sight seeing and, in the traffic
pattern, worry about some low-wing job letting down
on top of you. Visibility above is usually restricted
in high-wing aircraft.

The low-wingers boast that their configuration
is more modern, easier to handle in rough crosswinds,
easy to get into, lets you get a better tan, and you can,
if so inclined, sit around and worry that you might be
letting down on a high-winger. Visibility below a
low-winger is very restricted.

TOO HOT TO HANDLE?

By now you should have narrowed your preference to a point where there are not too many
designs to choose from.

Now is the time to consider your skill as a pilot.
If you are the average low-time weekend pilot, don't
even consider one of the hotter fast birds that are
available. Build an airplane you will enjoy flying. If
you have no access to an airport with a paved runway,
stay away from the hot little tomatoes with the small

Which popular biplane has excellent plans and
instructions too? (EAA Acrosport)

Perhaps a proven wood 2-seater with a 9G. structure?
(Jodel F-11 modification)

Say, why not a fast, reliable 2-seat homebuilt classic?
(Whitman Tailwind)

If it has to be a biplane, wouldn't a 2-holer be better?
(Steen Skybolts)

Wouldn't an ultra-modern single-seater and 2-seater make a nice set?
(Quickie and Varieze)

Need something out of the ordinary? (Varieze)

A good, solid, all-metal cruiser for two? (Zenith)

Worried about fuel? An ultra-light original can be different.
(Al Backstrom's Flying Plank)

Like to visit the bush country? Fish? Swim? Hunt? (Coot Amphibian)

Wouldn't a nice, 2-seater sporty biplane with classical lines be nice? Now, do you prefer it in the open cockpit version, or with the sedate, all-weather canopy?
(Starduster Too)

Have that Red Baron complex, do you?
(Fokker Triplane DR-1)

Why not a bit of nostalgia from the 1930s? It's easy to build in wood.
(Pietenpol)

How about a fresh-air 2-seater for a sight-seeing platform? (Woody Pusher)

Want to go fast in a 4-seater with built-in shade?
(Bede 4)

Want to go all the way with a sophisticated retractable. This one is mostly of wood.
(Cavelier modified)

Want to fly like a bird?
(Easy Rider)

Isn't this something? An advanced- concept 2-seater that is fast, slow and comfortable.

(Variviggen)

A simple, VW-powered job?
(Volksplane II modified)

Want to go fast in style?
(Mustang II)

A conservative, open-air for one, sir?   (Baby Ace)

How about a tiny, all-metal job?   (Windwagon)

Looking for an all-metal 2-seater?   This one is well-engineered.
(Pazmany PL-2)

wheels and tires. If your runway is short, pick a design that gets off quickly. Why build something you can't use safely and conveniently?

If possible, try to look at a set of plans for the airplane you would like to build. It could be that the plans are not very detailed or may be of poor quality. This can be a serious hinderance to a novice builder.

Don't let the cost of the plans exercise any influence at all in deciding what airplane to build. Let me emphasize that point. Don't permit yourself to think "I'd sure like to build that bird but the plans cost too much." If you do that, you may be a real loser. The cost of the plans become insignificant by the time you complete your project. Remember, an airplane may be under construction for several years. The redeeming feature of that condition is that the costs are also distributed over a like period. Heck, I used to spend more money on cigars than it cost me to build my last project. That's figuring about 5 cigars a day. If you just happen to like a design for which the plans are available at a modest cost, lucky you. If not, and you have to pay $150 for a set of plans, so what? After all, prorated over the length of the project, that's not much.

LET'S SEE NOW . . . . .

First, I have assumed that if you ever intend to build an airplane the best time to begin is as soon as possible no matter how severe the limitations on your spare time. If that is your decision too, all that remains is to determine whether you are most attracted to a single-place job or to a 2–4 place airplane. After having considered the type of construction that best suits you, as well as the type of configuration of air-

craft that tickled your fancy, your selection should be narrowed to a point where only a few designs will satisfy your requirements. The final step in your selection process is to assure yourself that the performance demands and characteristics of the airplane of your choice are within the comfort range of your own piloting skill and experience level.

Before you plunk down your money for some plans, why not do a little talking first? That's right, look up your local Experimental Aircraft Association (EAA) chapter and visit with some of the members who are building. Ask some questions. If possible, try to find a local EAA Designee. He will do his best to help you resolve whatever questions you might have.

PARTING SHOT

Now, if after all this sage discourse, you choose to select a design that merely appeals to your senses, what's so wrong with that? How can anyone argue with that kind of rational? It is always easier to do something that you want to do than it is to do what you should do . . . . so, why not build it?

Just one more observation. If you have ever in your life entertained the thought that you would someday like to build an airplane, you probably already regret that you didn't do it years ago when you were a lot younger. How young could it have been? I know a couple of gents 13 and 14 years of age who are busy at their first projects. Why wait until you are 50 or 60 to start? Remember, whatever age you are now, you will be some years older when you finish, even if you start today.

Time's awasting!

Pick one and take-off. . . .
(Emeraude)

28

Obtaining Parts and Materials

It seems that, sooner or later, just about any builder you talk with these days will say something like, "Man, if I only had the money to buy all new stuff for my project. I'd really have it made." Maybe, but it still takes one heck of a lot of determination, motivation, and persistence to build an airplane, new parts and materials notwithstanding.

NEW MATERIALS AND PARTS

First, (quite hastily too) let me assure you that having a complete collection of new materials and parts for a project would indeed be wonderful, and a guy would have to be some kind of a nut to use old stuff if he had the choice.

However, you folks who have already finished your first homebuilt, as well as those of you who are deep into a project, know full well that, while new parts and new materials are nice, they are no substitute for good workmanship. It is possible to do a lousy job even with new materials.

Something else needs to be said about new parts and new materials. They too, come in wrong types, sizes, and shapes. Unfortunately, even new parts can be defective, although most often this can be attributed to poor quality control during manufacture or packing and shipping. Therefore, do not allow yourself to be lulled into comfortable complacency just because your parts are all new. The careful builder must never overlook the need to inspect new parts and materials.

The ready availability and use of new parts would, of course, permit you to proceed at a much more rapid building pace with your project. And, at least until everything is painted over, it should look nicer than a similar project put together with hand-me-down parts.

SERVICEABLE USED PARTS

I often rationalized to myself that the best thing about used parts (besides the dollar savings) was the extra "education" that I automatically received. Certainly, before using a second-hand set of wheels and brakes, for example, the smart builder will clean, disassemble, and inspect them; replace worn, cracked or broken parts; and finally, reassemble and paint everything as necessary. Now, if that isn't educational, what is? If, on the other hand, a set of new wheels and brakes were in your grasp, you would not be as likely to check into them to the same extent . . . . now would you?

Other serviceable equipment is frequently found at reduced prices and is advertised as "used, re-manufactured, overhauled, etc." If obtained from a reputable outfit, the parts will usually be adequate for use.

As for the surplus hardware, most of it will be found satisfactory after a good cleaning and a close inspection. However, it would be mighty comforting to you later on if you knew you had new bolts in your wing attach fittings, in the landing gear fittings, and in your propeller. The same advice goes for used control cables or cables for wire-braced wings.

Without a doubt almost every homebuilt flying has a few surplus or used parts in its structure. Sometimes, it isn't a matter of cost but rather a problem of availability. In some sections of our country it is very difficult to obtain any kind of aircraft materials or parts. For this reason alone, it doesn't pay to be a loner. EAA chapter member/builders collectively have an unbelievable amount of materials and information. This includes good sources of supply.

THE NOT–SO–GOOD STUFF

All used parts of unknown origin are suspect and I hope that your own standards for quality control call for a leisurely and careful inspection in a well-lighted area before using them. Parts from a cracked up aircraft may be a bargain or they may be an invitation to another mishap. Here is where the extra eyeball power of a magnifying glass can be useful. In addition, your area EAA Designee can be of considerable assistance in helping you to examine such questionable parts. I am sure that in the case of critical steel components, a magnaflux inspection would probably be suggested by the Designee, and rightly so. If the slightest doubt arises regarding whether or not to use a part . . . . throw it away and forget it. Remember, an aircraft that has crashed has been subjected to sudden deceleration, impact, and high loads. No telling where a failure may show up as a result. Check and recheck.

USED MATERIALS (WOOD)

The most commonly used old wood materials are those obtained by salvaging old spars. Builders rip up the stuff for wing rib cap strips and for other strip stock. If the old spar is from a cracked up aircraft, it should not be used for spar stock in your project. Anyway, chances are the old spar will have some bolt holes in it that are not needed in your airplane.

Most FAA inspectors are rather aghast after viewing a spar with old bolt holes plugged with wood dowels. There have been too many cases in the past where a defective or split spar was not detected until too late.

In addition to the unknown element of risk, there are other disadvantages to using old wing spars for material. The old varnish and overlooked old nails really dull saw blades in a hurry. The resharpening of a 10-inch bench saw blade, these days, costs plenty. The material in old spars is often so old and dry that it splits easily. If you intend to make wing ribs out of the stuff and glue and nail your gussets on, you may wind up with a lot of split ends in the uprights. Furthermore, the job of ripping an old spar is very time consuming and there is a great amount of waste because of drilled holes, tapers, plates and bevels.

Now you know what I believe to be a few drawbacks to the use of old spars for materials. So in negotiating the price for an old spar or two, I hope you will have a better idea of what its real value would be to you.

On the other hand, well-selected wood from old spars is just as strong today as it was when it went into the original aircraft. As a matter of fact, because its moisture content might be somewhat lower now, its strength could actually turn out to be a bit higher. Just be sure to give it a thorough inspection before using any part of it.

USED MATERIALS (METAL)

How about used metal and tubing? Fine. Go ahead and use it if it is the right size, if it is in good condition, and if it is the correct material as called for in your plans.

When your plans call for 4130 steel tubing, that is what you should use. There is always a builder who just happens to have an old fuselage with some of the correct size tubing in it. However, unless you know for sure that the material in the old fuselage is 4130, you can get into trouble later. Some old birds used a much weaker 1025 carbon steel in parts of their structure.

Another possible source of trouble is old aluminum. If you don't know what specification it is, don't use it. Maybe these soft commercial grades of aluminum have a place in aircraft construction, but it certainly is not in structural parts. That goes for leading edges and cowlings too. It is bad news and the soft ding-prone metal makes for a doggy-looking bird in a matter of weeks after you have finished it.

SALVAGE A PLANE FOR PARTS

If the project costs are of paramount importance and you must keep the dollar cost for new parts to a minimum, consider a salvage job. As is the case with everything else, there will be good points as well as bad points to consider.

The idea is to purchase a wind- or hail-damaged airplane and salvage it completely for parts. The success of this type of venture depends upon a number of quality factors already mentioned. Before buying such an aircraft, consider carefully all alternatives. The more parts that you can use from the salvage aircraft, the more you can afford to pay for it. Most important, perhaps, is that it should have a usable engine. The engine can be a high-time one but, preferably, one that has not been subjected to a sudden stoppage accident or a major overhaul hundreds of hours ago. A low-time engine, naturally, would be a real find. You can figure on putting in at least several hundred dollars in overhauling the engine even if it doesn't have some cracked cylinders, a crankshaft to replace, or some other major defect.

In a salvage airplane you can get (besides the engine) the propeller (maybe), a minimum set of instruments, wheels and brakes, tail wheel or nosewheel assembly, and maybe a radio as well as a couple of pots full of miscellaneous hardware and parts. Items like primer pumps, strainers, rod end bearings, turnbuckles, controls, seats, gas tank, plumbing and all kinds of other odds and ends cost plenty when bought new or in small quantities.

Let me repeat it. The more parts you can use, the higher the price you can afford to consider for the salvage bird. Don't be too eager or too generous in your offer as you may not be able to use as many parts in your project as you think. Of course, any parts not needed by you might have a ready market with other homebuilders.

Buying the salvage package should give you most of what you need at less than half the price you would have to pay if you bought each item one by one. Sounds good, doesn't it? So what can be bad about it? Well, consider the following: To buy a salvage airplane, you will have to have a large sum of cash to spend all at once. Would you be prepared to put out about $2,500 to $4,500 at one time? Another thing, when you buy it, it is yours, and you'd better be prepared to haul it away . . . . to your own home most likely. How would your wife and neighbors react to a big junk airplane in the yard? After much work and after you have stripped the thing, then what do you do with the hulk? Of course if some of the components (wings, tail surfaces, etc.) are in good condition, they can be sold.

Well, those are some of the important things to consider before taking the plunge. The idea is sound, and for some sharp traders, very effective and re-warding. Still, unless you are careful you may be buying a hunk of junk that is, for the most part, unusable for your particular project. Remember, there are a lot of professional operators in the salvage business and they know how to buy and sell right (for their own profit).

Costs are a very real concern for most of us in this inflated economy, but never lose sight of the fact that the cost of your parts or materials must take second consideration to aircraft quality standards. After all, you are not building a go-cart or a birdhouse. Someday you'll be climbing into that thing and getting way up high in the sky with it.

**It might look like junk
to some people, but . . .**

(Photo by David Rivers)

You and the FAA

To obtain your homebuilt's original airworthiness certification you must prepare the airplane so that it will comply with certain rules applicable specifically to amateur-built aircraft. Fortunately, these rules are basically the same as they have been since the inception of the amateur-built program. However, to complicate matters, you also have to comply with elements of various Federal Aviation Regulations (FARs) governing the operation of all types of aircraft. Here's a brief overview of the requirements.

To begin with, any aircraft you present for certification must be in compliance with the 51% rule (reference FAR Part 21, Section 21.191 and Advisory Circular AC20-28A, Nationally Advertised Construction Kits, Amateur Built Aircraft). In short, you must have completed more than half of the construction yourself in order for your project to be eligible for certification under the amateur-built category.

If you purchase a kit, you should first check with the FAA to determine if that particular kit is eligible. That is, no more than 50% of the parts and construction are prefabricated. If you don't check beforehand and if all that will be needed on your part is a tinker-toy assembly effort, beware! You may be in for a tough time proving that you did, indeed, build at least 51% of the aircraft. Though you may consider the rule a bit severe, the amateur-built category was authorized as an individual education and recreation program and not as a shortcut way of acquiring an airplane to fly. Besides, the rule also has the purpose of preventing anyone from getting a bunch of airplane components and sticking them together into some sort of hybrid airplane.

If you do purchase a fairly complete kit for your project, you should have a signed invoice from the manufacturer of the kit as evidence of ownership. Those of you who build from scratch should keep all of the major bills and invoices as you will also have to establish evidence of ownership for your creation.

For the benefit of those of you who expect to field a homebuilt for the first time, and as a timely review for others who are coming up for the second or third time, let's continue with the essentials easily overlooked or slighted in the preparation for that original certification inspection. These include:
- Aircraft Log Book
- Registration Documentation
- Passenger Warning Placard
- Experimental Placard
- Minimum Instrumentation
- Aircraft Weight and Balance Data
- Other:
    Instrument Markings
    Radio Station License
    ELT
    Cockpit Checklist
    Pilot/Passenger Restraints

Although the foregoing may not, in your estimation, be items that affect the safety of flight, compliance is required by the rules of the land. In some respects, however, these items may, indeed, have a bearing on the safety of an "unsuspecting public"...and that is a matter of prime concern to the FAA. So let's take a look at each requirement in order to better understand its application and purpose.

Aircraft Log Book

There must be an Aircraft Log Book. In it you will record or have recorded all of the significant details regarding the aircraft's construction and inspections. It is your log book and you can enter into it anything you deem important or of future value. It must be maintained for the life of the aircraft. Separate engine and propeller log books are not required. Simply include engine and propeller data in your Aircraft Log Book.

For years, homebuilders have enjoyed an informal monitoring of their projects by the FAA. This monitoring was, actually, at the invitation and request of the builder. During these FAA visits the builder had an opportunity to ask all sorts of questions and receive timely reminders of things yet to be done. At some time during the visit, the FAA inspector would endorse, in the builder's Aircraft Log Book, some indications of the progress he was making. An entry such as "wing (fuselage, spar, tail surfaces, etc.) O.K. to close." Finally, after all of the aircraft structure had been completed, the builder would again call for an inspection. This time it was the long awaited "pre-cover inspection". It, too, was duly recorded in the Aircraft Log Book by the FAA with a notation like, "O.K. to cover."

Although the inspection ritual varied in number from FAA Region to FAA Region, the average homebuilt would have been subjected to at least 3 inspections before it found itself on the airport tarmac ready for that long awaited moment...its original certification.

The number of inspections performed by the FAA kept declining, and by the end of 1984 intermediate inspections had ended.

There will no longer be any other than an original certification inspection. It behooves all builders, therefore, to immediately start maintaining a construction log complete with dates and remarks similar to the type formerly entered by the FAA inspector. A more detailed separate construction log to supplement the brief entries in the Aircraft Log Book is highly recommended as would be photos taken of select construction highlights.

Aircraft Registration

All aircraft must be registered with the FAA before they can legally be flown in the U.S. About 6 months before your aircraft's estimated completion date you should write to the FAA (FAA Aircraft Registry, DOT, P.O. Box 25504, Oklahoma City, OK 73125) and request an identification number for your aircraft. You will be assigned some random number. If you prefer, you could request a particular number (a special number costs $10) and it will be assigned if it is available. Anyway, if you carefully followed their instructions you will, before long, have a permanent Aircraft Registration, AC Form 8050-3 or, pending its receipt, should have kept the temporary pink copy of the Aircraft Registration Application, AC Form 8050-1, which you had submitted to the FAA at Oklahoma City. One or the other should be on display in your cockpit or cabin.

The N-number (identification number) assigned to your aircraft must be affixed to the aircraft in the proper manner and location. Your guidance for this is FAR Part 21, Section 21.192 and FAR Part 45.

Essentially, a homebuilt may display its N-number in 3 inch block numerals and letters. They must be of a color that contrasts with the background and be legible. This means no fancy script or ornamentation.

Here's something else to think about. **If you make big talk that your snappy little homebuilt is extra fast and has a top speed of over 180 knots (207 mph), you will have to affix the standard 12 inch numerals...not the 3 inch size still permitted for ordinary amateur built aircraft.**

The markings must be displayed horizontally. On twin tail jobs (VariEze, Long-EZ, etc.) both outside surfaces must display the numbers. Single tail aircraft, of course, must be marked on both sides of the vertical tail surface. If you prefer, you could put the markings on the fuselage sides between the trailing edge of the wing and the leading edge of the stabilizer (conventional aircraft). If you have a peculiar problem due to insufficient structural surface, you had better make a call to your nearest FAA MIDO for instructions before applying for your certification inspection. The correct display of the N-number is an important requirement and non-compliance could mean certification will be denied until that discrepancy is remedied.

Identification/Data Plate

You must have an identification plate and it must be affixed in accordance with the same guidance governing the display of the registration numbers (FAR Part 45 and FAR Part 21, Section 21.182a).

It must be a fireproof plate. An aluminum plate of the type sold through some homebuilder supply sources is not considered as "fireproof" and, therefore, would be unacceptable.

NOTE: The EAA sells the proper type of Identification Plate and Passenger Warning Placard (stainless steel) as a set.

Your data plate information must be etched on, engraved or marked by some means that would assure its durability and fireproof qualities. If you prefer to make your own data plate, refer to FAR Part 45, Section 45.13 for the information that must be included.

The rules require that the Identification Plate be secured in such a manner that it will not likely be defaced or removed during normal service, or be lost or destroyed in an accident. It must be secured to the aircraft at an accessible location near an entrance. Almost any place in the cockpit or cabin is O.K. if it is readable by a person on the ground (of course, the airplane must also be on the ground). As an alternate choice, you could affix the data plate externally on the fuselage in the vicinity of the tail...if it can be easily viewed while the aircraft is on the ground.

A Data/Identification Plate is a major requirement so don't slight it.

Passenger Warning Placard

As mentioned earlier, the Identification Plate and the Passenger Warning Placard can be obtained as a very attractive set from EAA Headquarters finished in glossy black on a stainless steel background.

I guess it is very apparent that the purpose of the placard is to warn any member of the public who is about to embark in the aircraft, that he is about to be airborne in an experimental airplane and not in one of the common production-line models built according to the stringent safety standards established for the aircraft industry.

Your Passenger Warning Placard must be permanently installed in the cockpit in full view of all the occupants.

This is taken to mean that the placard is located on the instrument panel where the passenger (and the pilot) can stare at it and reflect on the wisdom of flying in an airplane bearing the stark testimonial:

PASSENGER WARNING - THIS AIRCRAFT IS AMATEUR-BUILT AND DOES NOT COMPLY WITH FEDERAL SAFETY REGULATIONS FOR STANDARD AIRCRAFT.

Kind of makes one think, doesn't it? And yes, the placard is necessary in a single seater, too. No placard. No certification.

Another note - don't forget that FAR Part 91 Section 91.42 pertaining to aircraft with experimental certificates requires you to "advise each person carried of the experimental nature of the aircraft..." (Passenger Warning Placard notwithstanding.)

Weight and Balance Data

Not only does the FAA require a weight and balance check as part of your certification documentation, it is a required part of your permanent aircraft records. Do your weighing and figuring before you call for the certification inspection to assure yourself that the aircraft balance is within limits.

Minimum Instrumentation

As you may not have been formally introduced to the required instrumentation for any aircraft, allow me to present it now:
- Airspeed Indicator
- Altimeter
- Magnetic Direction Indicator (compass, that is)
- Tachometer (one for each engine)
- Oil Pressure Gauge (for any engine using an oil pressure system)
- Oil Temperature Gauge (for any air cooled engine is installed)
- Fuel Quantity Indicator (for each tank)
- Landing Gear Position Indicator (for a retractable gear)

Although FAR Part 91 speaks only of the instrumentation required in standard category aircraft and is silent on the subject of amateur-built aircraft, Advisory Circular AC20-27B (as will its successor, I'm sure) gently remind you that it would be appropriate for your amateur-built to be equipped to conform with the applicable paragraphs of FAR Part 91 Section 91.33. Since you will be operating your aircraft in accordance with FAR Part 91, General Operating and Flight Rules, be convinced that the minimum instrumentation requirement does apply to your homebuilt, too.

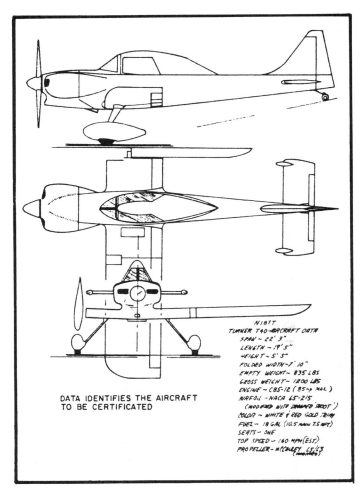

DATA IDENTIFIES THE AIRCRAFT TO BE CERTIFICATED

N187T
TURNER T40-AIRCRAFT DATA
SPAN ~ 22' 3"
LENGTH ~ 19' 5"
HEIGHT ~ 5' 5"
FOLDED WIDTH ~ 7' 10"
EMPTY WEIGHT ~ 835 LBS
GROSS WEIGHT ~ 1200 LBS
ENGINE ~ C85-12 (85 HP MAX)
AIRFOIL - NACA 65-215
(MODIFIED WITH DROOPED SNOOT)
COLOR - WHITE & RED GOLD TRIM
FUEL ~ 18 GAL (10.5 MAIN 7.5 AFT)
SEATS ~ ONE
TOP SPEED ~ 160 MPH (EST.)
PROPELLER - MCCAULEY 55/53 (MODIFIED)

Incidentally, although you might not consider it very important for a homebuilt putt-putt to have a magnetic compass, it is required. Not only that, it must also be graced with a compass correction card displayed nearby or on the compass. If you don't have one, the FAA inspector could rightfully conclude that your airplane is not yet ready for flight.

Experimental Placard

The Experimental Placard we have to put on our homebuilts is a source of great annoyance to some builders and an object of pride to others. However, the rules don't care whether you are annoyed or happy over having to affix that placard in huge 2 inch letters. Here is where the first vestiges of builder dissent surface. Two inch letters? On a small homebuilt two inch letters look as out of place as a sumo wrestler playing in a kiddie playground sandbox. Still, that is the rule requirement. (Your reference is FAR Part 45.)

When the U.S. registration ("N" plus the registration number) is displayed on an experimental aircraft, the operator shall also display on that aircraft, near each entrance to the cabin or cockpit, the word EXPERIMENTAL in letters not less than 2 inches nor more that 6 inches in height. Another section, Section 45.21, requires that the letters be legible, of a contrasting color and be free of ornamentation.

That is pretty specific, isn't it? Letters almost 2 inches tall are not 2 inches tall, so consider yourself alterted to the requirement. As written, the rule does not require you to have a 2 inch EXPERIMENTAL placard on each side of the cockpit. It says..."near each entrance to the cabin or cockpit". If you have but one entrance (flip-over canopy), one sign would get you into compliance, wouldn't it?

Don't think for one minute that the inspector has to or will grant you a certificate if just this one little thing isn't right. If the EXPERIMENTAL placard is not properly affixed at the time of inspection, you are not ready for certification.

Other Important Items

It would be impossible to delve into the acceptable fabrication and assembly methods, techniques and practices that would assure the certification of your homebuilt in this short account. However, a few other important areas can be singled out for your attention.

Your aircraft must have an acceptable (fire resistant) firewall.

You should make a fuel flow test to assure yourself that the engine will get all the fuel it needs at full throttle and at a steep climb angle.

Better make provisions for carburetor heat or be ready to convince the inspector that your fuel metering system doesn't need one.

You will have to mark your instruments for the normal range of operation, or at least indicate the "limits".

Label all engine controls as to direction of movement. Your controls should operate in the customary or standard direction. That is, for full throttle, the "go handle" goes forward (not backward)...mixture control, forward for full rich, etc.

And how about pilot/passenger restraints? (You know, seat belts, shoulder harness...Figure on installing a good set)

Although it is the Federal Communications Commission's prime responsiblity and not the FAA's, will you need to have an ELT (Emergency Locator Transmitter) and Radio Station License from the FCC with your documentation?

If you don't overlook any of the items we have covered, you should be able to submit your APPLICATION FOR AIRWORTHINESS CERTIFICATE with confidence.

Date: _____

Federal Aviation Administration
Manufacturing Inspection D.O. #_____

_____

_____ Zip _____

Gentlemen:

Request Experimental Certificate of Airworthiness be issued for aircraft described below:

Make _____   Model _____

S/N _____   Reg. No. _____

The purpose of the experiment is _____

_____

_____

The estimated time required is _____

The areas over which the experiment will be conducted will be

_____

_____

_____

Signature _____

Title _____

Address _____

_____

The EAA

EXPERIMENTAL AIRCRAFT ASSOCIATION

This organization any homebuilder should join. For more than two decades, the EAA has been bringing together thousands of people with a common love — airplanes and flying. Today it is the world's largest sport aviation organization, and it appeals to those who fly and build all kinds of sport aircraft including powered hang gliders, racing, aerobatic and rotary wing aircraft.

The EAA offers its members (more than 167,000 membership cards have been issued to folks in 91 countries) a splendid magazine – SPORT AVIATION, a variety of technical publications, an aviation museum, and a number of educational activities.

Through the EAA you can get involved in all facets of aviation from the grass roots activities of building and flying sport planes locally, to attending the world's greatest sport aviation spectacular, Oshkosh, the annual EAA Sport Aviation Convention and Exhibition. Nowhere on earth has there ever been gathered such great varieties and numbers of aircraft. It is a sight to be seen and remembered.

The man who has nurtured and provided the dedicated leadership for this international group is its founder and current President, Paul H. Poberezny.

If you love flying and looking and talking aviation, you will never find an organization that fits better than the EAA.

EXPERIMENTAL AIRCRAFT ASSOCIATION
P.O. Box 3065
Oshkosh, Wisconsin 54903-2591
Phone: (920) 426-4800

The EAA Technical Counselor

Designees are now known as Technical Counselors.

.... He is , in our case, a designated individual with a proven broad technical background and an avowed desire to be of help to his fellow EAA members who are building. He is selected (designated) by his EAA chapter as its own technical advisor and then by the EAA, which after reviewing his background and his qualifications, and in recognition of his willingness to serve, issues the necessary credentials.

Today the EAA has a volunteer task force of more than 1,000 technical advisors serving as Designees and I would imagine that just about every chapter does have one. Some chapters have more than one, especially those with large memberships. The services of the chapter's Designee and the large pool of knowledge and talent that is readily available are among the benefits that accrue to the builder who joins the local chapter.

Unfortunately, many members live in areas where there isn't an EAA chapter. These EAA members do not have the opportunity of being able to visit other builders, examine their projects or talk with experienced builders as their own projects progress.

Even though the builder knows that a Designee has no official status or inspection authority with the federal government, he is usually happy to have the volunteer look over his work before he calls for an FAA inspection. This voluntary bit of work by the Designee can often save the builder and the FAA inspector from an awkward or embarrassing situation. Of course it is always difficult for the Designee to point out that some work may not be good enough to pass inspection but most of these gents are usually up to coping with such a situation should it arise. . . . in their usually wily, round about, devious, casual manner.

Many of the fine tips, ideas, and suggestions passed around among the local builders by Designees, are ultimately printed in both SPORT AVIATION (the EAA's official magazine) and in the various technical publications that are primarily for the benefit of the builder.

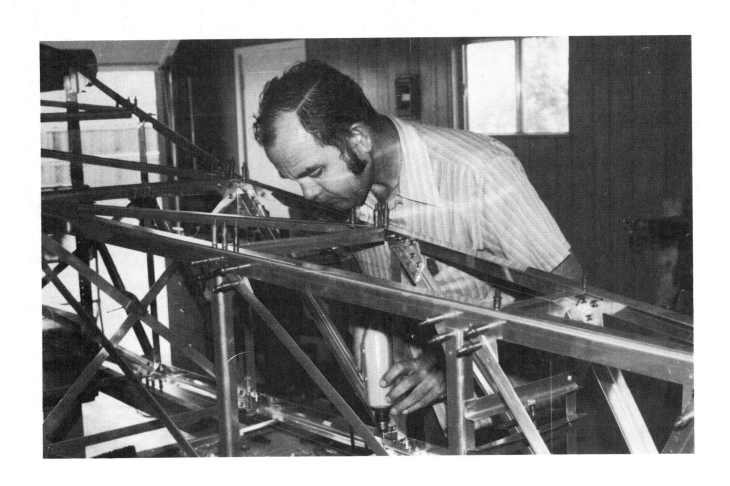

YOUR WORKSHOP

2

Cut the Clutter

Around EAA workshops, you find one of two very basic conditions. Either the workshop is crowded and cluttered with the makings of an airplane, or it is empty while the builder experiences the excruciating wait for plans or for the ordered materials.

Of course, there may be other conditions, but I'll wager that these two fit many more of us.

No matter what the status of your workshop, you probably can improve the conditions remarkably with just a little effort. If you are already deep into a project, it will be especially hard for you, even begrudgingly, to give up any work sessions to improve things around the shop. It could be worth it though.

Think about the problem for a minute. To build an airplane you need at least enough space to work on the fuselage, and later, on the wing(s). If space is very limited, it may mean that after you build the fuselage, it will have to be removed to some safe place for protective storage while you attack the wing construction. If you have the work space, naturally, you can afford the luxury of keeping the whole shebang together.

In the building of aircraft structures, you will be using a variety of materials and some tools and equipment. All of these occupy space .... valuable space. They are always in the way, or on top of whatever you need to get, or use, or find.

The materials, like tubing and longeron and spar stock, are long pieces and have a way of being around and in the way for a long time.... two or three years for example. Then there are the 4-ft. by 8-ft. sheets of plywood or aluminum. Boy, do they take up space. Last, engine parts, salvaged tubing, cables, pulleys, etc., etc., etc.

In the tool and equipment department you have, if you are fortunate or affluent, a band saw, drill press bench grinder, sanding disc, bench saw, and a welding rig. You may not consider yourself so fortunate after all when you have to provide the space for all of that stuff and your project too, in one very crowded workshop. Some of it, like the bench saw, may not be used for months on end. Well, that is the prologue. Now for the main event, 'How to cut all this clutter."

There is nothing messier than a bench grinder mounted on a bench. This is especially true where that bench has to serve also as a work bench. Not only does the grinder take up too much valuable space, but in addition, it always has a dirty area around it. The grinder always gets in the way and reduces the usefulness of the bench. If the bench grinder is mounted on a pedestal that is an improvement, as it does get the grinder off the bench. One thing about that though, you still have to give up about 3 square feet of valuable floor space for that one piece of equipment.

THE PORTABLE 4—WAY WORK ISLAND

Everything said of the bench grinder goes double for a sanding disc. It will create clouds of wood dust around the bench as the disc gnaws hungrily at expensive spruce. There you have it, two good reasons for the 4-way equipment bench. (Figure 1)

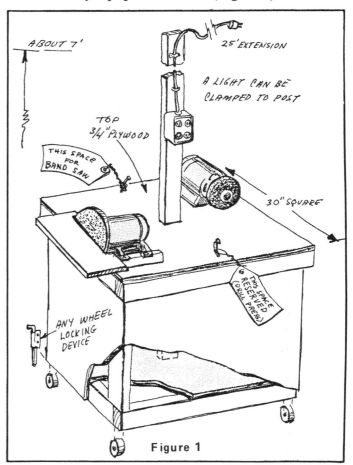

Figure 1

Although the bench can be built to any dimension, a 30-inch square configuration should be just about right for most shops. Perhaps its width should exactly match some existing bench so that you can push it up to that bench and against the wall out of the way.

It is an extremely versatile piece of furniture. You can mount the bench grinder and sanding disc opposite each other and leave the two other sides empty for work space. An alternate and very efficient arrangement would be to mount your band saw and drill press opposite each other in the empty spaces. If you don't have all of the equipment mentioned, you could mount any two to four pieces of equipment you do have in your shop and still save space. Some suggestions would include, in addition to the bench grinder, a disc sander, drill press and band saw, a jig saw, 18-inch sheet metal bending brake, medium-size vise, small hydraulic press and similar equipment.

The interesting feature is that all of these awkward pieces of machinery and tools can be grouped in just a few square feet of floor space and free your other benches.

The 4-square bench can be as lavish as you wish just as long as you make it solid and free from wobble. A central pipe or a 2 x 4 is used to mount a convenient 4-plug power outlet. This will give you a power source no matter where you roll the bench. Shelves and cabinets can be built into each of the four sides to provide storage for drill bits, blades, grinding wheels and sanding discs, freeing even more space to devote to building purposes.

The central power pole should be at least 7 feet tall and the 4-outlet electrical box wired with about 25 feet of extension cord attached. Several wire hooks suspended from the workshop ceiling will facilitate keeping the power cord up out of your way. As it is most unlikely that you will be using more than one electrical unit at a time, you needn't worry about overloading the cord. It would be wise, though, to make sure that the wire is of adequate size for normal use . . . . No. 14 wire would be fine and even No. 16 wouldn't be too bad unless you had some heavy load equipment mounted.

Before you get swept up with enthusiasm for the idea, remember that not all of your machines and equipment would be at a uniform working level if mounted on the same surface. Trying to install a bench grinder on a bench with the bandsaw may result in the working level being too high for one and too low for the other. Perhaps you can compromise the heights or even mount the grinder on blocks to help get things at a compatible level. The 4-square bench can even have its surface area built on two levels if necessary.

If the 30-inch by 30-inch size is a shade small for your purposes, increase the dimensions to suit your equipment. You could make scale templates of your equipment on scrap paper and try arranging the various tools to obtain the most efficient layout. No law says you must mount four gadgets on this bench. Even two would solve a lot of space problems for you and provide a good work island. When mounting something like a grinder, sander or band saw, be sure that no one tool will get in the way of long pieces being worked on one of the other 4-square bench machines.

Of course, the main asset to this rig is the ease with which you can move it about your shop. You can always have the equipment right where you are working. The time you save by not having to walk to each of the machines could reduce the time needed to build your plane by weeks.

THE TUBE AND METAL RACK

One of the best space savers you can rig up for a homebuilder's workshop is a rack for tubing and other narrow stuff like long spruce or Douglas Fir boards.

This really shouldn't take too long to do as you do not have to build a long shelf. You don't need long expensive boards. You will need perhaps one or two of these racks along the garage or workshop wall up near the ceiling where they will be out of the way and will not use up valuable wall space at the level where you need it most. A high one above any windows would be a good location. (Figure 2)

If you can afford to obtain a bunch of wall brackets and some boards to build long shelves (at least 16 feet long) that would be great. One drawback to board shelves though, is the fact that you cannot see what you have up there very well without climbing the wall — so to speak. Besides, shelves accumulate an unbelievable amount of dust in a very short time. Long material does not need shelves and several simple wood triangular frames spaced about 4 feet apart work as well. Take the time to run a taut string from one end to the other (properly leveled) to serve as an alignment for the brackets. Most builders sooner or later hit on the idea working independently of anyone else. It is just a matter of good clear thinking, a characteristic quite noticeable among builders.

PLYWOOD RACK

Plywood is mistreated in more workshops by more builders than any other material. Many of them just lean the sheets against the only clear wall space available. In a few months it takes on a permanent curved set. That is no way to treat something as expensive as aircraft-quality plywood. If you can't lay the plywood down flat on furring strips so that air is free to circulate under the sheets as well as over it, the next best storage arrangement is rack them against the wall. A rack nailed to the wall takes up the least amount of floor space, but you do lose some valuable wall space. A rack suspended from the ceiling is good if you have a sufficient number of cross braces to support the plywood. A wall rack should have outside strips that hold the plywood firmly against the wall to prevent sagging and warping. If at all possible when storing plywood or even structural spruce or fir, try to permit the air to circulate around the plywood sheet or board. Changes in humidity cause the wood to shrink and swell. For example, if the air becomes very dry, as in a heated shop in the winter time, the top surface of a sheet of plywood or a board will shrink and the material will curl up. If the same air is permitted to flow across the bottom, the shrinking will be uniform and the warping and curling effect will just about be eliminated.

ROLLERSKATE–MOUNTED BENCH DRAWERS

Perhaps one of the most versatile and useful of the shop spacemakers is the dolly mounted drawer.

(Figure 3) The space beneath the average permanent workbench is nothing more than a dirt trap where all sorts of things are poked away only to be forgotten forevermore. That alone, should be sufficient reason to salvage this valuable space and put it to good use.

What airplane builder doesn't accumulate many pieces of salvaged equipment, tubing, scraps of 4130 sheet, and an unbelievable amount of stuff that may not ever go into the airplane being built? In the meantime, where do you store it? Most of the material is too long to go into small narrow drawers. It is too valuable to leave lying around, and cardboard boxes take up much space and are always in your way, aren't they?

Well, you could be doing yourself a great big favor by taking the time to build a couple of free-rolling storage bins or drawers that could be scooted under your bench and pulled out when needed. Mine are mounted on dual rollerskate wheels. It takes two pairs of "cheapie" rollerskates to mobilize both bins. The wheels do not swivel and that is the secret of the success of the bins. They roll in straight and easy once they are aligned. You can pull them out as far as you want or roll them clean across the shop if you like. It makes a very neat and nice looking installation. If the drawers are built with about 3/4-

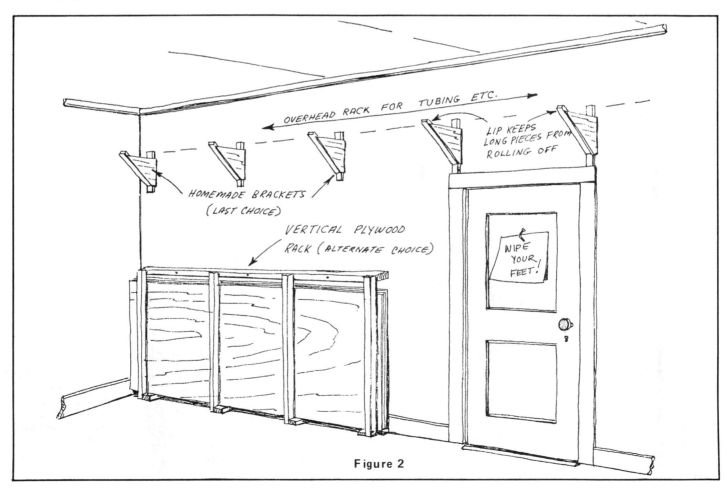

Figure 2

42

inch of space remaining above them when in place, you will find that you can slip material into these long bins without pulling them out. No protruding hardware handles needed.

Being a fair individual, I have foresaken the use of one of the two bins and have it reserved strictly for household junk and hardware. You know, pieces of lamps, light sockets, paint trays and rollers, antenna wire, light switches, brackets, screw eyes, cabinet hardware and anything else that would mess up my workshop for a good, but nonaviation purpose.

A parting observation. Lawn mowers, edgers, shovels, rakes and other alien equipment have no place in a guy's workshop. One of those small garden sheds or buildings is a wonderful solution especially if it is far removed from the shop (garage) area where you don't even have to look at the stuff. While I'm at it, I might as well go for broke and emphasize that the workshop is no place to keep the family car(s).

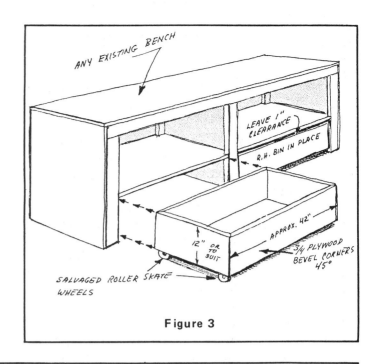

Figure 3

Most of the builder's shop equipment is concentrated in this offset area, leaving the 2-car garage area uncluttered for the project.

Shop Notes

As you will learn, if you haven't already, constructing your own aircraft requires an innovative approach to many problems. One reason for this is that even the best equipped shop will not always have all the tools and equipment needed for every job.

In some cases, the equipment needed is for a one-time use or for such a specialized purpose that you can't even buy it. Well, if you can build an airplane, why can't you also be your own tool maker and manufacturer of oddball shop equipment? Here are a few shop notes for some specialized equipment that is yours for the making.

THE DUMB ROBOT (ADJUSTABLE STAND)

Every shop needs one of these inanimate helpers. Its purpose is to hold the opposite end of any long piece of material or aircraft structure requiring precision drilling in the drill press. It will hold the other end of a spar, for example, in precisely the position you want it, and do it without giving you a running commentary or needless advice. Best of all, it will hold the spar or other heavy objects without getting

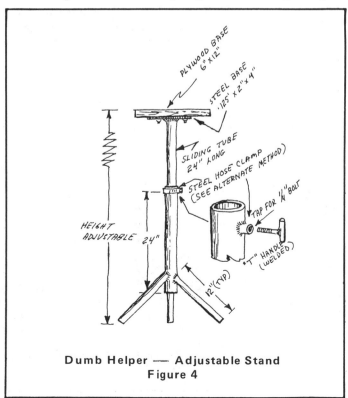

Dumb Helper — Adjustable Stand
Figure 4

tired while you piddle at the drill press end trying to get things adjusted there.

You can make the stand from any scrap tubing you might have around your workshop, provided that the smaller size tube can be slid into the larger size tube without too tight or too sloppy a fit. The dimensions are relatively unimportant and you can adapt any creative modifications that strike your fancy. (Figure 4)

When setting up for the drilling of a spar for its wing attach fittings, first adjust the stand to the same height as the drill press table. Then set one end of the spar on the drill press and the other on the stand. Next, place a level on the spar and readjust the height of the stand as needed. Now, you can proceed with your drilling chore and take all the time you need to do it right.

Incidentally, the stand doesn't take up much shop space and can be stored away most any place. It can also serve other useful functions. You can use it as a small tool stand, or better yet, a dandy mini-table for holding your drink while you are busy working on the airplane.

BENCH SAW SCARFER

Anyone building an all-wood airplane has probably considered a number of ways to speed up or to improve his plywood scarfing jobs. So, it's just a matter of deciding which method to try for yourself.

Illustrated is a technique of adapting your bench saw to serve as the foundation for a scarfing device. Figures 5 and 6 show the necessary details. To make the scarfer you will need an electric motor. One that puts out ½-hp at 3450 rpm would be just fine. My large sanding drum(3-inch) came from the local hardware store. The large turnbuckle and other items can be bought at any hardware store or perhaps even found around your shop.

The scarfing angle is adjusted with the large turnbuckle. Although a 10:1 or a 12:1 bevel is all you need, you can also make a nice 15:1 scarf joint just as easily. An important feature of the scarfer is the 24-inch wood slide strip that must be cut to fit the bench saw's slotted guide. Its function is to keep the plywood lined up properly for making the scarf cut. The plywood to be scarfed is laid with its edge aligned

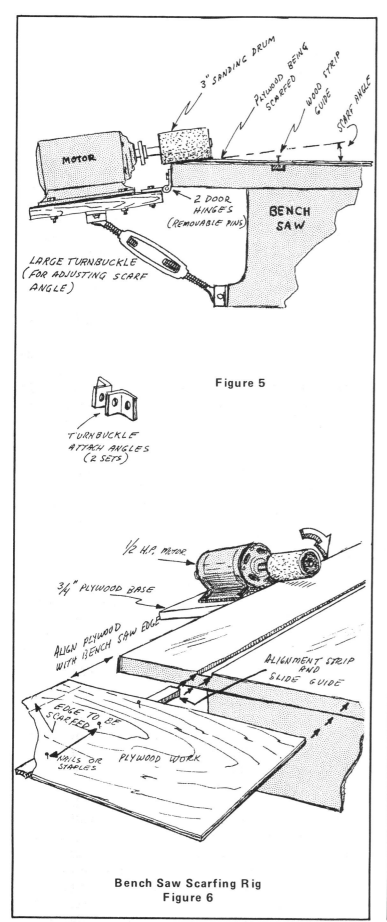

Figure 5

Bench Saw Scarfing Rig
Figure 6

along the edge of the saw table. Two or three small nails or staples are then driven through the plywood and into the wood guide strip beneath. The plywood piece can now be slid back and forth under the sanding drum in perfect alignment with the edge of the saw's table.

Now just turn on the motor and push the plywood piece (guided by the wood strip) into the sanding drum.

Caution: *Keep the plywood moving steadily. Don't stop in any one place as it makes an uneven cut.*

Several passes back and forth may be necessary to get your perfect scarf cut. Try a dry run on a scrap piece of plywood for practice.

When not in use, the rig can be completely removed by pulling the pins out of the hinges and unscrewing the turnbuckle. If you prefer, you can pull a bolt out of one of the angle brackets securing one end of the turnbuckle, thereby permitting the motor and drum to swing down out of the way.

CENTERING JIG FOR DRILLING TUBING

Take two 12-inch lengths of any common-size angle iron (1¼-inch x 1¼-inch x 1/8-inch was used for mine), place these two pieces side by side and tack weld the ends where they touch. Turn the angles over and finish welding by running a bead down the center joint line. After the work has cooled, grind the weld line as necessary to permit the device to lie perfectly flat on a level surface. (Figure 7)

To use this drilling jig, it must be clamped on the drill table and centered under the drill bit. For clamp-

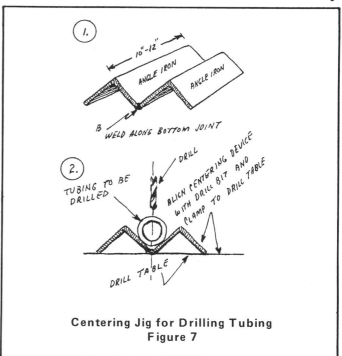

Centering Jig for Drilling Tubing
Figure 7

ing purposes, you might want to weld on a tab or two directly to the jig. In most cases, you can just slip a "C" clamp over one end of the device.

After the jig is clamped to your drill table, insert a small drill bit in the drill chuck and lower the bit until it just touches the jig. Now, move the centering jig around until the drill bit is centered over the center line of the jig. Tighten the "C" clamp and you are ready.

To drill any pipe or tubing, first make your punch mark as you usually do, and then lay the tube in the "V" groove of the centering jig. Drill completely through the tube as needed. The jig will automatically insure that your hole is centered in any size tubing.

SHOP FIRE EXTINGUISHERS

If you have no fire extinguishers in your workshop and have not even entertained the idea of buying any, read on. Why not at least consider using a few no-cost, "plastic jet-stream water dispenser types?"

Your wife probably buys liquid soap for dishwashing in a continuous effort to help maintain the American economy at its peak. And , just so the City will have something to do with all those garbage trucks they buy, she discards the empty plastic jugs regularly. Well, save those plastic containers, especially the quart (large economy) size squeeze bottles. These make fine, instant-action fire extinguishers capable of squirting a stream of water 50 feet. If you milk cows regularly or have a strong grip, you might get a 60-foot range. The caps on these plastic containers have a small hole in them that provides the proper nozzle action.

Now, whenever you get through horsing around with the jugs, why not refill them and place two or three strategically around your shop . . . . just in case you generate some long lasting welding sparks. Incidentally, they work equally well on itinerant cats or dogs which may, on occasion saunter by just to annoy you or to desecrate your project.

How to Use Taps and Dies

Lucky for us, somebody many, many years ago came up with the theory of the helix and its practical application to screws and bolts. Can you imagine how tough it would be to assemble an airplane without bolts and screws? Worse yet, would be the mess we'd have in trying to mate the proper nut to the bolt we wanted if there weren't some uniform standards for threads.

The first known attempt to formulate a standard for the many different screw designs dates back to the 19th century. A system conceived by an Englishman, Sir Joseph Whitworth, was rapidly adopted by the nut and bolt craftsmen of that time. Eventually, the Whitworth system was supplemented by other thread designs, the most notable being the United States Standard Thread.

However, times do change and by 1928, the name of the U.S. Standard Thread form was changed to American National Thread form. Incorporated into this category were the older ASME and the SAE systems of thread identification. That's why some of your older references and tables still list the standard threads as ASME and SAE.

This brings us up to the present. The general purpose threads standardized for use in the U.S. are known as the American National Thread. Although there are about nine common varieties of threads, we will discuss only three of them.

You, as a builder, have probably already been faced with an occasional need to cut threads on bolts or studs, or maybe on the inside of holes for special applications. How did you handle the problem? Did you have to farm the job out? Consider: You probably can buy the necessary equipment and do all the jobs yourself in the future for about what it would cost you to have it done once commercially. Let's discuss this business of tapping and cutting threads in detail.

WHAT IS A TAP?

To cut internal threads you need to use a tool called a tap. With this device it is possible to make your own special purpose nuts, thread holes in castings, pipes, and even in engine blocks. A tap will cut threads in many kinds of material used in building

sport aircraft, including steel, aluminum, plastics, phenolic blocks, and even hardwood.

THREAD CUTTING TAPS

There are three common types of thread taps. In ordinary engineering functions where conditions require the quick and easy assembly of bolts and nuts, the American National Coarse Thread series (NC) is used. (Figure 8)

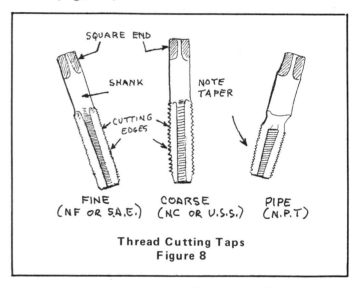

Thread Cutting Taps
Figure 8

In aircraft (and automotive) assemblies where structural design requires a reduction in weight with an increase in strength, you will find that the American National Fine Thread (NF) series is king.

The third type of thread is the American National Taper Pipe Thread (NPT). It is used where tapered external and internal pipe threads are needed for applications such as tank nipples and other fuel and oil system plumbing connections.

A good tap for the homebuilder is the plug hand tap available through most retail outfits handling tools and hardware. Each tap cuts only one size and one kind of thread. However, in aircraft work you will need only a few sizes of fine thread (NF) taps and, perhaps, one or two pipe thread taps (NPT) for building up the fuel system plumbing. The taper or pipe taps cut a characteristic taper thread which is essential in making tight, leak proof joints for pipe fittings.

The size of a tap or die is identified by the numbers etched on the tool. They indicate the diameter of the thread, the number of threads per inch, and the thread type. (On taps, the drill size to be used is also usually given.)

For example: *¼-inch x 28NF means a National Fine which will cut 28 threads per inch for a ¼-inch bolt or rod.*

HOW TO USE TAPS

First, determine what size bolt you intend to use and then select the appropriate tap and drill bit for it. The correct size of the hole to be tapped is very important. Drill the hole too small and you stand a good chance of breaking the tap in the hole. Then would come the problem of getting the broken tap out or, more often than not, the agony of having to discard the piece you tried to tap.

To produce a full 100 per cent thread height, the hole needs to be the same size as the minor diameter of the tap. Figure 9 illustrates that in order to control the thread height or engagement, you must vary the size of the drilled hole. If the drilled hole is too large, you will not get much of a thread and the bolt might strip out even under relatively light loads. In short, the degree of thread engagement is determined by the size of the drilled hole.

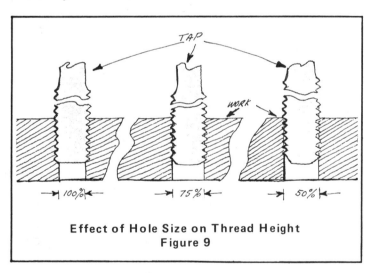

Effect of Hole Size on Thread Height
Figure 9

The recommended drill sizes for average use as listed in Table 1 will insure approximately 75 per cent thread. It is said that the difference between 75 per cent thread and 100 per cent thread is only a 5 per cent increase in strength, and yet, the force required to turn the tap triples. Somewhere, a long time ago, I read that the aviation standard for thread height was 80 per cent. This may be so, and it seems like a reasonable objective if you have a selective collection of drill sizes to choose from.

Aircraft Bolt Size	Tap Size/ Type	Drill Size	Minor Diameter Decimal Equivalent
AN 3 (3/16)	10 x 32 NF	No. 21 (5/32)	.159-inch
AN 4 (1/4)	1/4 x 28 NF	No. 3 (7/32)	.213-inch
AN 5 (5/16)	5/16 x 24 NF	No. I (17/64)	.266-inch
AN 6 (3/8)	3/8 x 24 NF	No. Q (21/64)	.332-inch

TAPPING PROCEDURE

Select the proper size tap. Insert the square end of the tap in a tap wrench and twist one of the knurled handles to lock the jaws of the wrench securely on the tap and you are all set. Incidentally, if the hole must be countersunk, do that before tapping.

It is best to secure your work in a vise for all tapping or threading operations on small parts. You will find it easier to start the tap if you grip the tap wrench at its center with one hand.

HOW TO USE A TAP

To cut clean, good quality threads, use the correct lubricant for the material being tapped. When tapping steel, apply standard thread cutting oil. For aluminum, just plain kerosene will do. Incidentally, it is better to do your tapping dry than to use the wrong lubricant.

Start the tap carefully. Keep it perpendicular to the work. After the tap has started, limit your turns of the handle to ¼ to ½ revolution, then reverse the action to break the chips (Figure 10)

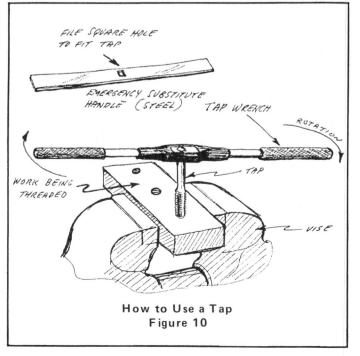

How to Use a Tap
Figure 10

Caution: *If, after starting to tap the hole, extreme tightness (and maybe even a squeaking noise) is encountered, your hole may be too small. Do not break the tap (especially a smaller size tap) by forcing it under these conditions. The proper feel, incidentally, will be acquired through experience.*

When tapping a blind hole, make sure it is deep enough for the required threads. Your tap, being chamfered at the end, will not cut a full thread all the way to the bottom of the hole. In addition, chips falling to the bottom of the hole need some space. For these two reasons it is accepted practice when drilling the hole, to permit the drill to penetrate to at least one drill bit diameter past the point where the stud is intended to reach.

HOW TO USE A DIE

The technique for using the tap's female counterpart, the die, is much the same as that for the tap. This tool is used to cut external threads on bolts or rods. (Figure 11)

Select the proper die. Insert the die into the die stock (handle) with the starting side as marked, next to the adjustable guide. There is a lock or set screw recess in the edge of each die and it should be inserted so that the recess aligns with one of the set screws in the die stock. With a small screw driver,

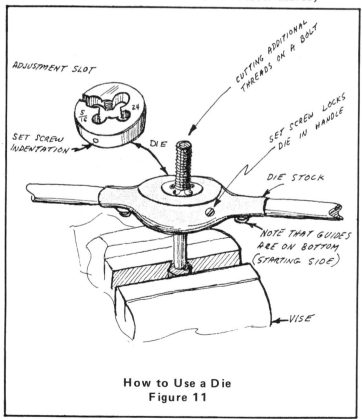

**How to Use a Die
Figure 11**

tighten the lock screws in the die stock against the die.

Check to see that the die stock guides are adjusted to the rod size. This is accomplished by loosening the knurled screws and by turning the chuck plate counterclockwise until the guides touch the rod. Retighten the knurled screws. These adjustable guides are important as they help insure the cutting of a straight thread.

To help start the thread on a rod, it is good practice to slightly chamfer or bevel the end of the rod. The rod to be threaded should then be clamped in a vise. As with the tap, to get the die started squarely, grasp the handle of the stock at the center with one hand.

To cut regular threads, the die stock is turned in a clockwise direction and reversed each ¼ to ½ turn to knock off the chips. (Left-hand threads require special left-hand taps and dies.) After the first two or three revolutions, the rest is easy. It is not necessary to press down on the die.

Never force the die to cut threads on an oversize rod or bolt. As a rough guide, the diameter of the rod should be the same size as the desired thread or about .005-inch to .010-inch undersize. Use plenty of cutting oil on the thread.

When you remove the die, it is fun to spin it off, but be careful as it nears the end of the rod. You shouldn't let it spin around on the end after it is free as that will damage the thread.

It's considered poor practice to cut additional threads on structural bolts that are too long. It is far better to get the right size bolt to start with.

Sometimes it may be necessary to cut thread all the way to the head of a bolt. In this case, proceed as far as you can with the die, then spin it off and screw the die on upside down. This makes it possible to make full threads all the way to the bolt head.

Any oddball special-use bolts requiring extra threads to be cut should always be treated against possible corrosion after the cutting operation. At the very least, give all newly cut threads a shot of zinc chromate primer.

FRUGALITY AND THE BUILDER

If your aircraft project and workshop budget is limited (and whose isn't?) buy your taps and dies only when you need them and only in the sizes you need. Undoubtedly, you will be using the 10-32 NF and the ¼-inch x 28 NF tap and die most frequently.

Although you will have to acquire a regular die stock for your 1-inch dies, you can make a temporary handle from scrap for your taps. A 10-inch length of scrap steel 1-inch x 1/8-inch with a hole drilled in its center will do the trick. The drilled hole must be filed square to snugly fit the square end of the tap's shank.

Caution: *Avoid using a vise-grip or a pair of pliers as a substitute tap handle. To keep from messing up the threads you need a handle which permits you to apply pressure equally on both sides of the tap, otherwise, turning the tap with a one-sided handle will result in an uncontrollable and thread damaging wobble.*

A Bit About Bits

Using a red hot wire or nail to burn a bolt hole in a wood aircraft structure is hardly an admirable practice. Yet, it has been resorted to as a desperate solution for making a bolt hole in an area inaccessible to a drill. Such techniques may have been common in fabricating Conestoga Wagons (and buggies), but in building an airplane some of us have enough trouble drilling just plain round holes with a nice modern-day round drill revolving precisely around its own axis, let alone resorting to such primitive fire rites.

Bolt holes, particularly those in primary structural elements, require close tolerances. A good job of drilling or boring in aircraft construction calls for holes that are round, smoothly cut, true-to-size, and drilled perpendicular (normal) to the surfaces to insure full bearing contact for the bolt head and shank. (Figure 12)

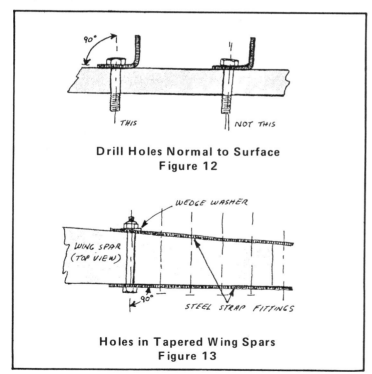

Drill Holes Normal to Surface
Figure 12

Holes in Tapered Wing Spars
Figure 13

Where one surface is oblique, a wedge washer must be made and used. Holes should be snug enough so that light taps of a mallet are required to insert the bolt. (Figure 13)

Unfortunately, once a bolt is installed, there is really no way to determine how good or how bad a job of drilling was done. If badly done, that could present a real danger. Nobody will know just to look at the installed bolt, not the EAA Designee, not the FAA inspector . . . . nobody. So guess who will worry about it later?

If the hole was poorly drilled or bored oversize, that material will not provide that ever-so-essential load bearing support needed. No use trying to fool yourself either. Tightening the nut down hard to compensate for a sloppy fit will not make the problem go away.

A big part of the blame for oversize, rough holes can be attributed to improperly sharpened drills. Twist drills should be machine sharpened or at least sharpened with the help of a mechanical aid of some sort. On the other hand, if you have critical holes to bore, as for wing strap fittings, it would be worthwhile to buy a new drill bit especially for that job. Although almost anyone can get pretty good at sharpening his own twist drills by hand, it does take plenty of practice . . . . especially on the smaller sizes. Anyhow, a new drill bit does tilt the odds in your favor.

What do you do if you find that the hole you have drilled is slightly oversize or elongated? The best solution is to make a new part. If this condition is in a spar, which is a time-consuming and expensive thing to build, the reluctance of the builder to build another spar is quite understandable. If for any reason you consider the making of a new part impractical, why not first get an unbiased opinion on the situation? Obtain advice from an FAA inspector or engineer, or the designer, or your own EAA Chapter Designee before drilling or reaming the hole to take the next larger size bolt. Going oversize is a logical and useful solution sometimes, but things like edge distances and clearances, for example, must be carefully considered to determine if such a solution is even possible.

DRILLING DEEP HOLES WITH A HAND DRILL

Another related problem, and equally as serious, is the problem of an internally enlarged hole due to the improper drilling from both sides of a structural member. (Figure 14)

The drilling problem here is in holding the hand drill at right angles to the surface. The requirement for correct hole alignment becomes acute when the hole is intended for the attachment of identical fittings on either side of a spar.

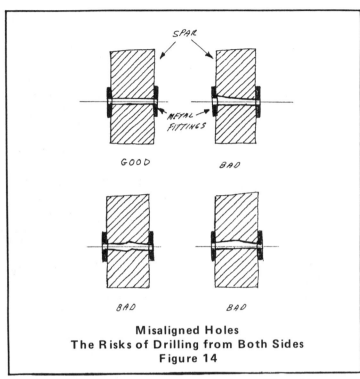

**Misaligned Holes
The Risks of Drilling from Both Sides
Figure 14**

Drilling from both sides is risky business. The odds are against both sides meeting exactly on center. Further efforts will only result in enlargement of the inner surfaces of the hole.

If you have no alternative other than drilling from both sides with a hand-held drill, proceed slowly and carefully. Try starting out with a small pilot hole to establish initial alignment. Slight corrections are then possible prior to the final drilling to exact size.

What else can you do? The obvious answer is to find a drill press somewhere and to level and jig the spar in the drill press for the drilling of critical holes. There are other aids too. The use of a drilling block or a small square to check the alignment of the hand drill is helpful but these are, at best, only pretty good techniques and cannot compete with the drill press for accuracy.

What else should you check when drilling with a hand drill? Well, make sure your work is backed up on the opposite side with solid blocking especially if the work is being done in place on the airplane. This is really important as there is nothing worse than the sight of torn wood fibers around an otherwise good hole caused by the drill breaking through the opposite side of the work.

WORKING WITH THE DRILL PRESS

Drilling holes can be dangerous. Small parts, especially metal pieces, should be secured to the drill press table to prevent their sudden wild rotation. Never hold small parts by hand, for very often, as the drill breaks through, there may be a dangerous tendency for the drill to jam or "hog in". If this seizing does take place and the work is not secured, the whole thing will whip around like a berserk meat cutter.

When drilling small fittings, it is usually quicker and better to place them on a board and stop or wedge them with nails. Of course you can't beat "C" clamps for doing the same job. Try to clamp or secure your work as close as possible to the drill.

PILOT HOLES

Since holes must usually be drilled precisely over a center punch mark, holes larger than 1/8 inch are usually drilled first with a smaller-size drill, which acts as a guide for the larger drill. A 1/8-inch drill, or one no larger than necessary is used because if the pilot hole is too large, it may cause the finishing drill to chatter, drill rough, and make an out-of-round hole.

FLEXIBLE SHAFT DRILLING

Where a hole needs to be drilled close to an adjacent structure and the chuck prevents your getting the drill in close, a length of steel rod or a short length of tachometer cable can be butt-brazed to the bit. The extended drill can then be used with any reasonable degree of flexing to clear obstructions and to work in close quarters. This rig is best used with a variable-speed electric hand drill that is held, lightly flexed, with your fingers to eliminate the danger of having the long drill rig whip around.

DRAIN HOLES IN WOOD AND METAL

Some people think drain holes are strictly for wood birds. This, of course, is not so. Water can also be trapped in metal compartments and can lead to corrosion or even result in an unsafe overload or critical c.g.

A preventative measure you can take is to drill a ¼-inch hole in the lowest portion of all compartments and sections that do not have natural drainage. These holes, in addition to providing drainage, will allow temperatures and pressurization changes to equalize throughout the structure.

When locating drain holes, and before drilling them, visualize in your mind how water would drain when the aircraft is at rest in its normal three-point attitude.

For wood aircraft structures, 5/16-inch or 3/8-inch holes are fine. Drill all drain holes before applying the top or cover skins. Don't forget to remove all burrs and splinters. No matter how watertight you think the top surface of your airplane may be, water from wind-blown rain and snow, condensation, washing and splashing is certain to find a way in. If you make it impossible for water to collect in any low places, you will have forestalled some of the problems of deterioration that come with the passage of time.

DRAIN HOLES IN FABRIC

Drain holes in fabric usually are reinforced with grommets. The usual procedure is to attach the grommet in the area where the drain hole is to be located, then, after the adhesive has dried, open the drain hole with a sharp X-Acto knife or a pointed, razor-sharp blade. Do not drill the hole open as this will make the edges fuzzy. Messy, fuzzy openings tend to catch dirt, which will ultimately block the holes.

There are those who claim it is unnecessary to use grommets with Dacron coverings if you use an electric soldering gun to melt a small drain hole in the fabric. They say the melted fibers automatically create a self-reinforced hole.

STOP—DRILL THOSE CRACKS

In metal as well as in plastics, the strains which cause a crack to occur tend to concentrate at the end of the crack. This condition is certain to cause the crack to further extend itself if unchecked. The remedy is well known. With a small drill (1/8- to 3/16-inch diameter) carefully drill the end of the crack. The hole helps distribute the strain over a wider area, relieving the tendency for the crack to continue its unwelcome propagation. This is not usually a permanent solution for primary structures

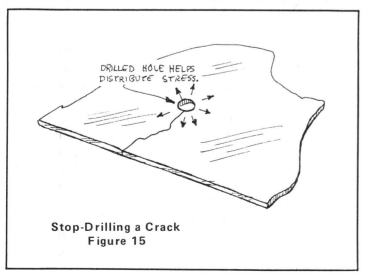

Stop-Drilling a Crack
Figure 15

and should be considered rather as a temporary fix. It is appropriately used on engine baffles, cowlings, windscreens and similar components. Do you question its effectiveness? I know of a cracked engine baffle with a stop-drilled crack that has been in continuous use for more than 11 years without any further deterioration. (Figure 15)

HOLE DUPLICATION

When replacing metal skin sections on a restoration project, the rivet holes in the new skins have to be drilled to exactly match the existing rivet holes. An accurate way to locate these new holes is to use a hole duplicator. Figure 16 illustrates one type of hole duplicator. A separate duplicator must be made for each diameter of rivet to be used in the replacement skins.

The duplicator consists of two thin metal straps riveted together on one end. The other end has a hole match-drilled (try for a snug fit for the rivet size to be used) through both straps. You will notice that in one side a rivet of the desired diameter is pressed in. If necessary, a dab of epoxy adhesive will insure that it doesn't fall out.

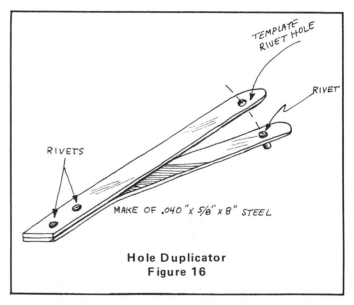

Hole Duplicator
Figure 16

To duplicate the holes in the new skins, the peg (rivet on leg A of the duplicator) is slipped under the new skin being fitted and into the existing rivet hole in the aircraft's structure. Voila! The exact location for drilling the hole in the new skin is automatically targeted. The proper-size drill is then used to drill through the template hole in leg B into the metal skin beneath, resulting in a perfectly aligned hole. If many holes of one size need to be drilled, I suggest a deluxe duplicator with a hardened bushing pressed in or welded on because the drill will soon wear the simple duplicator hole oversize.

The duplicator can also be used to locate holes for inspection covers and other plates where nut plates are already installed in a structure and you need to determine where to drill the holes for the fastening screws.

While on the subject of holes in metal work, here are some additional shop tips:

..... ON MAKING HOLES IN ALUMINUM SHEET

Here is an easy and reliable method for drilling on-size, clean, round rivet holes in thin sheet aluminum. Use a center drill to start and size the hole. These are available in all 1/32-inch o.d. increments from 1/16-inch to ½-inch, but who uses ½-inch rivets? The smaller sizes are available with pilots ranging .010-inch to 1/16-inch for an 1/8-inch o.d. You'll find that an A-2 (.125-inch o.d. with .040-inch pilot) is very satisfactory for .015- to .040-inch sheet aluminum. The completed hole diameter will range from .1250- to .1255-inch.

..... ON USING A HAND DRILL

Builders often encounter the problem of getting a drilled hole square and normal to a surface when using a hand drill. Mount your center drills in a 3- to 4-inch long extension and holder and watch the reflection of the holder on the aluminum skin. When the extension and the reflection are aligned in both axes, the drill is normal to the surface. The same method may be used with wood or other nonreflective surfaces. Tape a small mirror (or scrap piece

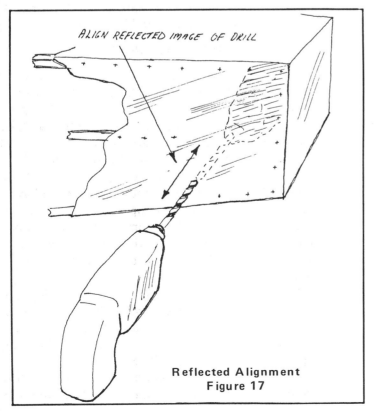

ALIGN REFLECTED IMAGE OF DRILL

Reflected Alignment
Figure 17

of aluminum) alongside the point where the hole is to be drilled. Tilt the 'easy' axis and use the reflection in the mirror to align the other axis. When the drill and the image are in a straight line, you have it. (Figure 17)

..... ON MAKING HOLES IN HARDENED STEEL

It is old hat to diemakers, but drilling a hole in hardened steel or heat-treated springs has brought many a builder to tears. It's not really a problem if you are willing to try this method. Heat the tip of a high-speed drill (definitely not a carbon-steel drill) to cherry-red, and quench it in mercury. (Dirty or contaminated mercury is cheap and can be obtained from many metals reclaimers and instrument supply houses.) *Be sure to have good ventilation when quenching. Mercury fumes are poisonous!* After quenching, proceed to drill the hole using steady pressure and moderate speed. A good cutting fluid helps but is not essential.

A BIT MORE ABOUT BITS AND BOLTS

Good high-speed drill sets cost plenty (carbon steel bits are cheap but don't hold up well in tough metal), but fortunately, in aircraft work it is unlikely you will need more than 8 or 10 different size drills. If you don't have a variety of sizes already, why not just buy what you will be needing?

Bits used to drill the common aircraft bolt holes are usually the same size as the diameter of the bolt. Therefore, a 3/16-inch bolt requires a 3/16-inch drill, and a ¼-inch bolt calls for a ¼-inch drill, etc. The common fractional drills you should have on hand are the 3/16-, 1/4-, 5/16-, and the 3/8-inch sizes. Other drills used in aircraft work are called numbered or letter drills because their sizes are identified by a number or letter. These are a bit harder to find locally as most places don't handle them.

Rivet Diameter	Drill Number/ Letter	Nominal Hole Diameter
1/16-inch	51	.067-inch
3/32-inch	41	.096-inch
1/8-inch	30	.129-inch
5/32-inch	21	.159-inch
3/16-inch	11	.191-inch
1/4-inch	F	.257-inch

After prolonged use some of the drill shanks are apt to get so marred that you cannot read the drill size. It is essential, therefore, that you check the size of the drill in a drill gage (or with a micrometer) before using it. Don't try to guess the size.

Heat Treating Metals

A lot of metal is used in a homebuilt no matter what the basic construction material. Most of it is aluminum and steel with some copper here and there.

Once committed to a project, a builder dutifully acquires the metal called for in the plans and specifications, and as far as he is concerned, that's all there is to the metal problem. A logical enough conclusion, but one that could get him into trouble because somewhere in the plans, there may be instructions for some metal parts to be heat treated to a specific condition. What does this mean? It means that even though the builder has acquired the proper material in the proper thicknesses, and has made the parts exactly according to the plans, the metal may not be in the right condition for installation and use.

We like to believe that designers do try to avoid complex structures and the use of exotic metals and difficult fabrication techniques in their designs. Nonetheless, as the designer develops the details for his creation, he often finds that a very high strength is required in certain units such as landing gears, control horns, or other highly loaded fittings. At this point he is confronted with a decision. Should those parts be made out of material heavy enough to resist the bending loads, or should he opt to save weight by making them of a lighter gage material and call for heat treatment after fabrication to obtain the necessary strength and stiffness? If he decides in favor of the thinner material, a builder working from his plans will be confronted with an unwelcome plans notation stating that certain parts must be heat treated . . . . "Heat treat to 125K," for example. The impact of such a requirement is that friend builder will have an additional complexity to cope with, an additional problem to solve. Many a builder will have to find someone, someplace who can properly heat treat his part because he can't do the job himself, especially if he does not even understand the concept.

As a homebuilder, you should understand a few basic characteristics and conditions of metals used in aircraft construction, and how these characteristics and conditions may be altered by heat treating.

NOT ALL METALS CAN BE HEAT TREATED

Pure aluminum and soft aluminum alloys such as 1100, 3003 and 5052 are not heat treatable. These metals are frequently used for gas tanks, fuel lines, brackets, fairings and nonstressed fittings. They are characteristically low in strength, soft and ductile, but also highly corrosion resistant. They are readily formed, and all can be welded. Their condition and characteristics can, nevertheless, be appreciably altered without heat, through what is called cold working or work hardening. The process is nothing more mysterious than subjecting the metal to bending, hammering, shrinking or stretching during the forming of a part. This cold working of the metal causes the material to harden and become somewhat stiffer and stronger.

There are non-heat-treatable ferrous metals too. Pure iron, wrought iron, and extremely low carbon steels (like the SAE 1025 steel used in some old aircraft) cannot be hardened appreciably by heat treatment because they contain no hardening element.

Like their aluminum counterparts, they are soft, ductile and relatively weak. This is why common low carbon steel should never be substituted for aircraft quality steel (4130 Condition N).

HEAT TREATMENT — GENERAL

Heat treatment is a process used to change a physical property or combination of physical properties in order to make the metal harder, stronger, and more resistant to impact. On the other hand, heat treatment can also make metal softer and more ductile although usually at the expense of some strength. No single heat treating operation can produce all of the characteristics in the metal you would like to have. There is a trade off. For example, if you harden the metal, it is very likely to become brittle. You must, therefore, know what properties are required in each part you use on the aircraft, and heat treat them accordingly.

All of the heat treating processes are alike in that they all involve the controlled heating and cooling of metals. The big difference is in the temperatures to which the metals are heated and the subsequent rates of cooling utilized.

Whatever the heat treatment of metals or alloys required, the process necessitates a controlled series of operations, always in the following sequence:

(1) Heating — First, the metal is heated to the proper temperature. Uniform heating is essential. If one area of a piece is heated more quickly than another, the consequence may be the cracking or distortion of the part.

(2) Soaking — Next, the metal's temperature is held within the correct range for the proper length of time, allowing the metal to become thoroughly saturated with heat. During the heat soaking step, the desired physical changes take place within the internal structure of the metal.

(3) Cooling — Finally, the metal is returned to a lower temperature through controlled cooling or quenching. The rate of cooling determines the final physical characteristics of the metal or alloy.

The rate of cooling is governed by the cooling method used. Cooling may be accomplished by using liquids, air or solids like iron chips, lime, sand or ashes. For most airplane building needs, the means most used are still-air, water or machine oil. A 10 per cent brine solution (sodium chloride) at a temperature of 65 degrees F has the fastest cooling rate, much greater than that of water. Although oil has a cooling rate considerably slower than the other two, it is a good general purpose quench and is quite a bit faster than still-air.

ANNEALING SOFTENS METALS

Steel, like most metals, can be annealed, that is, be made soft and ductile. In this condition it is easy to machine and to form, particularly where severe bending is required. Annealing also thoroughly removes internal stresses.

ANNEALING 4130 AIRCRAFT STEEL

1. Furnace temperature not to exceed 1,100 degrees F when parts are inserted.

2. Increase temperature gradually to 1,525 degrees F to 1,575 degrees F. Hold at that temperature for at least 15 minutes to ensure uniform heating.

3. Shut down furnace and permit it and parts to cool to approximately 900 degrees F. At 900 degrees F, remove parts and permit them to cool in still-air. Result: An ultimate tensile strength of approximately 75,000 psi. Steel is now in its softest, most ductile, and weakest condition.

It is difficult to fully anneal 4130 in the average shop, but this is of no significance, as annealed 4130 steel is not normally installed in aircraft.

ANNEALING ALUMINUM TUBING

Have you ever bought surplus stuff, or have you ever been given material, like say, aluminum tubing, and discovered that when you tried to flare one end to accept an AN standard fitting the end of the tubing cracked? This happened because the metal is hard and brittle. Now you know why the stuff was given away.

It may be that the tubing can still be used if it is annealed (heat treated to its soft condition). This you can do in your workshop with a propane torch. Of course, a welding torch also can be used to provide the heat source but greater care must be taken not to melt through the tubing with the concentrated, hotter flame.

Heat the tubing, with a torch, until it will char a small sliver of white pine or any other soft wood. Next allow it to cool in still-air. Obviously this is a trial and error way of determining the temperature of the tubing, and a risky way at that. Just a little too much heat from the torch and PLOP! You are no longer holding all of the tubing . . . . part of it is now

---

HANDLE COMPRESSED AIR WITH CARE

The FAA inspectors are a source of untapped knowledge for the amateur builder. I have received quite a bit of information from the various Texas GADO and EMDO gents. Some of these fellows have gone to a lot of extra work for themselves and have a variety of information sheets that they give to the builder during their inspections. The following is a good example.

"Handling an air hose filled with compressed air could be like handling a loaded rifle. Both are special tools that will do the job. And both could cause serious injury if used improperly.

"Although accidents resulting from the misuse of compressed air are uncommon, they are apt to be serious when they do occur. For example, it is the practice of many workers to dust themselves off with compressed air after the day's work. The compressed air hose is readily available and it does a good job of cleaning. Unfortunately, the hazards connected with such misuse outweigh any possible advantages."

lying on the floor.

A better way is to apply an even carbon coating to the tubing with a welding torch using an excess amount of acetylene. Then, readjust the flame to neutral and burn off all of the carbon on the tubing by playing the flame up and down the tubing. Be careful to keep the torch moving and don't try to rush the burning off of the soot or . . . . PLOP, there it goes again. As soon as all of the carbon disappears the tubing is annealed. Allow it to cool in still-air. It will then be soft enough to form and bend easily.

ANNEALING COPPER TUBING

Typically, a homebuilt will have at least a couple of copper tubing lines. The oil pressure and primer lines are two examples that come to mind. Brake lines too, may be made of copper tubing, and every year I see one well known Tailwind on the Oshkosh line quite brazenly sporting 1/8-inch copper tubing brake lines.

Although we think of copper as being a soft metal, it will, if subjected to prolonged vibration, become hard and brittle due to its natural work-hardening characteristic. Copper tubing on reaching its hardened state is prone to cracking.

There are two things you can do to minimize the risk of having the copper lines in your installation crack, leak, or fail completely. You can form a 2-inch loop (coil) in the tubing to minimize the effect of vibration. The loop acts as a sort of built in shock absorber. You can also anneal the tubing periodically, perhaps annually during your recertification inspection.

Copper becomes extremely plastic at temperatures between 1,200 degrees F and 1,650 degrees F. However, copper tubing can be brought up to its annealing temperature by heating it to 600 degrees F to 850 degrees F. Maintain the metal at this temperature until it is thoroughly heated. Then, allow it to air cool to room temperature, or quench it in water, if you are in a hurry. The cooling rate really has no effect on the copper's softness in this annealing process. It is worth remembering that quenching the copper in water produces better results because it eliminates scale. In its annealed condition copper has a tensile strength of approximately 35,000 psi.

You should also anneal your copper lines after they have been formed and fitted, especially if they were subjected to considerable bending and feel stiff when flexed.

In your shop you will find it easier to torch-anneal copper tubing at approximately 1,000 degrees F. Annealing at this higher temperature results in maximum softness. At this temperature the tubing will glow red in a dimly lighted work area, and rainbow-like colors will appear on the copper. This indicates that the correct temperature has been reached.

The container of water for quenching should be large enough to accommodate the entire length of the tubing at the same time.

HEAT TREATMENT OF ALUMINUM

Without doubt the most important structural aluminum used by the homebuilder in an all-metal project is 2024 T3 aluminum alloy.

In this alloy's tempered state (T3 for example) it is very stiff and has a tensile strength of approximately 62,000 psi. To make 90 degree bends or flanges in 2024 T3 (tempered state) requires a rather large bending radius to keep the metal from cracking. Therefore, when 2024 is used in rib designs that require severe forming, the designer sometimes specifies that the ribs are to be made of 2024-0 (soft or annealed condition) and then heat treated (and aged) to the 2024 T4 condition. Should your plans require this, do not install the metal ribs in their soft annealed condition, as their strength will be substandard (35,000 psi vs 62,000 psi).

Unfortunately, the heat treatment of aluminum alloy parts as large as wing ribs is generally beyond the capability of the average workshop. These require a furnace large enough to take the parts, and capable of heating them to a temperature between 910 degrees F and 930 degrees F where they must be held (soaked) at that temperature for the required time. After that, the parts are quenched in water. Following this heat treatment, 2024 aluminum alloy is exposed to room temperature for four days (aged). The 2024 parts then will have reached their theoretical tempered T4 strength of more than 62,000 psi.

If you must have heat treatment work done, plan to take all of the completed parts to a good commercial heat treating facility at the same time. You will get off cheaper because the charge is usually based on how many times the furnace must be loaded, and not necessarily on the number of pieces put in at one time.

You should realize that there is always the risk of warped or distorted parts being returned to you after heat treatment, particularly if the shop isn't familiar with the heat treatment of lightweight aluminum aircraft parts.

If you have an alternate choice of material, select the one that does not require heat treatment. It is a cheaper and quicker way to build.

HEAT TREATMENT OF 4130 STEEL

In addition to annealing, steel may be normalized, hardened and tempered by heat treating.

NORMALIZING — The primary purpose of normalizing steel is to remove the internal stresses caused by welding, forming or machining. This is the single most important heat treatment performed by the homebuilder on 4130 steel. All welded parts and tubing clusters should be normalized as soon as the welding is completed.

The normalizing of the metal is accomplished by heating the steel uniformly to a temperature of 1,650 degrees F and then allowing the part to cool in still-air. When done in a furnace, the heating and soaking times are the same as for annealing. However, normalizing is easily accomplished with your welding torch. Simply heat the welded area or entire part to a uniform bright red to salmon color (1,600 degrees F to 1,700 degrees F) with your welding torch and then allow it to cool in still-air. That's all there is to that.

The 4130 sheet steel is purchased, ordinarily, in its normalized condition, Condition N. Aircraft parts made of this annealed steel, if not later normalized, are much weaker than the normalized material required in your plans. A normalized part will have a tensile strength of approximately 95,000 psi, almost a third stronger than the same part in an annealed condition.

Parts requiring a higher tensile strength than 95,000 psi must be hardened. Before hardening steel, it is standard practice to first normalize it to give maximum assurance that the hardening process will consistently yield the desired results.

HARDENING STEEL — The correct way to harden steel, of course, is in a furnace. The steel must be heated to 1,575 degrees F to 1,625 degrees F and soaked at that temperature long enough to ensure that its desired internal condition has been reached throughout the steel. The steel is then cooled rapidly (by oil quenching).

Aircraft parts are never used in the hardened condition!

Hardening is really an intermediate step in heat treating steel to obtain the physical properties desired. So, after the hardened steel part is removed from its quench bath and well before it is completely cooled, it must be tempered immediately. Incorrect tempering action will almost certainly result in the sudden failure of the part.

TEMPERING — Tempering reduces the brittleness induced by the hardening step. Tempering always follows the hardening process. Not only does tempering reduce brittleness, but it also softens the steel.

As the still-warm, hardened steel is reheated, tempering begins at a very low temperature (212 degrees F) and continues as the temperature increases.

Therefore, the selection of the exact tempering temperature required should result in a predetermined hardness and strength in the metal. The minimum time at the tempering temperature will be approximately one hour for parts less than 1-inch in thickness, and longer for heavier pieces.

Generally, the rate of cooling from the tempering temperature has no effect on the results. Cooling in still-air to room temperature is the normal practice.

The chart gives the properties obtainable in 4130 steel by tempering it at various temperatures.

TEMPERING 4130 STEEL		
Tempering Temperatures (degrees F)	Tensile Strength (psi)	Hardness (Rockwell)
1050	125,000	C-25
900	150,000	C-33
700	180,000	C-39
575	500,000	C-43

Figure 18

In everyday practice, small heating jobs may have to be done in your shop. It is possible to visually determine the temperature of metal from the color change taking place in it when heated. This visual determination of temperature in metals is useful only for ferrous metals. (See chart below)

Temperatures needed for the hardening, normalizing or annealing of steel are hot enough that the steel changes color. This is a very useful characteristic. By observing these color changes closely, you can successfully determine the temperature of the steel.

A color chart, obtainable from many welding supply houses, would be helpful to you in differentiating between, say, medium cherry and cherry.

Color	Temperature F
Faint red	.900
Blood red	.1050
Dark cherry	.1075
Medium cherry	.1250
Cherry, full red	.1375
Bright red	.1550
Salmon	.1650
Orange	.1725
Lemon	.1825
Light yellow	.1975
White	.2200

Figure 19

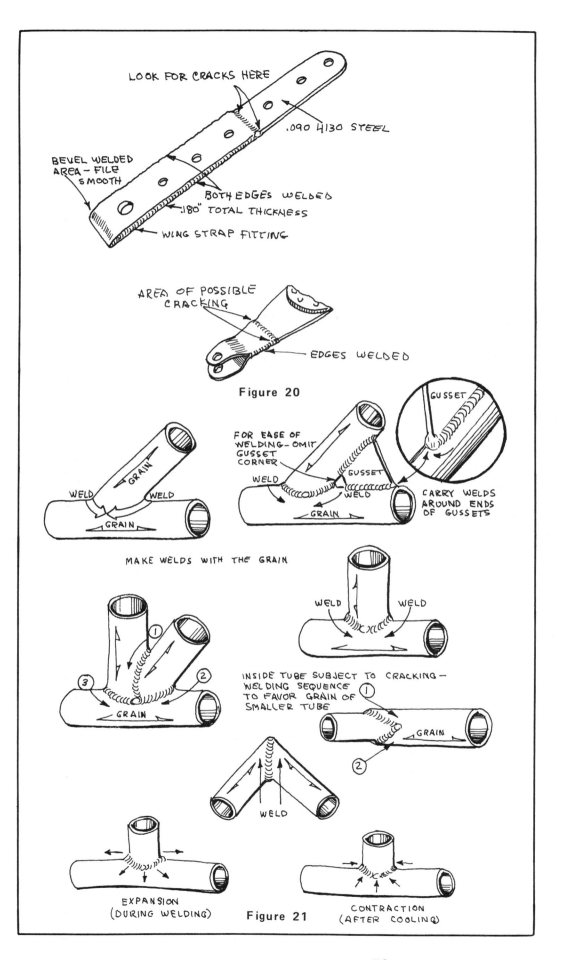

LOOK FOR CRACKS HERE

.090 4130 STEEL

BEVEL WELDED AREA — FILE SMOOTH

BOTH EDGES WELDED

.180" TOTAL THICKNESS

WING STRAP FITTING

AREA OF POSSIBLE CRACKING

EDGES WELDED

Figure 20

GRAIN

WELD WELD

GRAIN

MAKE WELDS WITH THE GRAIN

FOR EASE OF WELDING — OMIT GUSSET CORNER

GUSSET

WELD WELD

GRAIN

GUSSET

CARRY WELDS AROUND ENDS OF GUSSETS

WELD WELD

GRAIN

INSIDE TUBE SUBJECT TO CRACKING — WELDING SEQUENCE TO FAVOR GRAIN OF SMALLER TUBE

GRAIN

WELD

EXPANSION (DURING WELDING)

Figure 21

CONTRACTION (AFTER COOLING)

Aircraft Welding

The subject is controversial. Should the home-builder try to stress-relieve his 4130 welded structures with a torch?

The act of stress-relieving a weldment is simple, and although highly recommended by many expert welders, it is poo-pooed (no such word . . . it just sounds right) by others just as well qualified. The treatment requires that the weld, and the metal areas adjacent to it, be heated uniformly with an acetylene torch to bring the metal to a dull red condition (approximately 1,000 degrees F) and then be cooled in still air. That's it. Now, why should this be necessary?

When steel is heated as in welding, it increases in size in all its dimensions. While the weld is progressing, a rather narrow zone adjacent to it will reach a plastic condition and ultimately a molten state if the heating continues. This uneven heating sets up stresses in the metal. Metal that is a greater distance away from the flame will resist the expansion taking place in the weld area. Meanwhile, back at the weld, the tremendous initial pressures exerted by the heated metal become less resistant to the surrounding pressures of the cooler metal. The plastic center begins to yield to the compression force, which is now capable of buckling the plasticized metal in the weld area. This process continues along the line of the weld. And since all of the pressure or stress is not relieved in the process, these stresses remain trapped, or "locked-in," as the saying goes. Distortion also is a by-product of these complex changes in the metal.

As soon as the welding is completed, the molten metal, if it is permitted to do so, begins to cool down, somewhat more rapidly in comparison to the surrounding areas which will not have been heated much. This uncontrolled cooling causes an uneven contraction in the metal since the cooler metal, farther from the vicinity of the weld induces a quenching effect. This effect, of course, would be even greater if there were a nearby weld cluster or a welded fitting.

Anyone who has welded an engine mount or other structure requiring the exact alignment and positioning of mounting holes, will attest to the fact that, without rigid jigging, the assembly would crawl around during the welding as if it were alive. Indeed, the expansion of the metal from the heat of welding and from its subsequent cooling and contraction are usually so drastic that the builder must allow for this distortion.

Ordinarily, such stresses are not as severe, nor do they present a great problem in simple welded joints that are subjected only to static tension, torsion, or compression. No problem that is, provided the metal's ductility has not been seriously impaired by the welding. It is mostly with larger parts that are highly loaded, and perhaps subjected to vibration during their service life, that the prospect of cracking or failure of the weld must be faced.

So, we do have something to think about with regard to the locked-in stresses of welding. Is this a serious enough condition to require some form of stress-relief, or should it be ignored because the home-builder is unable to heat treat the entire assembly in a furnace?

Among those who say that the stress-relief of a weld with torch is not necessary or is not recommended are some very good welders. Undoubtedly, these welders follow a welding procedure much like this: preheat the metal, make the weld, and complete the process by playing the torch over the entire vicinity of the weld until the molten area has cooled down to a red heat. Then, and only then, is the torch finally withdrawn. What these welders are doing, in effect, is stress-relieving the weldment at the same time it is made. That makes good sense. After all, why leave a newly completed weld where the metal is already thoroughly heated without completing the job? Why should it be necessary to return some time later when the weld and the surrounding metal are totally cold? You would only have to start anew by raising the temperature of the metal to that dull red condition necessary for the stress-relief you wish to obtain.

It is easy to see that essentially the same results are achieved in both instances except that one welder is more experienced and more frugal with his time and energy. I can understand why such a welder would say that he never stress-relieves his welds.

Nor is there any conflict in my mind with the procedures adopted and practiced by manufacturers and the professional aerospace engineers, as well as factory representatives who believe that the best way to stress-relieve a welded 4130 structure is not with a torch but in an oven. Can't argue with that logic. But, I guess their stand is primarily based on the opinion that torch stress-relieving is undesirable because the area involved may not be uniformly and thoroughly heated. This is possibly true with some builders who do not take the time to switch to a larger welding tip and those who may not be as careful to heat the areas uniformly and methodically. After all, it's easy to inadvertently get some places too hot.

In real life, however, finding an oven to stress-relieve an entire fuselage is like finding the pot at the end of the rainbow. So, the option remains, either to stress-relieve the completed welds with a torch or to modify the welding technique to assure that the classic preheat, weld, and post heat applications serve to accomplish the same end result.

Recently, someone tried to convince me that when one attempts to stress-relieve a weldment with an acetylene torch (as opposed to using an oven) he simply moves the stresses outward from the welded area, but does not relieve them. That argument concluded with the observation that it would therefore, be more desirable to have these stresses in a welded cluster where the structure was the strongest, as opposed to moving them outward on the tubing where the structure was weakest. I don't know why but the remark was added . . . "this of course, is based on the assumption that 4130 steel was being used in a properly designed structure."

I find that supposition faulty for the most part. It might be true if there were some sort of heat sink a short distance away from the weld which might have a quenching effect on an unevenly heated weldment. However, it seems that during a properly executed stress-relief effort this would not be true. Here's why. The weld and adjacent area is thoroughly preheated and brought up to a dull red condition and therefore, the heated areas of the metal will range outward to an almost red, very hot, hot, not-so-hot, to a relatively cool and, ultimately, cool condition some distance away from the weld. How could such a gradual thermal change in the metal from the weldment to the remainder of the metal cause serious stresses to be moved farther outward on the tube? There could be an exception if an adjacent welded cluster, not included in the heating process, were near by.

The fact remains that people who obviously have much experience in this area do honestly disagree on this particular point. Maybe the real disagreement is not so much whether to stress-relieve or not, but with the technique utilized in making welds. Here are some other matters involving stress.

THE MATTER OF PREHEATING

What is the best way to begin a weld in 4130 steel? Certainly not with a concentrated application of the flame directly to the joint. Such a modus operandi may result in committing certain critical welds to a short-lived future even though a fairly good-looking, uniform weld was obtained. Additionally, a welding procedure like that introduces internal stresses in the adjoining metal in the manner discussed earlier.

The proper starting procedure is to always take the time to preheat the area before starting to weld. Play the flame over the entire area until it is evenly heated. This preheating is especially important when there is a nearby welded joint. It doesn't mean though, that the surrounding metal must be raised to a red hot condition . . . not at all.

WELD WITH THE GRAIN

Metal does have grain, you know. Somewhat like that in wood. It results from the manufacturing process and is a factor to consider whenever bending metal or welding it. The grain in tubing is noticeable and runs the length of the tube in straight lines. The grain in flat steel stock is likewise visible to the eye, and is further delineated by the orientation of the lines of painted specification numbers and letters across the sheet.

Experience has shown that cracks tend to develop in welds made against the grain. Therefore, whenever possible, welds should be made in the direction of the grain and not against it.

Once the metal is heated to a molten state and the welding puddle forms, air should not be permitted to reach the white hot metal at any time. Use the outer envelope of the flame as a protective blanket against oxidation. This protective blanket must not ever be totally removed even when changing to a new welding rod or readjusting the flame. Certainly not until the weld is completed and the heated metal has been allowed to cool down to a red heat.

END THE WELD PROPERLY

Do not immediately withdraw the torch and marvel at the good-looking weld you just completed. Instead, take your time and play the flame over the completed weld area until it cools to a red heat condition. The gradual withdrawal of the heat after the weld is completed minimizes the likelyhood of cracks developing, or, more likely, the appearance of small pin holes in the cooling puddles where the welds terminate. Furthermore, this procedure improves the ductility of the weld and minimizes the quenching effect the adjacent cooler metal may have.

Those gentle, caressing breezes drifting through your workshop during those hot, sultry summer days may be great for you, but they are bad for your welding. When welding 4130 steel, do not expose it to any cooling by air in motion. This is an air-hardening steel and it will develop cracks when subjected to any sudden cooling, however gentle it might feel to you. That means you should close any door near the welding area. Shut off those fans too, and make sure that your dog doesn't wag his tail.

A SUMMARY OF PRECAUTIONS AND PRACTICES

Although 4130 steel (chrome molybdenum or "chrome moly") is very tough and strong when cold, it is even weaker than mild steel, in the heated condition. Therefore, it must not be stressed or shocked while in a white hot state.

Do your welding in a draft-free area, otherwise the metal will probably chill too fast and thereby be weakened.

Never use tightly clamped jigs. Spring-type clamps are just fine for holding parts to be welded, and they come in various sizes.

Good welders say that starting welding on an edge is not a good technique. Rather, it is best to start at a point away from the edge and work to it. **CAUTION:** Heat builds up fast near the easily heated edges and it is very, very easy to inadvertently burn through the edge of the metal. Watch it, and draw the flame away slightly as needed when the edge itself is reached. If you ruin a piece, **make it over**, that's where the education part of homebuilding comes in.

In all cases where parts have been tack-welded together, it is most important that you melt completely through the tack as you complete the final weld.

Especially on thin metal and thin-walled tubing, care needs to be taken to clean any dirt, scale or oxide from the parts to be welded. Percentage-wise, as the parent metal becomes thinner, the chances of having dirty metal in the weld is increased. Take time to clean the weld areas.

As the thickness of the welded metal decreases, the selection of the proper tip and the adjustment of the gases becomes very important. Thin metals are easily buckled when too much heat is used.

Get in the habit of preheating the metal in the area to be welded.

Don't clamp your work in the vise and then try to weld on the part near the jaws of the vise, as the heavy metal of the vise will draw away the heat and you'll have difficulty getting the metal hot enough. Remember, any large or heavy metal areas near the weld area will draw away the heat from the joint and will require a larger flame, thereby increasing the risk of burning the adjacent metal.

Be sure your line of weld in the parent metal is heated to proper melting point. Try to keep your weld pool size as uniform as possible.

Hold the filler rod to the same melting point before introducing it into the melted pool of metal.

Add filler rod as evenly and steadily as possible.

Don't rush. Be sure that the added metal and parent metal are puddled together properly.

Keep playing the outer envelope flame over the pool to protect it from the oxidizing air.

Melt a certain portion of the parent metal on both sides for the entire length of the weld.

Avoid reheating of weld metal which has cooled.

CONSTRUCTION PRACTICES

To Nail or Not to Nail

In you are building in wood, you probably have have already decided whether or not to use nails. Undoubtedly, your decision was influenced to a great degree by personal preference as well as by the design details. If that is the case, certainly, there is no intention here to influence you to change your thinking on the subject. Be assured then that this impartial (chuckle) commentary may be just the thing for somebody else.

NAIL SELECTION

In determining the nail type to use, I would give preference to brass nails over ferrous types every time. This is true even though steel nails, as manufactured for aircraft use, will have been specially treated by cadmium plating, galvanizing, or cement coating to prevent rust. Equally important is the selection of the proper length and size of the nails to use.

Nail diameters are expressed in wire gage sizes. Lengths are expressed in inches. In most ordinary sizes, the more slender 20-gage nails are recommended for use as the thicker 18-gage size is heavier and more apt to cause the wood to split.

For an aircraft nail to hold effectively, it must be long enough to penetrate into the underlying structure to a minimum depth roughly equivalent to 3 times the thickness of the surface plywood. For example, in gluing and nailing 1/16-inch thick gussets to wing rib cap strips, ¼-inch x 20 gage nails would suffice. These ¼-inch nails would pass through the gusset and penetrate the structure 3/16 of an inch. Nails shouldn't be so long as to pass completely through an underlying structure. (Figure 1)

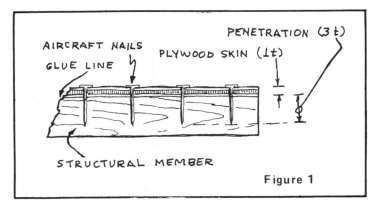

AIRCRAFT NAILS
GLUE LINE
PENETRATION (3 t)
PLYWOOD SKIN (1t)
STRUCTURAL MEMBER

Figure 1

HANDLING NAILS

Since most nails used in aircraft woodwork are small and difficult to handle with the fingers, a number of handling gimmicks have evolved. Each of these methods is lauded by some devoted adherent as being the best way to pick up nails and to hold them in position for nailing.

Some advocate the use of a magnetic tack hammer, but this method requires a steady hand and a good aim in order to land the nail exactly where you want it. It may be all right to use this technique when a random nail or two is to be driven to keep a panel from sliding around as you prepare to secure it, but rapid and accurate nail placement will be difficult for the average builder.

Another source seriously proposes that the plywood be pricked with a sharp awl or a pair of dividers and the nail then inserted by hand into the hole . . . . obviously a slow and crude procedure.

Still another way described in some ancient references goes something like this: Cut a long notch in the end of a slinder stick. Pick up a nail and slip the nail's shank into the notch with the head up. The stick can then be moved into position and the nail, without any risk of damage to the fingers, may be bravely hammered home.

Well, the method which merits my personal favor has several variations. First, scatter some nails on your work surface within a 3-inch or 4-inch area. Then, using a pair of tweezers (small-nose pliers or a small magnetized screwdriver blade for steel nails), pick up a nail, hold it in position, give it a light tap with a tack hammer, and you are on your way. Incidentally, most builders can handle the ½-inch or larger nails with little difficulty using only their fingers.

Your own practice run on a couple of the methods described, or a variation thereof, will help you determine the most effective method for you.

PERMANENT NAILING

Permanent nailing, as the term implies, is a method of applying clamping pressure on a glue line using nails which are not later withdrawn after the glue has dried. Instead, the nails become an integral part of the structure. Permanent nailing is used by many builders as a quick and convenient way to affix the various plywood gussets to wing ribs, fuselage frames, and control surfaces. Quite often, nails are even employed in the application of plywood skins to major structural units.

Any place where nails are permanently driven into external surfaces, or where appearance counts, strips of ducting tape or pinked tape should be doped down over the nail rows before the final covering and finish is applied. However, before using permanent nailing to any extent in any external plywood-skinned surfaces, think it over and then decide against it. Elsewhere, permanent nailing can be useful and quite effective.

Even in projects where the intention is to clamp all gussets and permanent nailing is not desired, it may still be expedient to drive a nail or two into the gusset to hold it in position while you are setting up the work for clamping. The nails will guarantee that the gusset will not slip out of position as the clamps are tightened.

Larger plywood pieces and gussets require prenailing in order to make the nailing go quickly. However, prenailing of plywood skins and gussets in thicknesses less than 3/32-inch is often more trouble than it is worth as some of the preset nails will drop out because of the vibrational shocks created during the nail hammering process.

Because the pressure exerted by nails is rather low, uneven, and unpredictable, avoid excessive spacing of the nails. The following is a suggested maximum spacing of nails for different thicknesses of plywood:

> For 1/16-inch plywood use ¼-inch x 20 gage nails spaced ½-inch apart.
>
> For 3/32-inch plywood use 3/8-inch x 20 gage nails spaced ¾-inch apart.
>
> For 1/8-inch plywood use ½-inch x 20 gage nails spaced ¾-inch apart.
>
> For ¼-inch plywood use 1-inch x 18 gage nails spaced 1 inch apart.

Normally, a minimum of one nail per wood member is required in gusset work such as is found in the construction of a truss-type wing rib. It may be possible to use two or more nails in each member, but it is not a good idea to space them closer than ¼-inch apart.

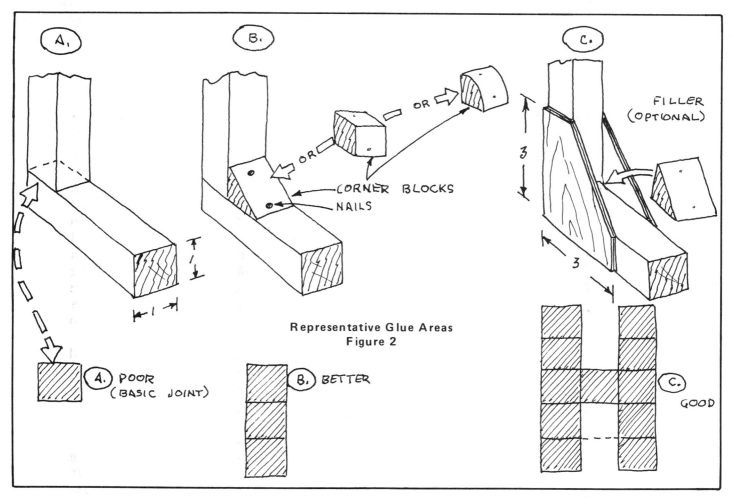

Representative Glue Areas
Figure 2

Corner blocks are almost impossible to clamp in place because of their awkward locations. Here is a place where a couple of nails will do a fine job of holding the blocks in position, and in obtaining the desired clamping effect. (Figure 2)

Another effective use of nails is in the attachment of ribs to spars. Established practice dictates that ribs be glued and nailed to the spar by nailing through the uprights at the spar openings. Check Figure 6 on page 75 to see what I mean. Don't nail through the capstrip. It weakens the rib.

Use of nails to attach the plywood webs to box spars isn't a very popular practice now, but if you do nail your webs, it is advisable that you avoid driving nails too close to the flange edges. Stagger the nail rows slightly but keep the nails at least ¼-inch from the edges.

As in any method of applying pressure to a glued joint, if the joint is visible, the indication of an adequate joint is the appearance of excess glue squeezed out in a continuous seam at the glue line. Any portion of the joint which does not display this evidence should be subjected to close scrutiny. Possibly additional pressure will be necessary, through clamping or by closer spacing of the nails. For joints that are hidden from view, you have no guidance except to follow accepted good practices which will normally yield good results. Tapping the structure lightly with a hammer along the invisible glue line, should result in a solid sound to your ears. An odd or hollow sound could indicate a poor glue joint.

Develop the habit of marking the internal structural outlines on the outer skin to serve as a guide to nailing, and for future reference.

It is just a little thing, but always remove and replace any bent nails . . . . do quality work. Drive the nails in snugly, but do not bury the heads deeply into the plywood fibers.

SOMETIMES NAILS CAN CREATE PROBLEMS

When you do use permanently-driven nails in the assembly of your glued wood components, all sorts of annoying results seem to crop up as construction proceeds and the smaller parts are progressively mated to larger assemblies.

Take the situation where you have just assembled an elevator and you must bevel and fair the trailing edge gussets in preparation for the fabric covering. The quickest way is to use a sharp knife or a block plane, but . . . . YIPES! NAILS! Never happen you say? Well, even if you carefully plan not to drive the nails to close to the areas that later will be beveled, I'll bet your plane or knife blade will look more like a comb than a cutting blade when you've finished the

beveling.

You might as well take time out to remove all of the offending nails even though that may not be the easiest of tasks.

It is better to be prudent and do the gusset beveling job safely with a file or disc sander as either will zip right through any overlooked nails. A file does a nice job and it can't be beat for final finishing, but it is a good bit slower than the disc sander.

Here's another irritating situation. Say you have to drill holes in the vicinity of a gussetted joint. You mark the spot and start. As luck would have it, you strike a nail and the drill wanders off center enough to affect the ultimate alignment of whatever component that hole was drilled for. This is really annoying, for once a hole is drilled, you are stuck with it.

Most of the classic arguments against the use of nails in wood structures are essentially statements of petty annoyances and may be summarized as follows:

1. Nails tend to work out in time and can cause ugly little localized bumps in the covering or finish of the aircraft.

2. The effects of the natural moisture content of the wood can cause 'iron' nails to rust, leaving messy surface stains and streaks. (Of course brass nails don't rust or stain.)

3. Three or four pounds of unnecessary nails used in the structure are just that much extra dead weight. (Figure 3)

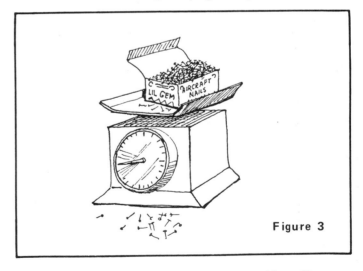

Figure 3

There is still another point to consider. Even though using nails appears to be an easy assembly technique for gluing operations, this nailing business is a time-consuming and tedious process.

It is generally accepted that nails contribute little if any strenght to a joint. Actually, they do no useful work at all once the glue has dried. Hence, it may be said that the nails are just so much dead weight and are going along for a free ride. Admittedly, however, it is mighty hard to argue down that "Steely-Eyed" craftsman of Ye Olde Casein Glue Days, who insists that gussets glued and nailed look mighty formidable and give a guy that nice inner feeling of security. If using nails in your gluing operations does this for you . . . . go right ahead. You will have plenty of company.

On the other hand, if you are going all out for weight control and appearance, and do own a dozen or two of assorted clamps, by all means clamp all of your stuff. Use as few nails as possible and save both weight and money.

So why use nails at all? Well, in addition to that vague feeling of security already mentioned, strong arguments for the continued use of the humble little aircraft nail do exist.

An example is in the construction of a truss-type wing rib. Should you decide not to use nails to hold the gussets in place, the gussets must then be clamped, right? If clamps are used, they must remain in place for a minimum of several hours and preferably overnight. To keep from marring the wood, it is necessary to prepare a clamping board or individual back-up blocks to prevent the metal clamps from sinking into your work and messing things up by crushing the wood fibers. Besides all of that, you probably will soon use up most or all of your supply of clamps, and your jig will not be available for assembly of another rib. Employing this method, your production will be limited to perhaps one rib per day with gussets still remaining to be added to the opposite side later, when once again, you must go through the whole process. As if that isn't enough, you have

to mix glue many more times to construct a given number of ribs, so your glue costs will be higher than anticipated. By contrast, using the glue and permanent nailing method, no clamps are needed and the rib may be removed immediately from the jig and another inserted for quick uninterrupted production and increased glue economy.

Of course, there are some places where clamps just can't reach. Then you realize that a nail is exactly what you need . . . . just one tiny little nail.

NAIL STRIP GLUING

When skinning wings and attaching plywood skins to larger structural assemblies, you may prefer not to use permanent nailing and yet you find it impossible to apply pressure with clamps as both sides of the structure are not accessible to clamps. In this case you will find it handy to use temporary nailing strips. (Figure 4)

A nailing strip is used to impose sufficient pressure along a glue line to assure good strong bonding of the wood parts. Once the glue has dried, the nail strip is carefully pried loose and discarded. This leaves a nice, smoothly-skinned surface unmarred by nailheads. You can also use the nail strips any place where permanently-driven nails would be objectionable.

I prefer to use nail strips made of scrap white pine, although plywood or any common wood 1/16-inch to 3/16-inch thick can be used. The usual widths are 3/8- inch and ½-inch, but in some cases these may be as wide as 1¼ inches. Actually the width of the nailing strip should approximate the width of the underlying member. If required, two or more strips

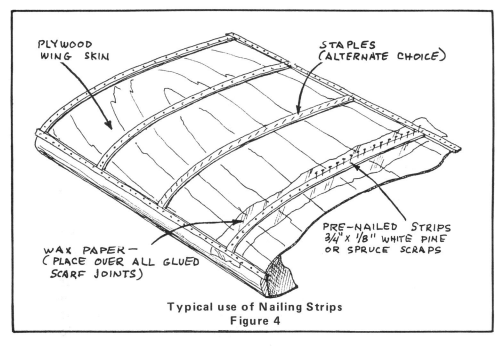

PLYWOOD WING SKIN

STAPLES (ALTERNATE CHOICE)

WAX PAPER — (PLACE OVER ALL GLUED SCARF JOINTS)

PRE-NAILED STRIPS 3/4" X 1/8" WHITE PINE OR SPRUCE SCRAPS

Typical use of Nailing Strips
Figure 4

can be nailed down side by side to effectively spread the pressure over a larger area. Make your strips as long as necessary to span the area of intended use.

Prepare the strips in advance by prenailing a batch of the battens. Remember the nail must be long enough to pass through the strip, plywood, and then into the structure.

As the strips will be carefully split away and the nails removed, it is not necessary to use nails of aircraft quality. Any nail of similar size will serve the purpose. Nail spacing in the strips is governed by the thickness and rigidity of the strip. As a rule, spacing of nails should not exceed 1½ inches.

Wherever nail strips might come in contact with glue, use wax paper under the strips to prevent them from being glued inadvertently to the structure.

Where there is a sharp curvature to the surfaces, it is better to make your nailing strips of plywood (short-grained) or use thinner, more flexible pieces of solid wood. This flexibility will permit them to conform more easily to the contour of the surface.

Nail strip clamping is not normally recommended when the thickness of the plywood exceeds 3/16 of an inch. Instead, use clamps or permanent nailing.

In nailing down the strips, always work from the center of a panel outwards. The first strip is usually nailed down along the primary structural support. The subsequent strips are then worked and fastened down outwards in all directions progressively to ensure that you do not wind up in one end with bulges or gaps in the joint. This sequence of fastening will ordinarily give good results, provided the surface being covered is free from compound curvature.

NAIL STRIP REMOVAL

As you may have suspected, the removal of the nailing strips after the glue has dried can be a bit of a problem to say nothing of the valuable time that is consumed. Whatever technique you may devise, take care not to damage the plywood skin or to excessively enlarge the nail (or staple) holes as the strips are pried loose. Sometimes it is easier to carefully split the wood strips away from the nails with a sharp wood chisel, clear the mess away and pull out the nails with a pair of diagonals.

Nail holes remaining after nailing strips have been removed may be filled with wood filler and surfaced before the final finishing of the surface. Filling the tiny nail holes may not be worth the effort if the plywood surfaces are to be later covered with fiberglass or fabric. Just sand the surface to remove roughness around the nail holes.

Let me sum things up by suggesting that you can use nails any place you want to provided you remember that the use of nails really has nothing to do with the ultimate strength of a glued joint. As a matter of fact, nails must never be used to carry structural loads.

Wood Wing Ribs

The very first part most of us undertake to build in our aircraft projects is a wing rib. We can't all be wrong, so it must be a good logical starting place for any project.

The skills required for wing rib construction are typical of those used throughout the remainder of the project. Ribs are economical to build, and constructing them permits you to get the project underway with a minimum initial investment. Furthermore, building the ribs enables you to gain the feel and experience needed for other construction. If you later find you don't like to do that sort of thing, or cannot discipline yourself to a rather long period of turning out wing ribs, maybe the project is not for you. Maybe you should't be building the airplane in the first place. With no large expenditure of funds to influence your decision, you can gracefully bow out at this point.

It's pretty hard to build a wing without utilizing some sort of ribbed foundation structure. The nearest thing to a ribless wing would be one of composite construction. But even here, airfoil sections akin to the lowly rib must be cut out of some sort of foam material, usually to an exact dimension, shaped, and then assembled prior to skinning the wing.

When you delve into construction methods you find that just about all imaginable materials and techniques have been tried at one time or another in wing rib construction — aluminum ribs hammered out of a single sheet, built-up aluminum ribs riveted together from preformed aluminum strips and extrusions, steel-rod ribs with silver-soldered or brazed joints, built-up wood ribs, solid wood ribs, and of course, a variety of plywood ribs. As you might expect, there are countless variations in design for each of the types of construction mentioned.

JIGS FOR WOOD RIBS

Ribs require some sort of jig during their construction to ensure uniform contours. If a tapered-wing design of any kind is selected, the builder should be aware that his jig requirement and rib building effort will cost him extra time and money. As a starter, it would be necessary to lay out and build a separate jig for each size rib. Lucky are those who are building a rectangular wing design, as they will

Rib jig in the foreground with another in background showing clamping required if no nails are used in the gussets.

only need to make one rib jig. But remember, whichever you build, if you only need to make 2 ribs in each jig, it is unnecessary to build as fancy and as durable a jig as you would if 20 or 30 ribs had to come out of that same form.

After the rib shape is accurately drawn on a piece of ¾-inch plywood, overlay it with wax paper or a sheet of polyethylene to prevent glue from sticking things you don't want stuck. Use headless nails to outline the rib shape and to locate the positions for the uprights and diagonal braces. Small blocks of wood can also be used.

These blocks should be a bit smaller in dimension than the rib stock used. You really don't need too many nails or blocks. Just locate them wherever necessary to hold the rib stock to the exact curvature required.

If you do not intend to glue-nail the gussets (assuming your rib type requires gussets) but prefer to save weight by gluing and clamping only, a slight modification in the jig board and procedure is suggested. (See photo) First, cut the jig board to the approximate shape of the rib, reducing its overall size as much as possible. Then, nail several small blocks (about ¾-inch x 1½ inches x 6 inches) across the bottom of the jig board so that it is elevated above your work table. This permits you to place clamps on each gusset as it is glued in place. The drawback to the glue and clamp method, of course, is that it will be necessary to leave the rib in the jig for at least 6 hours, preferably overnight. You will have the same delay for the attachment of the opposite side gussets.

The new miracle glues that dry almost instantly might change all this, but before using them you'd better check them out for water resistance and durability under adverse heat and cold conditions, then check on your bank account.

Another protective treatment for your jig board consists of drilling a large hole, 1- to 1½ inches, in diameter at each joint intersection of your rib jig. The idea here is that if there is no wood there, the rib cannot stick to the jig, and removal of the finished rib later will be a snap (oops). No need to use protective wax paper on such a jig.

To be assured that your spar openings are properly sized and shaped, secure a block of wood of the same dimension as the spars to the jig board.

The severe curvature at the nose end of most ribs dictates that the capstrips first be preformed by soaking or by steam bending. Soak the capstrips in hot water for about 30 minutes and then clamp them in a bending fixture similar to that illustrated in the photo. This will usually be sufficient for all but the curviest of ribs. To allow for spring-back, cut the bending jig from scrap 4-inch x 4-inch block to a curvature slightly greater than the rib shape at the nose end.

Before loading the capstrips in the bending jig, flex each one to see which way it bends easiest. Be sure to allow the bent capstrips to dry thoroughly before removing them from the fixture and doing any gluing. Unless the humidity is high, 24 hours should be sufficient.

QUALITY CONTROL

After the ribs are removed from the jig, there is really no need to get them all strung on a short stub spar and sanded with a sanding block until all are exactly alike. By the time they are glued to the spars, you may well have introduced slight misalignment in a rib or two. The wing will be sanded after assembly with a long 4-foot block to level everything anyway, so why do it twice?

After removing them from the jig, the ribs need to be trimmed and the spar openings cleaned up of glue runs . . . . so should the capstrips at the gusset areas. Your best tool for accomplishing this is not sandpaper but a 10-inch bastard-cut file. If you still prefer using sandpaper after trying the file, be sure to use a sanding block so that you don't round the areas you don't want rounded.

Capstrip bending-jig, cut on a band saw from a short section of a 4-inch X 4-inch block.

A file is a handy woodworking tool. For example, after you have slipped the capstrips and the uprights and diagonals into the jig for gluing, you can file lightly over each joint to be sure each piece is level with the other. Always level your joints before applying skin or gussets. Always.

TRUSS—TYPE RIBS

These are the ribs built up of strips of spruce, white pine or some other acceptable wood stock. Truss ribs are usually reinforced at their joints with small plywood gussets. When judged on a strength-to-weight basis, these ribs are always the lightest of the rib designs, if properly designed and well built. Unfortunately, they are also the most time-consuming

Lightened plywood ribs with spruce capstrips. Note use of corner blocks at rear spar positions.

to build.

Early in the 1930s a gent named Les Long used a truss rib featuring dual capstrips in an ultra-light design called the "Longster." At first, you might think such a rib would be very heavy, but this was not the case as that truss rib did not have plywood gussets. It was also an easy rib to build although it did require more spruce stock. Using ¼-inch x ¼-inch spruce capstrips, he slipped two of them into the jig for the top part and two for the bottom. Separating the two strips slightly, he slipped spruce uprights and diagonals between them. A dab of glue where needed and a single ¾-inch x 20 gage nail driven through each joint completed the job. That was it. The rough ends sticking beyond the capstrips were then trimmed with a model saw and the rib was finished. Supposedly, one of these ribs could be turned out in 10 minutes. It weighed a mere 3½ ounces (54-inch chord). Maybe builders should take another look at this design. You certainly can't build a regular truss rib in 10 minutes.

The order of efficiency (weight compared to strength) for the different rib types might be shown as follows:

1. Truss rib
2. Lightened, reinforced plywood rib
3. Solid plywood-web with stiffeners
4. Plywood-web with lightening holes and no reinforcements
5. Full plywood-web

While well designed ribs will generally reflect the foregoing order of strength-to-weight standing, the truss type may not always be the best type of rib to use. For example, when shallow or rather thin ribs are required, it is better to use the plywood-web type. This applies as well to some slim wing-tip ribs which do not lend themselves to the truss type of construction.

Truss ribs aren't very effective when used under plywood skins. The gluing operations are ordinarily accomplished by means of nail strips. When the nails are hammered through the skin, the capstrips, being quite flexible, will give and deflect in the process, making that hoped-for tightly-clamped skin joint somewhat questionable. Truss ribs, however, built with long one-piece plywood gussets could certainly minimize the flexibility of the capstrips and make the rib as suitable as a solid web type.

If you glue-nail your gussets and you are using 1/16-inch plywood gussets, ¼-inch x 20 gage nails driven about ½-inch apart will suffice. Use at least one nail in each upright or diagonal. Half-round or quarter-round gusset shapes prove the most effective and can be easily cut out in number with a 2-inch hole saw. Stack a bunch of them at one time for cutting into halves and into quarter shapes. The drilled hole left by the hole saw can be trimmed away or ignored. Always lightly sand or scuff birch plywood before gluing it.

PLYWOOD RIBS

In this category, we include the full plywood-web ribs, with or without stringers, and the plywood-web ribs with lightening holes. I guess it is pretty much true that the heavier the rib, the stronger it is. However, just how strong does a rib have to be? Rib failures are really a rather rare occurance.

Plywood-web ribs, although considered to be among the heaviest of the rib types are easier to construct than the others, hence quite popular with the beginner builder.

Whenever lightening holes are to be spotted on the rib layout, remember that one larger hole will lighten a rib more than two smaller diameter holes. (Figure 5)

The hole arrangement and size are critical since plywood rib failures usually occur around these holes.

METAL TO WOOD CONTACT

If you ever have the opportunity to take part in the disassembly of an old airplane . . . . take it. You will see plenty of rust, etc. It will remind you to protect the wood surfaces before attaching fittings. Here's why:

Wood, as used in aircraft construction, will always have moisture in it . . . . ideally about 12 per cent. We also know that it is necessary to attach to the wood structure, various metal fittings, brackets, and reinforcements made of either 4130 steel or aluminum.

To protect the steel and aluminum parts from corrosion, it is customary to prime them with zinc chromate primer or to have them plated with cadmium. To protect the wood structure, we generally give it two or more brush coats of Polyurethane or Spar Varnish. It would seem that with each of the metal parts being coated with a protective film, that corrosion or dry rot would not be a problem.

Ordinarily that is true in some parts of the country. However, in most localities there is considerable humidity at least sometime during the year. Furthermore, aircraft do not stay in one location and often roam to areas where there is high humidity. Then there are the rains, and (sob) snow!

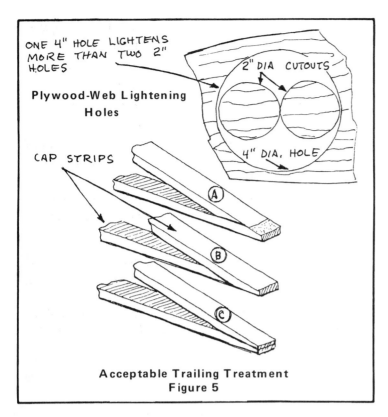

ONE 4" HOLE LIGHTENS MORE THAN TWO 2" HOLES

Plywood-Web Lightening Holes

2" DIA CUTOUTS

4" DIA. HOLE

CAP STRIPS

Ⓐ

Ⓑ

Ⓒ

**Acceptable Trailing Treatment
Figure 5**

When in doubt as to the strength in a particular area, use stiffeners close to the cutout.

Locate lightening holes so that they run longitudinally. Generally speaking, ribs with the face grains of the plywood webs oriented vertically, consistently demonstrate the greatest strength when a full solid web is used. Longitudinal face grain, on the other hand, is better when webs are lightened with holes and when stiffeners are used. Small stiffeners glued near the edges of the lightening holes are very effective in reducing buckling. Fortunately, the resulting increase in weight will often be offset by the increase in strength, but only if that added strength is really needed.

In some antique aircraft you will find plywood ribs featuring a single capstrip made of ¾-inch x ¼-inch spruce with a shallow center groove to receive the plywood web. Another common treatment was to glue and nail capstrips on each side of a plywood web. Both of these construction methods are still used to some extent, but the current trend is to use a ¼-inch plywood-web rib without any reinforcement around its periphery.

Years ago, most builders had to cut out plywood ribs with a small coping saw or jig saw, a very slow way indeed. Today, a band saw permits a more accurate cutting of the ribs and speeds the process remarkably. The lightening holes are cut out with a sweep cutter or a large hole saw that can be chucked in any drill press. Oh, my gosh, no! . . . . never in a hand-held electric drill. A lot of builders are also using routers to cut out both the rib and the lightening holes. An all-in-one jigged operation is possible with a router.

THREE–PIECE WING RIBS

Some ribs are built in three sections with a separate piece for the nose, the center section (between the front and rear spar) and the trailing edge portion. In assembly, each of these pieces is butted against the appropriate spar and nail-glued in place. This type of construction is used to permit building the spar to the maximum wing depth for strength. The alignment is critical in this type of assembly, as any deviation in the vertical uprights at any one of the rib ends could alter the incidence of the wing and/or cause assembly and alignment problems affecting the external contours of the airfoil.

I suggest therefore, that when the plans call for three-piece wing ribs, they be built in one piece in the jig and then later cut apart at the spar openings before assembly.

Each upright that butts against the spar must match all of the other ribs exactly to assure alignment.

HOW TO ATTACH RIBS TO THE SPARS

One-piece wing ribs are simply slipped onto the spars to previously-marked locations and nailed and glued into place. The rib openings for the spars must not be a press fit. Allow .010- to .015-inch tolerance for the glue and the swelling of the wood from the moist glue. (Figure 6)

Do not drive nails through the top or bottom capstrip when attaching the wingribs to the spars The proper attachment is always by means of glue, using cement-coated or brass aircraft nails driven through the rib upright member, on each side of the spar. A couple of nails through each upright should do the job.

When corner blocks are used, try gluing and nailing one of the corner blocks to each rib location on the spar before trying to attach any of the ribs. Positioning the rib after that becomes an easy job as you'll have a solid, fixed back-up against which you can easily position the rib and fasten it without it sliding all over the place while you are trying to nail it.

When gluing the individual rib sections of a three-piece rib to the spars, hold a block of wood against the spar and rest the bottom of the rib section against it for alignment. (Figure 6) Or, for aligning any kind of rib, you might try this: Mount the inboard and outboard wing ribs first. Then span across them with a long straight edge set on top of the ribs near the front end. Place another straight edge near the aft end of the ribs. As you position each rib for gluing, make sure that it touches both straight edges. Alignment is assured. Be certain that all ribs have been slipped on and are in their proper locations before permanently attaching the end ribs.

Assure yourself that the front and rear straight edges are parallel to the main spar when viewed from the front or rear of the wing, unless you desire to build in some degree of wash-in or wing-warp.

HOW ABOUT COSTS?

Well we know that of the wooden ribs, the truss ribs are lighter and more efficient, and that the plywood-slab rib is easiest to make, and that the plywood reinforced rib is somewhat heavier, but also usually stronger . . . . but how do they rate cost-wise?

Figuring the cost on a comparative basis for a typical 48-inch rib in 1976 dollars, we find that the rib costs work out to approximately:

Truss rib	$1.53 including spruce, plywood gussets, glue and nails
"Les Long" spruce rib	$1.18 including spruce, glue and nails
Solid ¼-inch plywood rib	$2.34 aircraft mahogany plywood
Reinforced plywood	$2.68 1/8-inch aircraft plywood, spruce, glue and nails
Reinforced plywood web	$3.52 1/8-inch aircraft plywood, spruce, glue and nails

Apparently, there is no single best rib design for all purposes. Rest assured however, that your designer did consider all the advantages and disadvantages of the rib type he finally selected. If you are designing your own, perhaps this discussion has given you a better grasp of the subject.

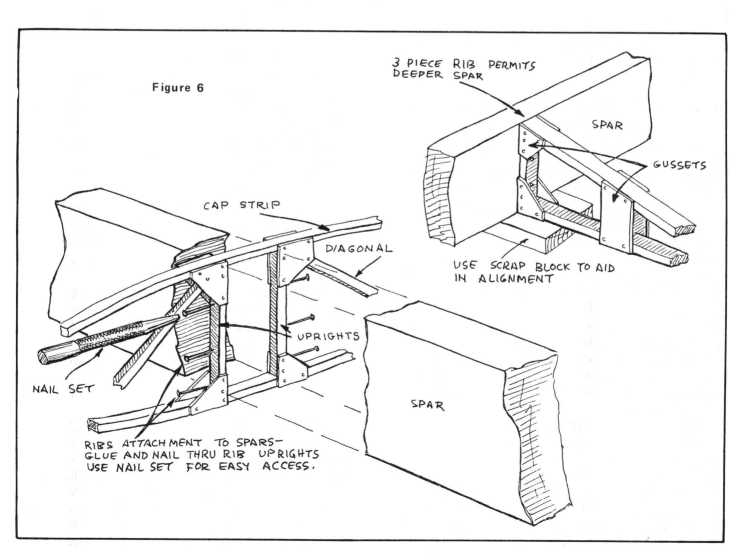

Figure 6

CAP STRIP

DIAGONAL

UPRIGHTS

NAIL SET

RIBS ATTACHMENT TO SPARS—
GLUE AND NAIL THRU RIB UPRIGHTS
USE NAIL SET FOR EASY ACCESS.

3 PIECE RIB PERMITS
DEEPER SPAR

SPAR

GUSSETS

USE SCRAP BLOCK TO AID
IN ALIGNMENT

SPAR

Metal Wing Ribs

A wood truss rib is built up of many small strips and gussets, while the ordinary metal rib is formed from a single metal blank. The work involved in cutting, fitting and gluing the small wood pieces and gussets is considerable. A metal rib, on the other hand, merely requires cutting, and the bending of a flange all around the rib. This is easily done. The metal rib blank is clamped into a forming block held in a vise, and the flange is bent with a plastic mallet.

Even if you compared a solid plywood rib with the metal rib, for ease of construction, the wood rib would lose out if it were necessary to glue and nail capstrips to the plywood. The cost and weight of plywood ribs make the aluminum rib positively shine by comparison (didn't quite mean it that way).

Here's a typical situation: Your plans call for a metal rib. A full-size drawing of the airfoil is included in the package you received as are all the necessary dimensions. Even the rib lightening holes are shown, but there is not a single word about making the ribs.

If you have selected one of the time-proven metal designs, you're in luck because there is much good material written about the construction methods utilized in the older designs. The designers of these and other aircraft have provided much material in the past on aircraft metal construction. You can make most of this valuable information your own by obtaining the manual you need from the designer or, in some cases, directly from the EAA. Buy the manuals, they are cheaper than the materials you might otherwise waste. "Knowing what to do makes learning how to do it easy." (Famous quote by Tony.)

Incidentally, the procedures for making metal wing ribs are identical to those for making bulkheads and all sorts of formers and riblets for the remainder of the project.

TYPICAL BUILDER REACTION

"Build a metal airplane? Not me! I don't have the equipment."

What equipment? Most of us do-it-yourselfers possess quite a few hand tools including tinsnips of some sort. Over and above these, the only special tools which might be needed to make metal wing ribs are:

A plastic mallet and a rubber mallet.
A bar of solder and, possibly, fluting pliers (can be homemade).
A bench vise. A good 3- to 4-inch jaws vise (the the bigger the better) is nice and solid.

Come to think of it, you might already have those common workshop items. If not, a quick trip to the neighborhood hardware store will fix you up pronto. (Pronto is the Texas word for the Japanese word "Hayaku.")

It is easier to be precise when working in metal than in wood. Therefore, you should program yourself to be meticulous and methodical when working metal. Any sloppiness will show in the crudeness of the completed part, or worse, result in a cracked unusable part.

As you may have already surmised, a piece of metal used to make the wing rib is called a blank. This blank is cut out at least 1-inch larger than the form block to allow for the flange, which will have to be bent. The edges of the blank should always be deburred with file and emery cloth before handling and working. The smooth edges will save the part some cracked bends and you some cut fingers.

For some builders, cutting a small piece of metal from a large sheet poses a problem. How in the world do you handle a large, floppy, uncooperative hunk of aluminum?

If extreme economy is of no great concern to you, it would be very nice to have the sheet sheared to approximate rib-size pieces at some sheet metal shop. Of course the shearing will be along straight lines only, hence some waste of metal would occur.

Another way, and perhaps the best way, is to cut out the rib blanks on a band saw. If the sheet is large, you will need somebody to help you support it. A fine-tooth metal cutting blade, running at normal speed does a wonderful job on aluminum sheet.

Still another way is with an electric saber saw using a metal cutting blade. Cutting aluminum sheet does not require slow blade speeds as is necessary when cutting steel . . . . simply use a fine-tooth metal cutting blade. Using a saber saw is something less than a highly-recommended method because it requires the development of a suitable technique and the proper support of the material. Be prepared for a rough job otherwise, and, I would suggest you leave plenty of margin when cutting out the blanks this way.

Since the rib metal is very thin, you can even cut the blanks with a hand-held hack saw blade to which a wood handle is taped. It is a slower method, but effective nevertheless. Again, a fine-tooth blade should be used.

Naturally you can cut out the blanks with tin snips. One of those new type of offset snips is the best, but the standard aviation tinsnips are all right too. Using this method, cut the blank about ¼-inch oversize on the initial cut and then gradually work down to the scribed line. This minimizes the crimping effect on the metal that results each time you squeeze the handles for the cut.

A word about bending metal . . . . no sharp corner bends are permitted in aircraft work. Metal can, however, be bent to a "minimum radius," depending upon the hardness and type of metal involved, with reasonable assurance that it will not crack. When you make the minimum-radius bend, the edges of the metal must be smooth and you must make the bend one time only. (Figure 7)

Your plans undoubtedly call for the use of tempered 2024 or 6061 aluminum. Both of these alloys can be bent and formed into ribs and then installed in the aircraft without heat treatment. For example, I see no earthly reason for using nontempered 2024-0 (soft condition) aluminum, and then hauling the whole batch of ribs to some furnace for heat treatment before they can be used. Sure, soft aluminum is a snap to form, but for simply forming the flanges on wing ribs, the other two grades of metal can be worked almost as easily.

Since wing ribs are made from thin material (.025- to .032-inch) the minimum bend radius will be about 1/8-inch, or as set forth in the plans. Remember, no square corners are permissible in making metal bends on aircraft parts. All edges must have a curved radius, otherwise the metal will crack and fail in use. So much for preliminaries.

MAKING TEMPLATES

Naturally you will want to keep your plans intact and in good condition, but somehow you must transpose that full-size wing rib shape to the hardwood material you will later use to make a rib forming block. This duplicating process is accomplished by using a template. You can make a template directly from the wing rib drawing without ruining the plans. Simply tape the full-size layout of the rib over a

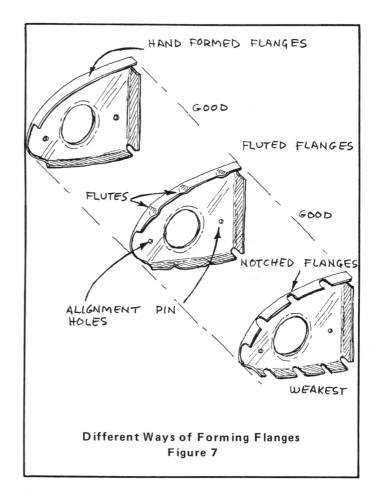

Different Ways of Forming Flanges
Figure 7

sheet of aluminum or galvanized metal and make punch marks through the drawing at each coordinate or significant point along the rib's profile. After removing the drawing, connect the punch-marked points using a flexible batten or French curve. Use a scribe to make the connecting lines through the coordinates. This is more accurate than a felt pen or pencil mark.

Here's another way to transfer the full-size drawing to your template material. Lay a piece of vellum over the drawing and trace it. This vellum tracing is then cut out roughly and stuck to the metal template material with contact cement. Proceed by cutting out the template through vellum and all. The drawing lines will make it easy to trim to exact shape with a file. Leave the drawing attached permanently.

If at all possible, cut the template out on a band saw. Finally, trim the template carefully with a smooth-cut 10-inch file. At this time, mark and remove from the outer edge (flange edge) an additional .025-inch, or whatever the rib material thickness is, to allow for the flange. The template must have this dimensional margin removed from all edges before the final finishing of the template, otherwise, you'll end up with "fat ribs" that could cause all sorts of problems during assembly of the wing.

Two ¼-inch holes to serve as alignment pin holes are now drilled wherever convenient in opposite ends of the template and along the centerline where no structure or attachments might interfere.

Each rib blank will also have to be punched and drilled, from the template, to provide two alignment holes. This ensures that each rib will be properly keyed to the forming block during the flanging operation. (Figure 8)

THE FORM BLOCK

The next step is the construction of a forming block around which the flanges of each of the ribs will be bent.

Select a clear-grained hardwood board for making the rib form block. Birch, maple or a similar material that can be cut and shaped are equally suitable.

Do not use soft wood if more than a single rib must be made, because, during the forming process, the edges of the form block will give way under the metal, and the original radius will get larger and larger.

Two separate form blocks should be made, one for the left-hand ribs, and one for the right-hand ribs. They will, of course, be made from that template you have already completed.

Scribe the outline of the template onto the wood using a sharp-pointed X-Acto knife or a scribe.

Cut the form block out with a band saw or by any other means at your disposal. Clamp the forming block in a vise and carefully work its edges down to the scribed line.

If you have a disc sander with an adjustable table, set it for about 5 degrees and carefully bevel the edge of the forming block all around. Otherwise, handplane and file the edges to this angle. This bevel will compensate for the natural spring-back characteristics that metal has when you try to bend it. The 5-degree bevel may be insufficient in some areas, but this can be determined after you have made a rib and can adjust the bevel accordingly. (Remember, you have to make one right and the other left.)

Round the high edge of the bevel with a file to a nice 1/8-inch radius all around the form block.

If you intend to use just one form block instead of making a left and a right, you might as well round both edges of the block and use the same form block for both the left and right ribs. Of course, since you will have no bevel, in this case, you will have to hand-hammer the flange a few more degrees of bend after the rib is removed from the form block.

THE METAL RIB BLANKS

Cut the blanks about 1-inch larger (all around) than the form block. This allows plenty of margin for forming the flange. Punch and drill the two alignment holes using the template as a drill guide.

Do not scribe the metal blank directly from the original template as that scribed line would be the bend line. No scribe mark must ever go on the metal

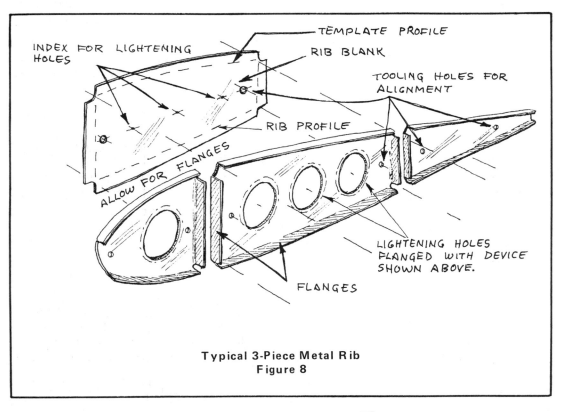

INDEX FOR LIGHTENING HOLES

TEMPLATE PROFILE

RIB BLANK

TOOLING HOLES FOR ALIGNMENT

RIB PROFILE

ALLOW FOR FLANGES

LIGHTENING HOLES FLANGED WITH DEVICE SHOWN ABOVE.

FLANGES

Typical 3-Piece Metal Rib
Figure 8

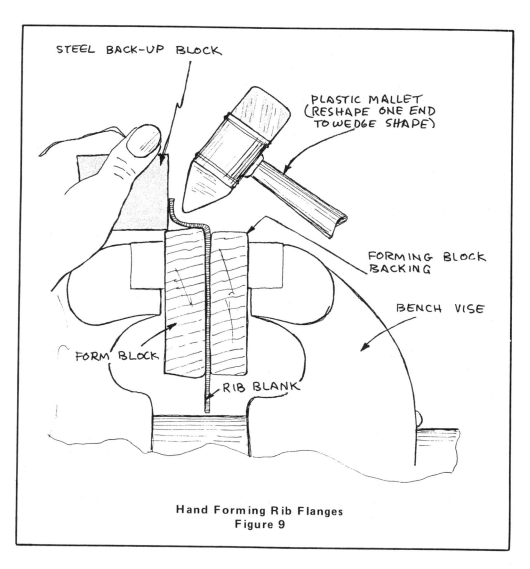

STEEL BACK-UP BLOCK

PLASTIC MALLET
(RESHAPE ONE END
TO WEDGE SHAPE)

FORMING BLOCK
BACKING

BENCH VISE

FORM BLOCK

RIB BLANK

Hand Forming Rib Flanges
Figure 9

of the blank before bending!

FORMING THE METAL RIB

This is anticlimactic after making the template and the forming block, and the easiest and least demanding of the preparatory steps . . . . if done properly.

You will need a plywood back-up block similar to the forming block but somewhat smaller. It should be drilled to accept the two master alignment pins pressed into the basic form block.

Slip the metal blank onto the alignment pins of the forming block and sandwich the blank between the form block and the back-up block. Place the whole thing into a good vise and you are ready to begin hammering the flange down. (Figure 9)

There are three common ways to form a rib flange.

Method one, and the easiest of all to work with is the notched-flange method. Unfortunately, it also creates the weakest rib, as the cut-out areas in the flanges result in reduced strength. Very few current

designs feature this super-simple rib.

Both of the other methods of getting the rib flange to lay down involve some degree of stretching and shrinking of the metal in some manner.

The second method requires fluting of the metal after it is bent, and works best when the flange is bent gradually using a light plastic mallet and numerous light blows rather than a few 'healthy licks". The idea is to avoid stretching the metal any more than necessary. As the bend in flange becomes more pronounced, the metal, because of the curvature of the part, will gradually develop ripples, or a rather scalloped effect, along the flange. Don't worry, this is normal, and the wavy-ness can be removed later.

After removing the rib from its forming block, use fluting pliers, homemade if necessary, to crimp the excess (unshrunk) flange material around the entire rib. This causes the rib to straighten out, and changes its ungainly arched appearance. Do the fluting only in the areas where there will not be any rivets. The depth of the flutes will vary from practically nothing to about a 1/8-inch depth. Use only enough

79

pressure on the fluting pliers to straighten the part. Do this a little at a time noting the effect as you go around the rib. Remember, fluted areas must not interfere with subsequent rivet installation — nor do you want the flute humps to protrude above the rib profile. (Be sure the flute is made in the proper direction.)

Some builders might prefer to file flute shapes into the forming blocks with a ½-inch round file. The flute can then be hammered into the rib flange as the flange is being formed. In theory, when the rib is removed from the forming block, it will be perfect.

The third method of forming the flange is by using the classic metal-forming method involving a shrinking and stretching technique. This requires holding a steel back-up block against the flange while you hammer the flange back and down. The metal is thus forced to flow into the angle area formed by the back-up and the form block. The method is not recommended for use on 2024 but it does particularly well with the softer 6061 aluminum material. A plastic hammer modified to a wedge-shape is the tool to use to force the metal into the corner and down. In the end, there will be a short turned-up standing edge on the flange remaining after the flange has been worked down. Trim this standing edge with tin snips and then slap the flange down smoothly with a bar of solder to finish the job. As an alternate to using the solder bar, you can accomplish the same results by holding a piece of hardwood over the flange and striking the wood piece smartly with a rubber mallet as you move it along the newly-formed flange. It will do just as good a job.

RIB LIGHTENING HOLES

After the rib is formed, the lightening holes can be cut by clamping the rib in the drill press and using a sweep cutter or hole saw. If you don't have either tool, it may be a long, rough road to go as you may have to resort to drilling small holes all around the diameter of the lightening hole and then chiseling the thing out. Man, that is no way to go. Do a little begging if necessary, but try to find someone who has the equipment to do the large hole-cutting thing the easy way.

These lightening holes do significantly reduce the weight of the rib, but the holes, being rather large, also make the rib a bit flexible and somewhat weaker. To restore some of the rigidity to the rib, it is customary to bend a flange around the circumference of each of these holes.

Some builders use a pair of ordinary flat-nose pliers and bend the flanges manually. Of course they do wrap the nose of the pliers with protective tape to prevent scarring the metal. They proceed by going around the hole slowly, bending the flange up gradually until it is bent approximately 30 degrees. For my part, I think this is a slow primitive way of doing it, and if your effort is no more effective than mine, it will result in a crude-looking flange. If you have to use this method, be careful and do not try to bend too much at one time as you might tear the metal. Go around the hole several times, each time increasing the degree of bend slightly.

A somewhat better way to bend the lightening hole reinforcing flanges is to make a lightening hole in a block of wood with a ¼-inch wide bevel of the desired slope (30 degrees will do). Flanging of the

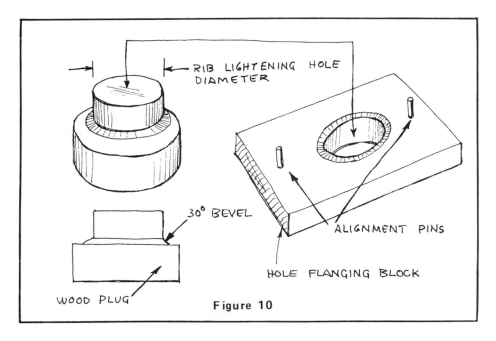

Figure 10

rib lightening holes is done after the rib has been formed. Use a small mallet to gradually hammer the metal down around the beveled lightening hole in the form block. Use alignment pins to keep the rib centered.

The most satisfying way to lay down the reinforcement flange, however, is by utilizing the plug illustrated in Figure 10.

Using it, the flange can be squeezed into the rib by clamping the rib between the plug and the female back-up block and squeezing the whole thing in the vise.

It is not worth the expense and time of making metal lightening hole forming dies of different sizes if they are only to be used once for a single project.

Always, always smooth-finish the edges of metal parts with fine grit emery cloth before bending and forming.

One thing about making metal ribs . . . . once you've developed the knack for it, making the other parts, such as fuselage bulkheads and formers, is merely more of the same.

Fairing Fuselages

As long as fabric-covered aircraft are built, the installation of fairing strips will continue to be an element of construction having a greater effect on the looks of the aircraft than on its structural integrity.

Naturally, none of the essential internal aircraft structure — no matter how beautifully executed — is evident in the finished aircraft, while the fairing strips, supporting and shaping the aircraft's fabric surfaces, are all to obvious. The external appearance of the fuselage is determined not only by the shape and the location of the formers, but also by the lofting of the fairing strips (stringers).

Fairing strips must blend into the structure at their forward and aft attaching points to obtain the best possible effect. Furthermore, the fairing strips should be so positioned that the impression of long, smooth flowing lines is created. After all, this effect is what makes fabric-covered aircraft so appealing to the eye. Crudely or carelessly installed, the fairing strips alone can ruin the appearance of the aircraft.

It is unfortunate that there are instances where the builder finds, after the fabric has been put on and shrunk, that the strain on the fairing strips and their attachment points was more than anticipated, and the fairing strips distorted under the fabric's tension. He learns too late that fairing strips must be stiff enough to withstand flexing under the lateral loads imposed along their length by the fabric, and that they also need to be secured rigidly and supported at sufficiently close intervals to forestall the unattractive consequence of the "sags."

FAIRING WOOD FUSELAGES

Installing the fairing strips on a wood fuselage can be a satisfying stage of construction. Everything is accessible and visible and the results fairly predictable.

Wood fuselages, however, ordinarily have external gussets in the area aft of the cockpit where they can create a "cosmetic" problem. For example, no matter how severely the gussets are beveled along the longeron edges, they nevertheless show up as unattractive bulges beneath the fabric.

A first-time builder may not realize that there is a simple remedy for this condition. Small strips of wood about ½- to¾-inch wide, and of the same thickness as the plywood gussets, should be glued to the longerons as filler strips between each of the gussets. (Figure 11)

A typical fabric-covered wood fuselage sports at least one, maybe two fairing strips along the sides, perhaps three more on the bottom, and several others

Note how smoothly the fairing stringers blend into the plywood turtledeck skin at the cockpit area.

Typical stringer installation on an EAA biplane.

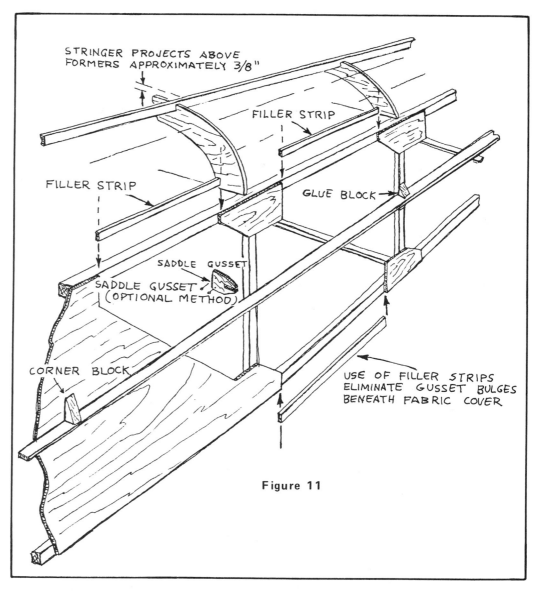

STRINGER PROJECTS ABOVE
FORMERS APPROXIMATELY 3/8"

FILLER STRIP

FILLER STRIP

GLUE BLOCK

SADDLE GUSSET

SADDLE GUSSET
(OPTIONAL METHOD)

CORNER BLOCK

USE OF FILLER STRIPS
ELIMINATE GUSSET BULGES
BENEATH FABRIC COVER

Figure 11

on the top of the fuselage comprising the turtledeck. While some plans indicate locations for each of the fairing strips, others do not show this detail or how the installation is to be made. The details are left to the builder. In the absence of guidance as to the material to be used, you might consider making the fairing strips from spruce, Douglas fir, or aluminum.

Although fir is stiffer and stronger than spruce, it does splinter and split easily and is somewhat heavier. The size of the strips varies a bit from one design to another. Essentially though, for a given size, stringers or fairing strips seem to be quite effective when their cross-sectional dimensions approximate a 4:1 ratio. That is, a ¼-inch thick strip would be approximately 1-inch wide. Fairing strips are normally mounted edgewise. They should be supported at a number of places along their length to minimize deflective bending. However, it is difficult to be specific as to the spacing of attaching points. Sometimes bulkheads

and formers are not spaced closely enough and additional supports may be needed.(Figure 11)

Before permanently securing a fairing strip in place, temporarily tack or clamp it in place and give it one final eyeball check. Back off and view it from the side. Does alignment in relationship to the longerons and overall fuselage shape look natural? Take a look at it from the front end of the fuselage and then from the aft end. By squinting your eyes a bit you can get a better overall visual impression. Does it look right? Are both sides uniform?. Do the stringers (fairing strips) appear as smooth, flowing lines?

FAIRING STEEL—TUBE FUSELAGES

Anyone who has had the unique experience of re-covering an old "tube and rag" job will assume, and naturally so I guess, that fairing strips are almost certain to be found badly warped, rotted or split, and that all fairing strips will ultimately develop a per-

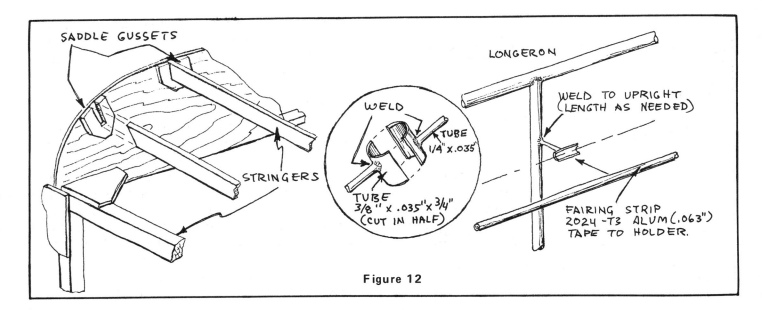

Figure 12

manent sag between the attach points.

When re-covering an older aircraft, it would probably be easier to replace the sagging, suffering stringers than it would be to salvage them. A builder aware of this chronic sagging problem should attempt to minimize the condition with a fairing strip installation that is well supported. (Figures 12 and 13)

Sometimes, warpage is caused by inadequately secured fairing strips. Fairing strip attachment difficulties are a bit more prevalent with welded steel-tube fuselages than with wood fuselages. While wood can be glued to wood in one simple operation with permanent results, steel-tube fuselages require a different treatment. Ingenious use must be made of welded brackets, clamps, cord, rivets, tape and bolts or machine screws to obtain good results. (No amigo, bubble gum does not work just as well.)

Brackets or tabs may be accurately located for welding by using a long temporary stringer clamped to the fuselage as an aid to marking the tab locations. It might be necessary to shim out the strip to obtain the exact curve desired. The length for each tab can be determined at this time by measuring from the fuselage upright to the outside edge of the temporary stringer at each intended attachment point.

The blending of fairing lines and curves is more complex in some steel-tube designs than in most all-wood varieties. For example, in many small biplanes it is difficult to achieve a pleasing appearance around the area of the fin. These small aircraft customarily incorporate an aluminum skin over their turtledeck which ends abruptly at the juncture of the fin. Inevitably the transition of the fin is marked by a harsh edge beneath the covering. Extra attention and preparation is required in this area, particularly if small details are important to you.

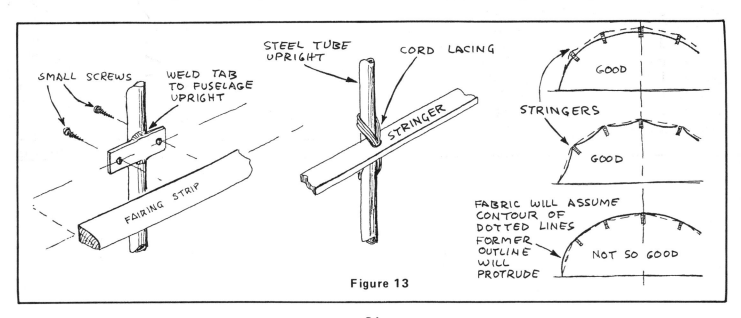

Figure 13

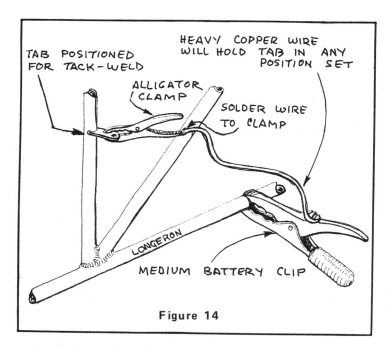

Figure 14

HOLDING DEVICE FOR WELDING TABS

Preparing a welded steel-tube fuselage for the attachment of the stringers or fairing strips generates the need for scads of small metal tabs. As previously mentioned, these must be welded to the structure in order to provide a means for securing the fairing strips to the fuselage frame.

Similar tabs are used to secure formers, instrument panels and other components. With so many to install and align, it becomes quite frustrating when you can't keep the tab positioned where you want it until it can be tack-welded in place. Figure 14 shows you one way to solve this problem.

The feature that makes the device practical is the short, ductile piece of heavy gage copper wire (about 3/32- to 1/8-inch in diameter) which has a small alligator spring clamp soldered to one end, and a medium size battery clip secured to its other end. In using this rig as a holding device, the wire can be bent to any position you want. It will retain that position indefinitely, assuring you of precise positioning of the tab. With both hands free, tack-welding it in place is a breeze. If you cannot obtain a heavy gage copper wire for the purpose, you might try using

a couple of strands of lighter gage wire twisted together. The wire or wires used must have sufficient rigidity to support the weight of the clamp and the tab in whatever position it is bent.

ALUMINUM FAIRING STRIPS

There is a type of aluminum channel strip utilized by companies making aluminum windows and doors that is suited for use as fairing strips and stringers. The channel is sold in 12-foot lengths. It is very light and extremely rigid when secured in place as a fairing strip. In its natural state, each of these strips of channel material seem to have a long, gentle curve along its entire length. This may be due to the manufacturing process, but it in no way presents a problem in its use. The channel can, of course, be bent, drilled, cut, or contoured to whatever shape you wish.

These metal fairing strips may be secured in place with a cotter pin or, if only a single attachment tab is provided on a tube fuselage, fastened to the tab with a small bolt or machine screw. (Figure 15)

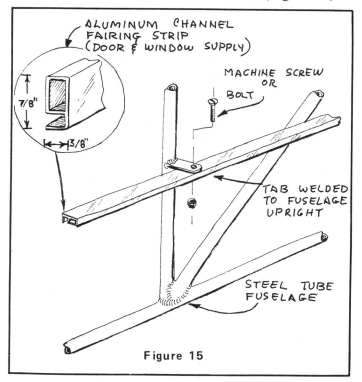

Figure 15

Access Panels

A builder should be aware that plans rarely show where to place inspection doors and access openings. The first-time builder usually is unaware of the importance of having easy access to certain areas for the maintenance and inspection of his aircraft. As a result, he provides access only to those areas necessary to the assembly of the airplane. After all, doesn't everyone preach simplicity of construction? Aren't you supposed to keep the weight down and not add all sorts of things that aren't really essential?

A point well taken, but anything done in the interest of safety must always be considered as essential. Human nature is such that the more difficult and restricted the inspection access, the less likely the aircraft will receive the thorough inspections and the necessary maintenance required to keep it in top-notch condition.

Broadly speaking, you need to provide for three types of access in your homebuilt:

1. Quick access for servicing the aircraft.
2. Easy access for inspection and maintenance.
3. Access for the assembly or disassembly.

ACCESS FOR SERVICING

Most builders do accommodate the need for servicing access. At least they see to it that the oil can be checked and that fuel can be taken aboard. Sometimes there might even be a special door or cover plate permitting access to a remotely installed battery. More often than not, however, this was installed not so much with the idea of providing for future inspection, but rather as being the only way to get that thing in there in the first place.

Sometimes the need for servicing isn't obvious during construction, and the builder simply does not realize it until much later, when he really finds himself face to face with an access problem. Brake master cylinders are frequently accorded this forgetfulness.

One builder ruefully relates that he has to remove his windshield and gas tank before he can get to the brake master cylinders. What makes his servicing situation even more difficult is a center console housing the radio, instruments, fuses and switches that overflowed his regular panel.

Easy access . . . . just like on a fine car.

ACCESS FOR INSPECTION PURPOSES

Those familiar round, concave and aluminum snap-type inspection covers (commercially available) are the most commonly used means of providing inspection access. Although they are used most on fabric-covered aircraft, they also work well on all-wood and metal homebuilts too. This sort of inspection access provides an opening large enough for a look-see, and access for lubrication purposes, but not much else. They are most effective when installed in pairs on opposite sides of the internal mechanisms requiring access. This permits use of both hands for manipulating wrenches, etc.

ACCESS FOR ASSEMBLY, MAINTENANCE, ETC.

Any access opening can, of course, be used as well for servicing, for inspection, and to a limited degree, for maintenance. Sometimes, larger openings must be provided to fulfill a special function. An example of this is the airplane with a three-piece wing. The fairing covers over the wing joint may be removed, not only to reassure yourself that the bolts are still holding the wings together, but also to utilize that entire opening for other purposes.

With the cowling and the metal side panels removed, the heart of the airplane is opened for easy inspection and maintenance.

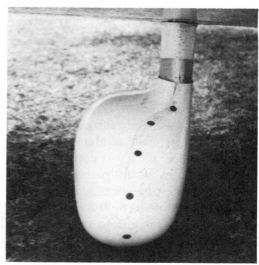
Inspection of the totally enclosed scissor mechanism is made possible by installing quick fasteners.

During construction, you will be installing all of the internally housed systems and controls. As you install each, visualize what access to them would be needed if at some later date it were necessary to remove and reinstall that same component. Certainly, you will never have the same easy access after the aircraft is completed, even though you do install a number of rather generous inspection openings. Special-purpose maintenance openings should be large enough to accomplish whatever work you would need to do in that location.

The gas tank should be installed so that it can be dropped or removed without a major disassembly of the aircraft. Think about it. Gas tanks sometimes cause a lot more trouble than any other component of the aircraft. Make the tank accessible and removable and you will not regret having that capability even if it never has to be used.

WHERE TO PUT INSPECTION OPENINGS

First, let's begin with the assumption that only a minimum number of access holes (only the necessary ones) will be cut into the structure. Often access is afforded through other openings. In the fuselage, for instance, access through the cockpit openings should not be overlooked. In the wings, consider using the access permitted through the landing light openings and that provided by removable wing tips.

Cutting a hole in the structure will weaken it to some degree. For this reason, cut-outs should be located with care and should always be reinforced by the installation of doublers.

Locate wing access holes near the center of a bay (spanwise), if possible, and as close to the front spar as you can. Never put more than one opening in

the same bay. Avoid installing access holes and plates in the top of the wing.

Access holes in wings should be staggered forward and aft of the front spar in adjoining bays to provide maximum access for maintenance functions.

Here's a surprise. The best location for an inspection or access opening is not necessarily where you would expect it should be. In order to reach some mechanisms and control assemblies, you will find it easier to put a wrench to the nuts and bolts if the inspection hole is located slightly off to one side.

Consider adding an access opening wherever there is a control connection. Provide access to the attachment points for the landing gear, wings and tail.

The attachment points for control hinges, especially those installed on wood spars, require access behind the fittings. A few builders might question that concept, though, pointing out that once controls are installed, there is no need to provide for the disassembly or removal of the hinges. Furthermore, they say, if access ever is needed for such purposes, they could cut out some of the skin and make a cover plate for the area at that time. Nevertheless, it would seem a lot easier to anticipate future need rather than to react to it in desperation. Alternatively, the control hinge brackets could be installed with nut plates. Since these hinge brackets have been known to loosen with age, a nut plate installation would permit them to be re-torqued if necessary from the front side. The need for access openings from behind would then be eliminated.

Two access openings on opposite sides of a structure (as those near the tail-end of the fuselage) are much more practical than a single, larger opening. Such an arrangement permits the use of both hands for the job at hand.

MAKING AND INSTALLING ACCESS COVERS

The foundation piece of any access plate is the back-up frame (doubler) which is glued or riveted inside the access hole to the structure's skin. In wood aircraft, these doublers are cut out of plywood and clamped in place while the glue sets. Metal aircraft utilize doublers made of aluminum. These must be riveted in place. In either case, it is easier to make the doublers and install nut plates on them before attaching them to the openings.

The function of a doubler is to reinforce the opening in the skin and to provide a small shoulder against which the inspection plate (cover) will be se-cured. Keep the inside opening of the doubler as large as possible in order not to unduly restrict hand access through the hole. The shoulder it provides need only be about 1/8-inch wide all around except where the nut plates must be attached. (Figure 17)

After the doublers are permanently secured to the openings, the cover plates can be fitted. Allow about 1/16-inch play around the edges because even a single coat of paint on them could make them too big to fit.

Aluminum inspection covers are recommended and will, in the long run, prove to be more practical than those made of fiberglas or plywood. Unlike wood or fiberglas, aluminum covers do not warp or distort with age. Another advantage of aluminum

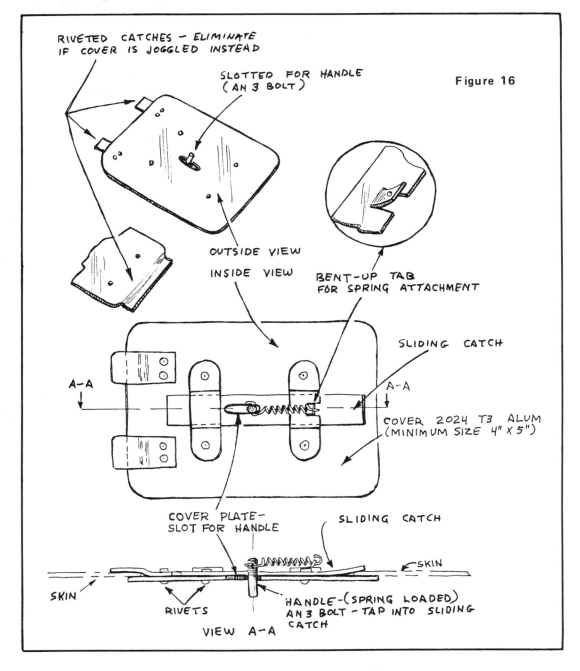

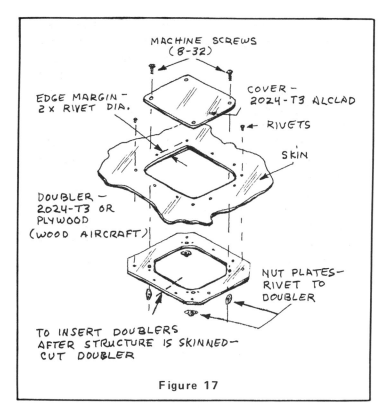

MACHINE SCREWS
(8-32)

EDGE MARGIN -
2 x RIVET DIA.

COVER -
2024-T3 ALCLAD

RIVETS

SKIN

DOUBLER -
2024-T3 OR
PLYWOOD
(WOOD AIRCRAFT)

NUT PLATES -
RIVET TO
DOUBLER

TO INSERT DOUBLERS
AFTER STRUCTURE IS SKINNED -
CUT DOUBLER

Figure 17

plates is in their adaptability to curved areas. Make the covers of thin material (.025- to .040-inch 2024 T-3 aluminum). Tape, or a thin gasket should be used to bring the cover out flush with the surrounding skin, if necessary, to adjust for the difference in thickness.

FITTING INSPECTION PLATES

The big trick in fitting screw-on access covers is in the drilling of the attachment holes to match the nut plates already in place. Naturally, if access from beneath is still possible, it would be easy to hold the cover in place and insert a sharp scribe into the nut plate to mark the locations of the holes for drilling. Without access from behind, however, the spotting of the screw holes gets to be an exercise in problem solving. You can, for example, make a stiff paper pattern of the cover and hold it in position while rubbing the area of the nut plate holes with a rounded dowel to cause an indentation in the paper pattern. These locations can then be transferred to the metal cover with a center punch. Or, maybe, it would be easier to fold the pattern half way back and, while holding it in place, mark it from underneath using a piece of bent welding rod or wire.

More popular in Europe than in this country are the homemade quick-access inspections plates. I don't know why more of us don't use them because they do appear superior in every respect to plates that have to be screwed into place. It is necessary, however, to handcraft these, and therein may be the reason. (Figure 16)

I saw an example of such inspection plates by an English EAA'er. These inspection plates are quite nice, easy to remove, yet secure and fairly flush. The elevator bell crank inspection plates as shown in Figure 17 are about 4 inches x 3 inches in size. Elevator and aileron pulley inspection plates are quite similar to these.

A final reminder . . . . remember if you can't see it and can't get to it, it'll be awfully hard to fix!

Where and How to Install Nut Plates

Sometimes it is years later that you realize you should have taken the time to install a nut plate, or anchor plate as it is sometimes called. A most shameful example is my own. Some years ago, I had quite smugly bolted my voltage regulator to the firewall and stepped back to admire my own skill in putting it in exactly the right place and aligning it perfectly. (I don't recall what it was supposed to be aligned with, but it sure looked good.)

About three years later, I noticed that the ammeter wasn't indicating a lick of work. In time, I determined that the voltage regulator was guilty and derelict in its duties. I decided to remove it and bring it back to my workshop. Egad! Suddenly it dawned on me that I would have to drain and remove my gas tank to get a wrench on the nuts on the back side (front side?) of the firewall just to remove that voltage regulator! What ordinarily would have been a simple five-minute job, suddenly developed a very real potential for a half-day ordeal. Two 10-cent nut plates would have made all the difference in the world right then.

Fortunately for me, this episode had a happy ending as a good friend of mine, an ignition wizard (homebuilder, too), saved me from the slave labor bit. He drove his big ol' Chevy station wagon right up to my bird and hooked up a mess of wire, did some magic tapping and twisting, and in about ten minutes the agony was over. The ammeter became its nervous, but healthy self again. Obviously, the original threat remains. If that regulator ever has to come off . . . . !

From now on all of my voltage regulators, battery boxes and other goodies fastened to the firewall are going on with anchor nuts.

WHERE TO USE NUT PLATES

You can install a nut plate in just about any place that a regular nut would be used. It is apparent that the installation of a nut plate where it is not needed is a bit foolish. You are merely making extra work for yourself. The nut plate becomes priceless, however, when you have a bolt or a machine screw to install and you cannot easily get at the back side of it to put a wrench on the nut. It is especially ef-

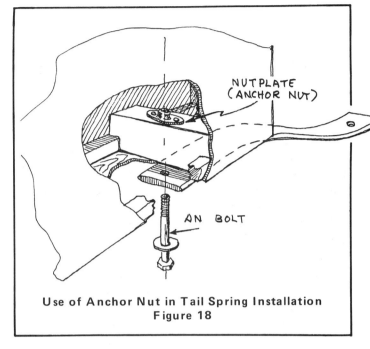

Use of Anchor Nut in Tail Spring Installation
Figure 18

fective where the bolt installation goes through a bulkhead and you would need the services of another person on the other side to hold the wrench for you.

Where else can you use them? Anchor nuts are use extensively in attaching the spinner bulkheads to propeller spinners, in fastening landing gear covers, inspection plates, control hinges, instrument panels, cowlings and fairing strips. How about the attachment of a tail spring? (Figure 18)

WHAT KIND TO USE

The type of nut plate or anchor nut you use does not matter much if it is adaptable to the location where it is to be used. Anchor nuts are even made with a 90-degree offset so that they can be used in that peculiar place where nothing else seems to work.

Among the assortment of self-locking plate nuts (anchor nuts) are the standard AN366 non-countersunk, and the AN373 100-degree countersunk plate nuts. They are satisfactory for use in both tensile and shear applications.

As is the case with most aircraft hardware, these nuts are identified by their AN number. The dash numbers and the thread sizes used for the AN366

Nut Size	Dash Number Steel	Dash Number Aluminum	Thread Size	Attaching Hole Size	Spacing Between Holes*
No. 8	F832	DF832	No. 8-32 NC-2	.098-inch	.688-inch
No. 10	F1032	DF1032	No. 1032 NF-3	.098-inch	.688-inch
1/4-inch	F428	DF428	1/4 x 32 NF-3	.098-inch	1.0-inch
5/16-inch	F524	DF524	5/16 x 24 NF-3	.130-inch	1.0-inch
3/8-inch	F624	DF624	3/8 x 24 NF-3	.130-inch	1.0-inch

AN366/AN373 Self-Locking Plate Nuts

*NOTE: There is such a large variety of nut plates that it would be best to check the spacing between the wing holes from the nut plate you have in your hand. Rather than take a chance on precise measurement and layout of the hole pattern, I prefer the foolproof method of drilling the holes by using a nut plate as a drilling template.

and AN373 plate nuts are quite similar to other AN items. To be specific, an AN366F428 nut plate will accept an AN4 bolt (¼-inch). It is a ¼-inch x 28 (NF thread) self-locking steel plate nut, either all-metal or with a nonmetallic insert. The chart above shows other examples.

Illustrated in the photos are a number of the more common nut plates that can be purchased or scrounged as well as an assortment of the different kinds of fasteners that can be used with the nut plates.

If bought one or two at a time these little jewels are pretty costly. Through surplus sales and at Oshkosh you can buy them in little packages or by the handful and at very reasonable prices.

When buying the nut plates in small grab-bag packages, they may be of assorted sizes. Therefore, if you need a certain number of a specific size, you'd better make sure that you get enough of the size needed for your purposes.

I already mentioned that it really doesn't matter much what kind of nut plate you use provided it fits the bolt of intended use. Perhaps that is too generalized a statement to make. It does matter

for instance, if you use an elastic fiber insert-type of nut plate where it is subjected to high temperatures. Such conditions may be found on heat muffs and in certain areas of the engine baffles. In such locations use all-metal nut plates with self-locking features. Some nut plates are not of the self-locking variety, and this you should know at the time of installation.

Another point to consider: some of those exotic anchor nuts, now available as spin-off items from our space program, are really mini-size all-metal nut plates. These tiny nut plates, while they may fit your bolt, are so small that they present very little bearing surface if installed on a wood surface or at any location where the bolt is subjected to considerable load. In such locations use the standard (larger) AN366 self-locking plate nut or the AN373 100-degree countersunk plate nuts, as they are better for use in tensile or shear applications. However, they are not used where the temperatures will exceed 250-degrees F.

Nut plates are attached to the structure by making use of the holes in each of the wings of the two lug anchor nuts that jut outward from the nut

Nut plates will accept an infinite variety of machine screws, bolts, and other threaded hardware.

There is a nutplate for just about any purpose. Some are even made to go into corners and some have 90-degree offsets.

portion. The fastening means used includes rivets, screws, welds, nails, and even epoxy adhesive. Whatever the method of attachment, you must be sure that the nut will remain secured. I can't think of anything worse than to have an anchor nut start turning on you when you have to remove the bolt. If you use small screws you may have to drill the holes in the attachment lugs a bit oversize to accommodate the screws to be used. If the screws are very tiny, or the wood very soft, or if you use nails, it might be good insurance to put on a dab of epoxy adhesive under the anchor nut before you secure it. Rather than drill tiny pilot holes for the screws, an icepick or an awl will make a good starting hole. Don't be misled by an assumption that rivets are strictly for use in attaching the nut plates to aluminum, and that screws must be used in fastening the nut plate to wood frames. You can also use rivets in wood. If you can obtain soft commercial rivets for this purpose, it would make your task much easier, especially if the installation has to be made in some hard-to-reach place on the aircraft.

ATTACHMENT OF THE NUT PLATES

The holes drilled in the member through which the bolts pass need not be "close-drilled." What are known as "clearance-drilled" holes are snug enough for anchor nut installations. For example, a No. 12 drill is usually specified when drilling a hole for a 3/16-inch bolt. This would be too snug a fit for a bolt going through the structure for a nut plate. Therefore, a slightly larger (clearance-drilled) hole using a No. 8 or a No. 10 drill bit permits easier installation and assembly.

There's no big trick to installing nut plates. If you have never done it before, however, you are apt to make a few false starts before you figure out the best sequence of events. Installation preparations require the sequencing of two different size holes that need to be drilled, and the countersinking of two of them. Naturally, these holes must be properly located and spaced. So you see, even the simple anchor nut installation takes a bit of preplanning. The sketches(Figure 19) show the sequence of the pre-

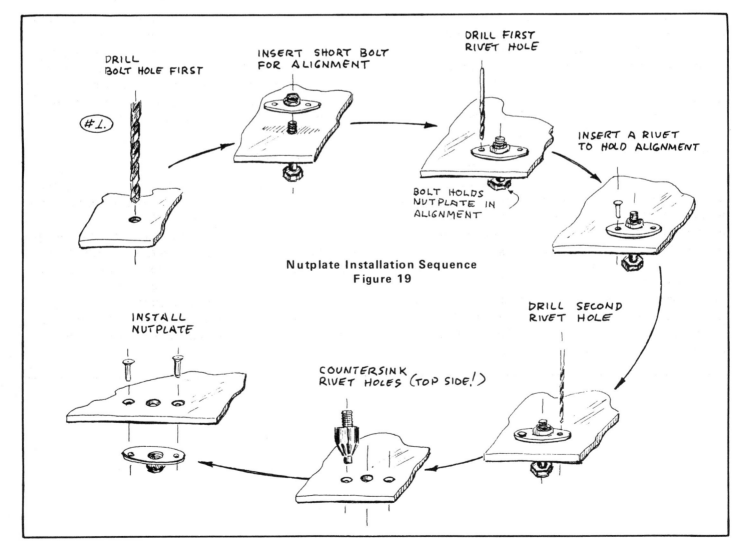

Nutplate Installation Sequence
Figure 19

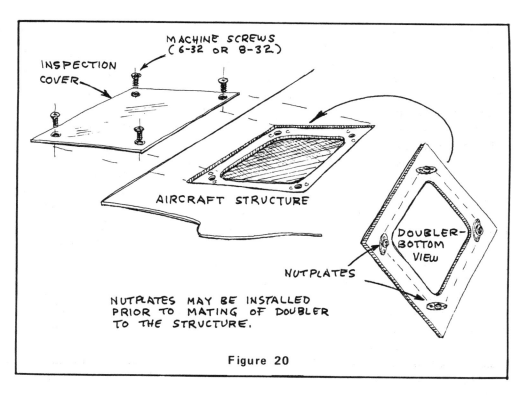

INSPECTION COVER

MACHINE SCREWS (6-32 OR 8-32)

AIRCRAFT STRUCTURE

DOUBLER-BOTTOM VIEW

NUTPLATES

NUTPLATES MAY BE INSTALLED PRIOR TO MATING OF DOUBLER TO THE STRUCTURE.

Figure 20

paration steps required for installing an anchor nut. You can see that if you are installing several nut plates, switching to another drill size, and then to a countersink, can be tiresome and time-consuming. It would help if you had a couple of electric drills handy.

Sometimes it is far easier to install the nut plates on the frame of an inspection plate opening prior to building it into the airplane. This would permit the riveting to be done in a vise. Squeezing rivets in the vise is preferable to setting them by hammering. You could use a riveting gun, of course, but setting things up for bucking 8 rivets seems kind of foolish . . . .unless you are building an all-metal project and are doing a lot of riveting most of the time. (Figure 20)

Fitting a cover plate to an inspection opening sometimes takes a bit of figuring. This becomes a bit of a problem when you do not have access from behind the plate and you need to spot the places to drill in the inspection cover to match the installed nut plates. One way to do it is to grind a point on a bolt or machine screw of the proper size and screw it into the nut plate so that the point projects slightly. Place the inspection plate or cover in place and tap it ever so lightly with a tack hammer directly over the area of the nut plate with the protruding point of the bolt. A slight prick point will be made in the cover and the hole can be drilled with confidence that it is in exactly the right place.

WILL YOU REMEMBER?

Incidentally, the EAA Service Manual is the homebuilder's equivalent of the store-bought aircraft manual. One should be activated by the builder for his project as soon as construction starts. In it would be recorded anything and everything about the airplane. Where you have installed nut plates is an important bit of information. Should you ever have to remove an elevator, aileron, or rudder hinge in some distant future . . . . it is almost certain that you will have forgotten whether you were clever enough to use nut plates, and in what places.

Cowlings

How many homebuilders will candidly admit that their cowling was developed for its looks . . . . its nice lines? Often it is not until after the molds have been painstakingly formed, waxed and the cowling completed, that the problem of cooling the engine finally receives its share of attention. Common practice seems to call for two uniform air inlets up front somewhere where they won't louse up the nice lines, and some sort of exit for the hot and bothered air. Oddly enough, most of the builders are quite successful. Some, however, are not. We read of them often in SPORT AVIATION magazine. It is becoming something of a treat to read of a test flight during which the builder did not experience excessive oil or cylinder heat temperatures. Such excessive engine temperatures are usually caused by a poor baffle installation or a poorly designed cowling, sometimes both. Some of the homebuilts currently flying without apparent trouble may not be as trouble-free as their owners believe. Their engines may be suffering from hotspots inside the cowling.

How important is this cowling business? Plenty important!

Some old time homebuilder types knew and practiced the art of cowling refinement, not cosmetically as is the current rage, but with efficient cooling as the primary objective. I think I can make my point better by sharing with you a few candid remarks from Harold "Pop" Emigh (Helicom, Inc.), a real pioneer among homebuilders. Pop says:

"Cowling an engine can be a very scientific job, as I learned back in 1947 while attempting to pass all climb tests in the Emigh Trojan airplane during its certification. There can be as much as 15 mph difference in top speed by designing the proper cowling, as I learned!

"In one test I had a small opening at the bottom just ahead of the nose wheel strut. The engine was overheating but I had a good top speed. I moved the opening forward 2 inches and riveted a lip on it to block some of the air that may have caused a reversed flow. The engine temperature was satisfactory, but the airspeed was about 15 mph slower than with the first opening.

"I then made an adjustable scoop that could be operated from the cockpit. To my surprise the scoop

Note the similarity of the cowls between this Varieze and the Sonerai in the adjacent photo. One's a pusher and the other a tractor.

The NASA duct just under the spinner feeds air under the VW crankcase for cooling purposes. Essential to VW engines.

found its own level. The temperature went down . . . . the airspeed went up and the noise level was reduced. I measured the opening and nailed it solid at this point.

"Another problem was the right front cylinder (looking aft) was overheating. I had some experience in a small Stinson back in 1941. The right front exhaust valve kept burning up in the Franklin engine. A little study showed that the prop, in passing the opening, was dragging the air with it and blocking this cylinder. I did some looking around and found that a Bellanca was using an extended lip to catch the air.

"I thought that I would use turbulence instead. So, I indented the lower edges of the opening and cured the problem in the Trojan. I did it to both sides just for looks.

"In looking back to 1941, I would bet that the Stinson had the same problems with the Franklin engine. It seemed unreasonable that the cylinder closest to the opening would overheat, but it did. Of course, we had thermocouples all over the engine during these tests.

"In our helicopter cowling we use an axial-flow fan on top of the engine and enclose the front of the engine to force the air under pressure between all cylinders and as far around the cylinders on the back side as possible to take advantage of the fins.

"I leave the back half of the fan wide open to cause a scavenging flow of air past the cylinders.

"If this isn't done I call it stagnation. I have a heck of a time keeping the homebuilders from shutting off this flow on the back side. They seem to think that they can force more air down the front side by blocking the aft side of the fan.

"One man was talking of chasing down an anemometer, or whatever they call the gadget. Upon my suggestion we simply ran the airspeed line into the cowling and got all of the answers. We shoot for 60 mph in the cowling, for what its worth.

"It takes horsepower to cool an engine, and the most efficient cowling will do the job with less power. So it pays to do a little research on the subject.

"I believe I must have climbed to stabilizing altitude a hundred times and cut up a 4-foot x 12-foot sheet of aluminum in cooling the Trojan to my satisfaction." Signed: Harold "Pop" Emigh, Helicom. Inc.

That's the way it was 37 years ago when Pop Emigh was developing the cowling and baffles on his Trojan, and it is still true today.

As enlightened as most of us think we are, it is always surprising for me to find that sometimes even the experienced builder neglects to take advantage of the techniques and experiences available to him.

Cowlings having wide openings such as this should never be split vertically. Long, flat opening would require reinforcement.

If you are willing to accept the challenge. Metal cowlings can be made with compound curves and welded at the seams.

This cowling has a single air inlet to handle all of the engine's air needs. Requires careful engineering and ducting.

There are many good features that can be worked into the average cowling installation to make it better and more efficient.

Before you make any molds or cowling components, it would be a good idea to build and install your complete exhaust system . . . . first! If you do not take the time to do this little chore, you may well discover some surprises when you later try to fit your exhaust system within the confines of a too-snug cowling. You often see cowlings with cute little (unwanted) streamline-bumps and covers . . . . mute evidence usually of a builder's hurry to make the cowling before his engine was completely installed. Strive to obtain about ½-inch minimum clearance between the engine and the cowling in all close areas. Greater clearance is advisable around the exhaust stacks because the hot stacks could cause problems like burning of paint or buckles and bulges in fiberglass. Of course, insulation with asbestos could be resorted to as a partial solution, but it is better not to have to make remedial fixes in the first place.

Hot air is difficult to route downward as it has a natural tendency to rise. If you had your outlet in the top of the cowling, it would dispose of the hot air off the engine nicely, but who wants a hole in the top of his airplane, or to have hot air dumped in his face or over his windshield?

Actually, most aircraft engines used in custom-built aircraft are designed to be cooled by routing the air down through the engine. To alter this natural arrangement usually creates more difficulties than most of us would be willing to accept.

For the low-wing job, exhausting the air through side outlets allows a natural flow of the air with the minimum of drag, as it is dumped into the relatively low-pressure area over the wing. This is quite a popular arrangement in the T-18 and on some other high-performance aircraft.

One thing most experienced hands will agree on is that having the air exit in more than one area is pretty poor practice. I saw one biplane that had five air outlets, two on each side and one on the bottom. It was a sign of desperation no doubt.

You are much better off if you will decide to either have side outlets, or the more common under-the-fuselage-outlet. Sometimes routing the air out the bottom is not as easy as you might think, as there may be a rather turbulent area of higher pressure there that is not conducive to the proper scavenging of the hot air. Some builders and manufacturers (also in desperation) resort to the installation of a large, deflected lip along the bottom opening in an effort to create a sort of venturi-like low pressure area to improve the airflow through the engine cowling. If you have to depend upon this double-ugly solution,

This simple, straight metal cowling requires no nose-piece. It takes advantage of the spinner's size.

Another metal cowling. Simple, but pleasing to the eye.

Just about the ultimate in simplicity. Such a large air inlet area is not ordinarily needed, even on a slow airplane.

Air outlet gills on either side of fuselage are very effective for low-wing aircraft.

the air inlet openings help maintain a smooth flow of air into the engine by reducing turbulence around the propeller hub inlet area. So will a good spinner.

Since cooling effectiveness is greatly influenced by the velocity of the aircraft, or rather, the airflow through the engine, you can see that if an aircraft is operated at lower speeds, as in climbing attitudes, cooling becomes a serious problem. This condition is also experienced in prolonged ground operations where the flow through a tightly-cowled engine is drastically reduced. Aircraft with lower cruise speeds tend to sport larger air inlets in their cowls.

THE TROUBLE WITH MOST COWLINGS . . . .

The complete removal and installation of some cowlings can waste close to an hour of your time. This is as true for some mighty fine production-type aircraft as it is for many homebuilts. On one very nice retractable store-bought, I counted more than 40 screws securing the cowling on just one side. Can you imagine removing more than 80 screws just to take the cowling off? Here is a place where improvement is needed in a big way.

The use of an excess number of fasteners seems to be a universal fault with homebuilders, too. The idea being, I suppose, that better too many than not enough. On some cowlings (including my own) it would seem that every other fastener could be omitted without impairing the cowling's security.

You should definitely make your cowling as easy to remove as possible. I guess it is no secret that most EAA Designees advise builders to check under the cowling of an operating homebuilt (any aircraft, for that matter) as often as practical. But

you should probably restudy your cowling and cooling installation and rework it.

The location and size of the outlet opening in the cowling should be as carefully worked out as the inlet opening. Ordinarily most builders provide a slightly larger area (about 10 per cent larger) for the air outlet than for the inlet opening. This is necessary as the air, after it has passed through the engine, loses some of its velocity on entering the cavernous engine compartment.

To assure an adequate supply of cooling air, the inlet opening should be the minimum area necessary for the job, and it should be located as squarely as possible to the flow of air. Well-rounded edges around

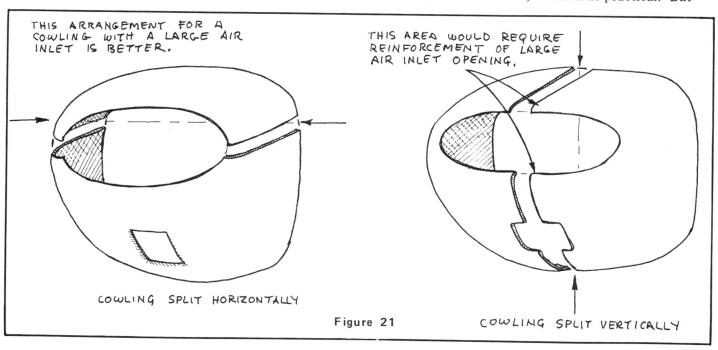

THIS ARRANGEMENT FOR A COWLING WITH A LARGE AIR INLET IS BETTER.

THIS AREA WOULD REQUIRE REINFORCEMENT OF LARGE AIR INLET OPENING.

COWLING SPLIT HORIZONTALLY

Figure 21

COWLING SPLIT VERTICALLY

how often do you suppose that would happen with some 40-50 machine screws in the cowling holding hands with their nutplates? The way to prevent trouble is to look for the signs first. In this regard, the engine is numero uno as far as aircraft health, and your own are concerned.

BEFORE YOU SPLIT THAT COWLING

While we have but two choices of material for making cowlings, aluminum or fiberglass (the expense of the exotic Kelvar or Carbon Fibers is still too high for most of us), we do have an infinite number of ways of assembling the cowlings to the aircraft.

First of all, the single-piece cowling should not even be considered for any sport aircraft installation. Its great drawback is that the propeller and spinner must be removed before you can remove or install the cowling. A one-piece cowling does look good, but it is an invitation to neglect the engine.

The decision facing the builder when he first takes a good look at his newly-acquired fiberglass cowling is how to split it for installation. There are two basic ways, split it vertically or split it horizontally. Both methods have advantages and drawbacks. Properly installed (with quick-release fasteners), you can remove either side of the cowling for easy access to one entire side of the engine. Of course, if there are a lot of nutplates and screws along the upper and lower seams holding the two sides together, you are really gaining very little because by removing just a few more screws you can remove the entire cowling. In such cases it doesn't matter whether the split is vertical or horizontal. (Figure 21)

There is one more thing to point out if you plan on a vertical split. Do not use it with a cowling that has a single large air inlet opening in it. This wide area across the front would have to receive special reinforcement to support it adequately against the slipstream, and any reinforcement in this area runs into problems of clearance and extra work and weight . . . . conditions that cause allergy outbreaks in most builders.

What was said of the vertically split cowling can be applied to the horizontally split cowling. You should make it easy to remove either half without disturbing the other. This is very important when it is time to change oil and clean the oil screen.

It could be that you would prefer to make a couple of large, hinged doors on either side of the cowling to give the required access to the engine for inspection and maintenance. The question, however, remains . . . . can you change oil easily with such a set-up?

The opening side panels are ideal for the fiberglass/aluminum combination cowling. (Figure 22)

This cowl features a quick-opening hood and a buried air outlet gill with a controllable opening.

Air scoop apparently is an attempt to cope with a cooling problem. Could feed air to the carburetor of course. Who knows? It's impressive though.

If your cowl opens up quickly, inspections are easy and will probably be more frequent.

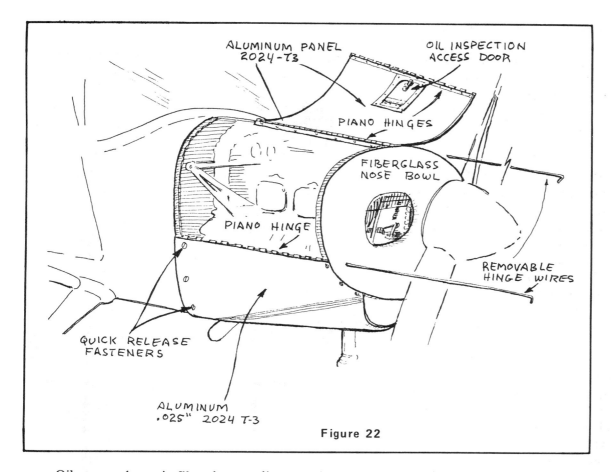

ALUMINUM PANEL 2024-T3

OIL INSPECTION ACCESS DOOR

PIANO HINGES

FIBERGLASS NOSE BOWL

PIANO HINGE

REMOVABLE HINGE WIRES

QUICK RELEASE FASTENERS

ALUMINUM .025" 2024 T-3

Figure 22

Oil access doors in fiberglass cowlings are best made of aluminum sheet (about .032-inch 2024 T3) unless there is considerable compound curvature in that particular area. An aluminum door will not warp with heat and age as a fiberglass piece might. If the metal door is thinner than the cowling in that section, attach a cork or rubber weatherstrip to build it up so that the little door is flush with the cowl when it is latched shut. Latches in oil inspection doors should be of the quick-release spring-type made especially for that purpose. You should not have to go search for a screwdriver or a coin just to check your oil. The door should be large enough and positioned so as to make the job easy and quick.

Fiberglass cowlings are at their best if there are a lot of compound curves in the desired shape. If there are fairly large flat areas, however, fiberglass doesn't come out very well when compared with aluminum sheet. Study the general shape of the cowling you intend to make from the drawings to determine if it wouldn't be better to just make a good nose-piece out of fiberglass and then to use aluminum sheet for the sides, top and bottom. It may be that you will need to make the bottom of fiberglass too, to achieve the curvature you want. There is absolutely no reason why you cannot mix both fiberglass and aluminum to obtain exactly what you want in a cowling.

Caution: *Never use commercial or soft aluminum for cowlings (and leading edges); use the tougher 2024 T-3 or similar tempered aluminum.*

A lot can be said for the combination fiberglass/aluminum cowling. Such a combination provides a cowling with the minimum of work, since all that has to be molded is the nose-piece. Quite often even a stock nose-piece can be obtained that is suitable for your aircraft. If you can't find a stock nose-piece, you might be able to borrow one and make a plaster mold of it. A number of advertisers in SPORT AVIATION manufacture a large variety of cowlings and components to satisfy most needs. With a nose-piece it's a simple matter to secure it in position and fit the aluminum sides, top and bottom pieces. Compound curves, of course, are virtually ruled out for such a cowling. Nevertheless, a surprising choice of forms or shapes is possible so don't be too hasty in ruling out the combination aluminum/fiberglass cowling for your own aircraft. Ordinarily, the cowling will be lighter than an all-fiberglass bonnet.

The fitting of the aluminum panels requires that the exact shapes first be determined by the use of heavy paper patterns and the exercise of a whole lot of patient cut-and-trim work. A roll of masking tape can be used to fill places on the paper patterns where your cut-and-fit technique turned out too short here and there. Simply stick small pieces of tape on to fit into the exact contour you desire. The paper or cardboard pattern, when removed, will carry the masking tape bits with it making the exact outline you wanted all along. Lay on another strip of tape to the back side of the pattern following closely the new outline formed by the masking tape correction. This will stiffen the pattern, making it easier to use.

A good place to start fitting is on the bottom piece after the nose-piece is clamped in place. Mark a centerline on the paper and work outward from it on both sides. Incidentally, do not try to save time by making a pattern for only one-half of the cowling and then transferring the pattern to the opposite side. Remember, in the 4-cylinder aircraft engines, the cylinders are not exactly opposite each other. This peculiarity alone can throw your shortcut plans off.

In trimming your patterns (and later the metal), trim a little at a time until you obtain the snug fit you want. Never try to get your perfect fit in a one-shot attempt . . . . it won't work out most of the time, and all you will have is a large sheet of ruined material on your hands.

As a rule, cowlings are not attached to the engine at any point. The reason is obvious as the rubber shock-mounted engine does dance about somewhat. If the cowling were secured to the engine, it wouldn't be long before it would begin to self-destruct at the fasteners or attachment points.

Attachment of the cowling sections to the aircraft along the firewall area is accomplished by the use of small aluminum brackets with either nut plates or some other quick-release receptacle attached. The brackets are secured to the firewall by riveting, bolting or even welding, depending on the type of con-

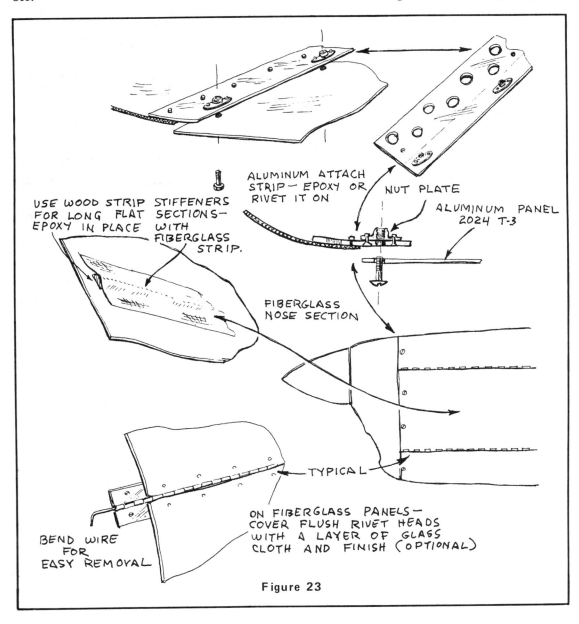

Figure 23

100

struction used. (Figure 23)

A practice that could be improved, as I have already mentioned, is the use of nutplates and machine screws to attach the cowlings. While this is an excellent way to do it, it is very time-consuming in terms of cowling installation and removal. A better way would be the use of one type of the quick-release fasteners such as the Dzus, the Camlock, etc. It could be that economical sources for the purchase of these quick-release fasteners are harder to locate. I think that because many builders have never installed such fasteners, they may not even consider trying to do so. The fact that such fasteners require special tools also contributes to the reluctance of the builder.

Every reasonable attempt should be made, however, to install the cowling with quick-release features.

The easiest way to accomplish this is through the use of piano hinges. The reliance on piano hinges not only as attachment hinges, but also a form of a quick-release type fastener, is becoming quite common. More and more cowlings utilize easily removed piano wires to provide the access needed. The system is neat, light, and very adaptable to most locations. Do not think, however, that you cannot use this piano hinge-type of fastener where there is a curved section. You can, and very effectively so. Naturally the radius of curve has to be within reason. You can check this out by bending a piece of piano hinge to whatever curve is needed and then see if you can remove and reinstall the wire. Naturally, if the piano hinge is installed on a curved surface you will not be using it as a hinge, but as a means of securing two sections.

A FEW FINAL POINTS

If we accept the premise that as much as 90 per cent of the air in the path of the engine is deflected around it and only 10 per cent of the air makes its way through the engine, we can also conclude that the design of an effective cowling must provide a good clean profile with a smooth flow of the air around it.

As only 10 per cent or so of the air is forced through the cowling for cooling purposes, it is necessary that this relatively small amount of air be efficiently utilized to cool the engine with the minimum expenditure of power.

A useful test for cooling adequacy is to see if you have what the engineers refer to as a pressure differential of at least 5 inches of water. One way to check the equivalent of this was described earlier in Pop Emigh's remarks. Use an airspeed pitot tube in the engine inlet area and locate a static tube at the outlet area. As Pop said, if you get a reading of 60 mph or more, you're alright. However, in the case of the faster aircraft, such as the 150-mph plus types, a reading of about 100 mph would be expected.

Fuselage Alignment

You want your airplane to track through the air like an arrow, not sort of sidle along like a scavenging land crab. So, you will have to control its alignment carefully during the construction and assembly phases.

A well built structure is one whose alignment is inconspicuous. If everything looks reasonably aligned, nobody notices it as most of us are blissfully oblivious of the obvious norm. Let the alignment of the rudder, wing, or stablizer end up leaning a bit from that imaginary reference line though, and you will find yourself

cringing everytime you look in that direction. And you will hear your share of snide remarks about it as a constant reminder of your transgressions.

If, for example, the incidence of one wing is greater than the other . . . . bad news. Likewise, if one wing is warped during the skinning process, poor flight characteristics will result. It is a matter for concern, because even a slight twist in one wing can lead to control difficulties and undesirable stall behavior. A large error can even render the aircraft uncontrol-

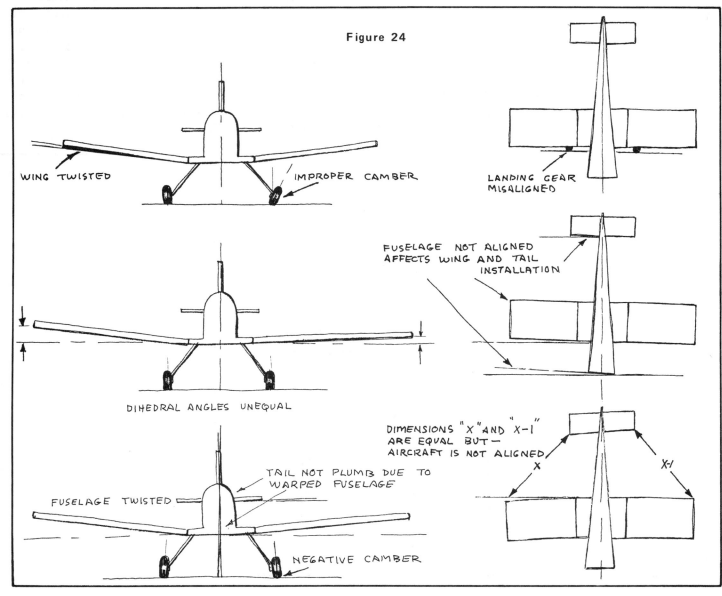

Figure 24

WING TWISTED

IMPROPER CAMBER

LANDING GEAR MISALIGNED

DIHEDRAL ANGLES UNEQUAL

FUSELAGE NOT ALIGNED AFFECTS WING AND TAIL INSTALLATION

TAIL NOT PLUMB DUE TO WARPED FUSELAGE

FUSELAGE TWISTED

NEGATIVE CAMBER

DIMENSIONS "X" AND "X-1" ARE EQUAL BUT — AIRCRAFT IS NOT ALIGNED

X   X-1

lable. (Figure 24)   The illustrations show some of the common boo-boos that any builder can make without even trying (Notice the statement reads any builder, not just an inexperienced one!)

A misaligned fuselage can generate more problems than anyone deserves. This becomes apparent when you realize that the fuselage, in most designs, is the foundation for the rest of the airplane. Quite often, the wings, tail surfaces, and even the landing gear attach directly to some part of the fuselage. The attachment of these structural components is often by means of metal fittings bolted or welded to the fuselage at a particular station or bulkhead. If a builder is not careful, he will assume that the bulkhead or station location automatically locates his fitting for him, and that no further alignment measurements are necessary. How wrong!

It is easy to be lulled into a premature sense of well being after you have completed two identical fuselage sides in the same jig. How could anything go wrong with the assembly after that? Aren't both sides exactly alike, and isn't it simply a matter of cutting and fitting the cross members? True, but if the symmetry of the fuselage and the proper placement of the firewall and the various cross members and bulkheads is not geometrically controlled, the whole fuselage can be thrown off alignment. If that happens, then your wing, tail surfaces and landing gear may go on cockeyed. (Figure 25)

Before you start the assembly of the fuselage, a reference line should be established on your work surface over which the fuselage sides will be erected. This reference can be a drawn line or a tightly stretched wire or cord. An inked line, drawn with a felt pen makes a very visible and effective reference. A stretched line can only be used if the fuselage is erected on raised supports that permits the presence of the line beneath without interference with the assembly. At

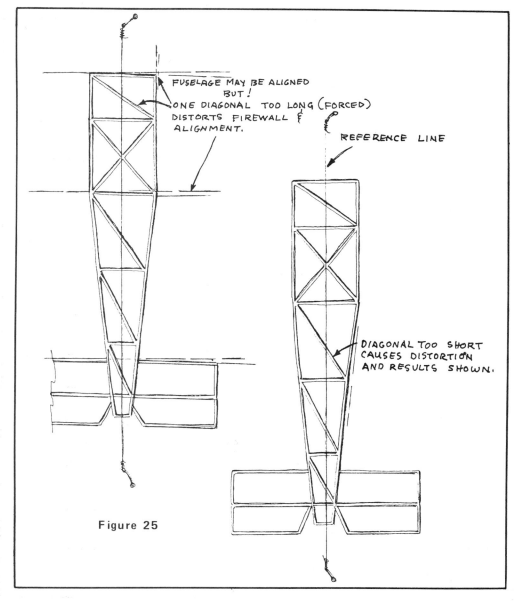

FUSELAGE MAY BE ALIGNED BUT! ONE DIAGONAL TOO LONG (FORCED) DISTORTS FIREWALL & ALIGNMENT.

REFERENCE LINE

DIAGONAL TOO SHORT CAUSES DISTORTION AND RESULTS SHOWN.

Figure 25

one end, a line should be drawn across the reference line at a 90 degree angle. This is a very important starting point since the firewall will be positioned over it. If the firewall is not perfectly oriented with the fuselage reference line, any error at that point (station) will be locked in and will be continued all the way through the assembly of the rest of the fuselage. This can be serious if not caught in time, and compensating corrections made to the engine mount, wing and tail attachment points. Another way the fuselage can be off is in its cross section. If the fuselage sides are not monitored continuously for squareness with a large carpenter's square, it is very possible that the cross section may assume the semblance of

a parallelogram instead of maintaining the desired rectangular shape. Such a cross sectional warping would undoubtedly also have an adverse effect on the wing alignment, the fitting of the gas tank, and perhaps, the alignment of the instrument panel.

If the symmetrical and cross sectional integrity is not maintained, the rudder post and the stabilizer installation can become very difficult, as their location and alignment is definitely influenced by the fuselage and its reference points. (Figure 26)

In low-wing all-wood fuselages the alignment of the wing with reference to the fuselage is usually fixed by the location of a main bulkhead. If this bulkhead is not positioned squarely and at the proper vertical angle to the fuselage reference line, you may have difficulty with the alignment of the wing, and with the establishment of the proper incidence. Incidence error can result in an abnormal nose-low or nose-high flight attitude in cruise. Either condition is undesirable because of increased drag.

When installing a wing center section in the fuselage, an alignment error as small as 1/8-inch on one side of the fuselage could be compounded to a 1½-inch error at the tip of a 12-foot wing. It is best, therefore, to use the full length spar or the assembled wing to make those first alignment trial fits.

WHAT CAUSES ALIGNMENT ERRORS?

1. The most common cause is the builder's failure to establish and work from a centerline or reference line during the assembly of the fuselage. (It is also a common mistake to abandon reliance on the centerline too soon.)

2. Failure to align the firewall at right angles to the centerline.

3. Failure to mark the center of each station's cross member or bulkhead and then . . . . failing to make sure, with a plumb bob, that this mark straddles the fuselage reference line.

4. Permitting the structure to be moved accidentally. Even a slight jar will change the reference points. Keep checking periodically.

5. A glob of dried glue, a nut, a bolt, a file, or almost anything else lying on your work surface, can accidentally find itself under one of the longerons, causing it to be raised slightly off the work surface. If you don't notice it, you may proceed with the assembly of the fuselage with one side of it slightly raised.

6. Forcing any diagonal into place, however gently, will deflect the structure at that station, and either the top or bottom cross members will no longer inter-

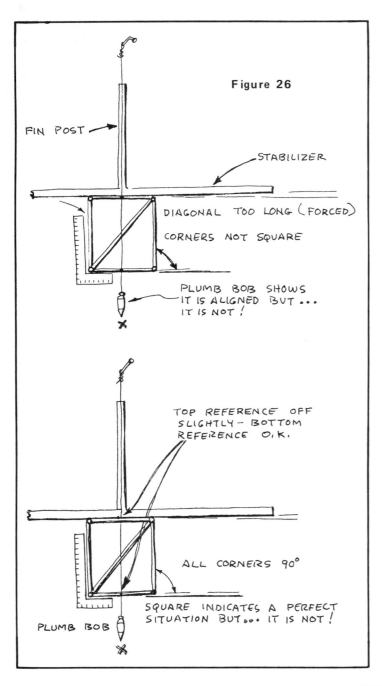

Figure 26

FIN POST

STABILIZER

DIAGONAL TOO LONG (FORCED)

CORNERS NOT SQUARE

PLUMB BOB SHOWS IT IS ALIGNED BUT . . . IT IS NOT!

TOP REFERENCE OFF SLIGHTLY - BOTTOM REFERENCE O.K.

ALL CORNERS 90°

SQUARE INDICATES A PERFECT SITUATION BUT... IT IS NOT!

PLUMB BOB

sect the reference line. A too-short diagonal member will have a similar effect.

There are three ways to check your alignment. Eyeball it; measure it with a steel tape; or use instruments such as a square, spirit level, combination square, protractor, and beam trammel. In practice, however, you will find it more practical to use any combination of the three methods to the degree best suited to the job at hand. Often a point is reached where the accuracy becomes more of a fetish than a practical requirement. For example, to achieve the ultimate in accuracy, a guy can become frustrated trying to split a 1/16-inch difference in wheel alignment as measured at a point well ahead of the wheel.

Rectangular fuselages are checked at each station using a plumb bob and a large carpenter's square. When constructing any fuselage of which the bottom longerons are closer together than the top longerons, the cross sectional check at each station must be accomplished using a plumb bob. (Figure 26)

An alternate method would be to use a combination protractor head to check the angle formed by each of the fuselage sides. The angle reading for each side should be identical. In using this method, however, make sure that the fuselage is resting on a perfectly level surface.

Still another check should be made along the side profile when bulkheads are installed to insure vertical alignment. A bulkhead that leans forward or backward could, in some cases, alter the incidence angle when the wing installation is attempted. When fitting and installing the cross pieces in the typical welded steel tube or wood fuselage, each member should be centered over the reference line and fuselage sides checked for squareness using a large square. The greatest single source of fuselage misalignment occurs during the fitting of the diagonal members. If the fit of a diagonal member is a bit snug, it will almost certainly deflect the fuselage from the reference line. Likewise, if a diagonal is just a bit too short and you have to use clamps to draw the fuselage sides in, that too will cause the fuselage to distort. As you work from the front of the fuselage toward the tail, you will be tempted to prematurely abandon the checks because everything seems to be going well . . . . don't give in to this temptation. Keep close check on your reference line and each station until you get to the tail end.

Wing Alignment

Building an airplane seems to be a series of alignment problems. Each component requires some sort of an alignment check in mating it to some other part. Some alignment procedures are simple and obvious, and we don't even consider them as alignment exercises. Here are a few which require careful attention: landing gear alignment; wings for twist, incidence, sweepback, etc.; propeller; tail surfaces; and engine installation. Useful materials for alignment purposes would include as many of the following as you can get:

- ☐ Straight-edges (straight pieces of ¾-inch square x 6 feet, or ¾-inch x 2-inch x 6–8 feet)
- ☐ Plumb bob
- ☐ String (rib stitching cord is fine)
- ☐ 50-foot steel measuring tape (it doesn't stretch)
- ☐ Protractor head from a combination tool
- ☐ Level
- ☐ One or two willing helpers (nice, but not mandatory

WING ALIGNMENT

Here is a critical alignment problem indeed. Many an airplane has been built with warped wings or excessive "wash-in" or "wash-out." This leads to unpleasant flight characteristics like a persistent roll tendency or a vicious stall characteristic, to say nothing about reduced cruise performance. In the case of fabric-covered strut-braced wings, you merely have a rigging problem on your hands. However, if you have a metal or plywood-skinned wing that wasn't aligned and jigged securely during the skinning process, you have yourself a major rebuild job. So, always carefully check the wings for warpage before skinning them.

EYEBALL CHECK METHOD NO. 1

Let's call this the "parallel stick method." This is an accurate way of checking rectangular wings that do not require any wash-in or wash-out at the tips. (Figure 27)"Wash-in" is when the trailing edge of the wing is warped downward, or washed **into** the slip- stream. "Wash-out" is when the trailing edge is washed **out** of the slipstream, or warped upward.

Obtain two straight-edge strips of wood, and lay one across both spars at a 90-degree angle at the root end of the wing. Place the other straight-edge across the spars anywhere near the outer end of the wing, just before any taper of the spars for the wing tip.

Step back from the root end of the wing several feet and sight down towards the tip. Raise or lower your line of sight to almost block out your view of the tip-end second straight-edge. Now it is easy to see if both strips or straight-edges are in perfect alignment; if so, so is your wing.

EYEBALL CHECK METHOD NO. 2

This is merely a variation of the principle illustrated (Figure 27). Make your sighting check from a point about 8 feet in front of the wing. (Figure 28) When the top surfaces of the spars are parallel with each other, you've got it! Clamp or jig your wing solidly and proceed with the plywood or metal skinning.

Make each part right, and the airplane will turn out right too!

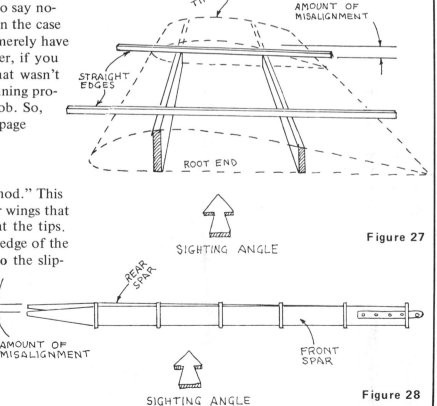

TIP END

AMOUNT OF MISALIGNMENT

STRAIGHT EDGES

ROOT END

SIGHTING ANGLE

Figure 27

REAR SPAR

AMOUNT OF MISALIGNMENT

FRONT SPAR

SIGHTING ANGLE

Figure 28

Think Light, Build Light

"Tony," the letter begins, "My plane flies like a man-hole cover on edge when I chop the power. It stays in the air ONLY because of the souped-up VW 1600 and Bernie Warnke's prop. I think I could remove the wings and see little difference in its performance. This surely dumbfounds me! I built the thing because I wanted a floater. Then, I got carried away and added extras until I built myself an ungainly bird. It's about 105 pounds overweight. It will jump into the air with a minimum run, but once you get to about 200 feet it quits climbing. In fact it seems to have a service ceiling of about 3,000 feet. It takes me three trips around the field to get to pattern altitude. That's 2,800 feet here. Now what . . . ?"

Yes, now what? What do you do about an overweight homebuilt?

Unfortunately, it is too late when the aircraft is completed to do anything about weight control. The absence of a consciencious effort from the very beginning to control the weight of the aircraft during its construction, more often than not, results in an airplane that is a disappointment to its builder. Indeed, his unhappy reward can be an airplane so heavy that it suffers from poor takeoff and climb. Often it's too hot to handle comfortably and is endowed with high approach and landing speeds. And, the deadly likelihood will always exist that the structure may someday be overstressed in even very gentle manuevers or light gusts. Equally dismal, assuming the owner is fortunate enough not to hurt himself during its early test flights, is the limited future of the plane.

Here is another homebuilt that will fly around for a season or two and then change hands several times as each owner passes it on. The airplane's poor reputation grows, and in time, if somebody doesn't crack it up, it will be scrapped to provide parts for another project.

Each time a builder says "Heck, it doesn't weigh much more anyway, so . . . ," look out. This is faulty reasoning. You simply cannot add a little here and there and expect your airplane to make a good showing on the weighing scales and in the air. Anyway, many of us have been at least slightly disappointed when we first saw that empty weight . . . . don't join the pack.

It is a rare homebuilder who can build an air-

Let's see . . . . if I added a bubble canopy, a pressure cowling, wheel pants, prop, electrical system, navigation lights, landing lights, full instruments. . . .

plane from plans that will weigh as little as the designer's original prototype. Why? Well, for one thing, the designer's first interest was in getting the design airborne as soon as possible to prove his concept. Sophistication, he reasoned, could come later.

Does that mean the designer is deliberately misleading his enthusiastic followers? No, he has no control over the eager builder who has aspirations of equipping his airplane like the reconnaissance fighter he once flew. Or, over the guy who wants to install a bigger engine than called for in the plans, and in anticipation, begins "beefing" things up here and there because they look like they'll need it. Nor does he have control over the builder with a nice VW conversion who wants to modify his to something with full IFR capability and maybe a retractable gear, tailwheel and all.

Don't let this discourage you from building the airplane to suit your fancy, but do let it influence you to think light and build light. Any airplane can be built much heavier than it needs to be, even yours.

The idea of thinking light and building light is not as dull as you may think. In reality it is a fascinating challenge. Give it a try. The suggestions that follow just might help you build a lighter airplane . . . . sensibly, without violating the basic design and without jeopardizing the good reputation of the designer.

Substituting materials and beefing it up — Don't beef up the design anyplace if it is not your own creation unless you are willing to accept the consequences, pay the weight penalty, and are able to work a stress analysis for the change.

Why a stress analysis? In strengthening one area you may inadvertently subject another to overstress. For example, substituting thicker outboard wing skins than those required in the plans, can impose higher bending loads in the center of the wing, just where you happen to be sitting. A wing separating at this location can be a definite problem, especially if it happens in flight.

If you are serious about weight control, never substitute a heavier gage metal than called for, or make a part oversized . . . . not even once. Don't get in a rush and proceed impulsively. Wait until you can obtain the proper size material. Substituting one type of material for another usually works against you. Substituting Douglas Fir for spruce is such a case. Oh yes, it will be stronger (even if it doesn't need to be) but the weight penalty is an automatic 25 per cent increase for those parts made of the Douglas Fir.

Wings — A large portion of an aircraft's net weight is in its wings. This is a good area in which to effect weight control. If you have an option between building a three-piece wing or a single-piece full-span

wing, opt for the one-piece wing. You can save 30 to 50 pounds of weight and at least 100 hours and up to $100. Unfortunately, the one-piece wing will be more difficult to manage single-handedly while building. It will require more work space, and present a bigger challenge in transporting it to the airport. However, remember that the travails of the construction period last but a couple of years, while the benefits of a lighter airplane last and last and last.

Bolts — Always use the correct length and size, no longer, no larger. Bolts one size longer add needless weight and usually require extra washers.

Washers — Eliminate washers where possible. Of course, always use a large washer against wood surfaces and a washer against metal surfaces where there is movement between the bolt and the part There is really no need, ordinarily, to use washers under bolt heads bearing on fixed steel or aluminum parts.

Electrical systems —— Supposing, after your aircraft is completed, it exceeds your empty weight expectations by far? Even then it is not too late to lighten it, if an electrical system is on board. Consider the removal of the electrical system or, at least a part of it. A battery and case weigh about 22 pounds. Another 16 pounds is contributed by the starter, 10 to 11 pounds by the generator (or alternator), and about 1½- pounds by the voltage regulator and wiring. Shedding that 50 or so pounds will improve any airplane's performance.

Wires, cables, hoses — Make them as short as possible without subjecting them to tension. Route them as directly as possible.

Battery cables are heavy, so locate the battery in the engine compartment if weight and balance permits. You often see wires, cables and lines with their excess lengths neatly coiled and secured to the structure. This can add more pounds than you might think. Why should they be so long?

CAUTION: **Do not cut precalibrated wire leads used in engine instruments which rely upon temperature differential (cylinder head temperature gages, etc.) for their operation.**

Electrically operated equipment in aircraft made of wood requires ground wires. Consolidate their routing wherever possible to minimize the number of ground wires running hither, thither and yon.

Nav and landing lights — Why wire the plane for night flying if it will never be used at night?

Composite structures and fiberglass parts — A build up of weight is caused by the application of too much resin in wetting out the fiberglass cloth. This is one of the biggest bloopers made by inexperienced builders when working with fiberglass.

Fiberglass cowlings and fairings do not require as many layers of cloth as most builders use. They do not have to be completely rigid and 1/8-inch thick. Look how thin and flexible metal cowlings are. The secret is to make your fiberglass parts with as much curvature (compound curves) as is possible and to adequately support the parts through proper mounting. Reinforce only the areas of high stress. If no compound curves are required, consider using aluminum. It will be lighter and more fire resistant.

Metal fittings — Radius the ends of metal fittings. Often fittings are squared off at their ends. Sure it takes extra work and it won't save much weight, but it all adds up. Always cut out lightening holes in large metal parts where optional.

Many nonstructural angles and brackets should be made of aluminum rather than steel. Take care though, a 4130 steel fitting is almost twice as strong in the same thickness as is 2024 T3 aluminum.

Wheels — If propeller clearance permits, and you will be operating mostly from fairly smooth airport strips, consider using 500 x 5 wheels and tires instead of the bigger and heavier 600 x 6 wheels. Another benefit . . . . wheel pants could then be smaller and lighter.

Instruments — Save weight by using small instruments where practical. Better yet, install one of those engine instrument clusters combining oil temperature, oil pressure, cylinder head temperature, ammeter, fuel, etc. in one installation unit (Cessna and Beechcraft, or similar).

Fasteners — Increase the spacing between screws and fasteners. Is it really essential to install cowling and fairing fasteners 3 inches apart? Wouldn't 6 inches or 8 inches serve as well? Check some factory-built airplanes for guidance. Homebuilders overdo it.

Drainage — Use seaplane drain grommets at the drain holes in the bottom of the fuselage. There is no immediate weight saving, but regular grommets permit oily mist and dirt to be sucked into the fuselage, accumulating as an oily film which traps dust and dirt. Over the years this means considerable weight.

Painting — Consider not painting an all-metal aircraft, particularly if you live in a relatively dry climate. Polished aluminum, and just a bit of painted trim can look just as nice as a full paint job.

Don't be too generous with the number of coats of paint or dope you put on fabric-covered aircraft. An average airplane will have gained 20 pounds after it has been painted. If it is a "for show, trophy-hunter airplane," you are building, naturally you will shrug off the consequences as you put on coat after coat of hand-rubbed weight.

Don't become a finish fanatic. Skip the heavy treatment with BONDO; that 12-pound-per-gallon imperfection hider is best used on Mack trucks.

Engines — Remove all accessories, brackets and clamps not needed for your installation. Shielded ignition harnesses weigh almost twice as much as the unshielded ones. If no radio will be installed, why pay extra in weight and cost? Try to use the exact length of throttle cable and tachometer cable. Tachometer cables are made up to exact lengths on order without extra cost.

WOOD CONSTRUCTION

Nails — Instead of using nails in building wood components, rely more on clamping and temporary staples for gluing pressures. Eliminate permanent nailing where possible. For esthetic reasons, use no nails in external skins, as they always manage to work out and bulge under the fabric. About 2 to 4 pounds of nails can be used needlessly in an all-wood airplane. Even small rib gussets can be clamped instead of nailed.

Ribs — If you have the option, use built-up spruce ribs rather than the so called easy-to-make solid plywood types. Plywood ribs, even with lightening holes, are heavier. Some of them are weaker too. If you do use plywood ribs, always cut out the lightening holes where permitted. Remember, one 4-inch hole removes more weight than two 2-inch holes.

Corner blocks — Triangular corner blocks are lighter than square blocks or half-round blocks and still provide as much glue area.

Oozed glue — Clean up all excess glue that has squeezed out of joints. This saves weight and minimizes the glue's tendency to draw down the plywood skins along joint edges, distorting the outer surface contour.

Plywood skins — Why cover the all-plywood structures with cloth before painting? It might increase the strength somewhat, and undoubtedly will provide additional protection against the elements, but it is heavier than just paint. The new epoxies, paints and finishes are remarkable. Besides, if the plywood finish doesn't weather well, you can always cover it with fabric later.

Carpeting — Make sure you shop around first. Use lightweight aircraft carpeting. There is a difference and a 5-pound weight saving can be realized in a typical two-place aircraft.

War surplus components and scrounged gadgets — Don't use accessories and parts off fighter planes, bombers and 747s . . . . they are simply too heavy for the light job to be done. Let me put it another way. If you don't use it, it won't add any weight.

Fabric covering — Some fabrics are lighter than others. Do you really need the heavier 3.7-ounce-per-yard fabric, or will the 2.7-ounce fabric do? A 2 to 4 pound saving on cloth alone can be realized. Lighter fabric doesn't take as much finishing material either.

Upholstery — Shy away from extensive use of Naugahyde, leathers and other heavy materials. Use the lighter aircraft quality fabrics for cushions and panels with small accent areas for effect.

Get the idea? Think light . . . . the cumulative results will show up where it really counts . . . . in the air.

Metal Fairings

Not all fairings are being made of fiberglass. Many homebuilders prefer to make some of them out of aluminum, especially those fairings having simple bends. These include all flat fairings and gap covers without compound curvatures, and quite often, some of the large trailing-edge wing root fairings (if you prefer, call them fillets).

Besides being lighter, metal fairings are not susceptible to sunlight deterioration or warpage from aging, and once installed, should retain their good fit indefinitely.

Sheet aluminum (2024 T3) in thicknesses of .016-inch to .032-inch are the gages most frequently used for fairings. The thinner .016-inch and .020-inch gages are more difficult to fasten in place smoothly because the thin sheet tends to bulge between fasteners. It often helps to crimp (break) straight edges of thin metal slightly to obtain a better fit. In addition, you'll find that the lighter gages of metal cannot be countersunk without causing a drastic enlargement of the drilled holes. So, if flathead screws or countersunk rivets are to be used for installation, the holes must be dimpled. This, in turn, leads to other complications, because the underlying surface to which

you will be fastening the fairing must also have its holes dimpled. This dimpling might be quite difficult to do on a fuselage or wing having little or no access from behind.

Annealed (soft) aluminum should not be used for flat fairings or those without compound curvature. Hammering or stretching aluminum into compound curvatures work-hardens it, making it somewhat more durable. The common hardware store variety is peculiarly not suited to aircraft use because it will soon become distorted and full of bumps and dents from even the slightest of external contacts.

You should never let price be your main consideration if quality and longevity of the structure are at stake. You may end up paying more in time and material if you have to replace the cheap metal.

Long, relatively narrow pieces of metal are very difficult to form into fairing shapes by hand. Even very thin sheet is quite resistant to hand-imposed bending forces. Hand-bending a tight curvature in a tapered or narrow strip of metal is virtually impossible until you figure out how to do it.

Here are a few easy to remember suggestions to help make the forming of your metal fairings easier.

A flat fairing of metal over the aft portion of the wing. Very simple and very effective.

It's difficult to put a compound curve into metal fairings. This is a factory solution.

1. Use a wider piece of material than is necessary. This is very important. You can always cut it to size <u>after</u> the forming is completed.
2. Don't rush the bending. Keep working it down with a constantly increasing application of pressure.
3. Check the results frequently. Don't overbend it. Quit when the curvature is about right. Final adjustments of a minor nature can be done later.

The use of a metal bending brake is out of the question, except for using it as a clamp or for making a slight break along a straight edge . . . . if there is one. The bending of a wing fairing is strictly a hand and eyeball operation.

You cannot, of course, form a single-piece wing root fairing of 2024 T3 aluminum as is generally done with fiberglass. The 2024 T3 will not accommodate compound curvatures. Using this tempered aluminum stock for fairings, therefore, limits your options to some curvature around radiating straight lines with perhaps a bit of reliance on optical illusion.

There is one sure way to determine whether a simple aluminum fairing can be successfully bent for a specific area. First make a cardboard pattern to fit. If the cardboard pattern lays in well enough to obtain perimeter contact with the structure to which it will be attached, you can be assured that it will do as well in metal. Sometimes, the cardboard pattern will not lay in there because of an improper fitting. That can usually be corrected. If, on the other hand, it will not fit in spite of everything, that is an indication that compound curvatures are present and a simple straight bend will not work in that area.

A metal fairing can be formed to fit the aft portion of the average wing without encountering too much difficulty. The secret is in the making of an accurate pattern before you bend and cut the metal. Incidentally, the kind of cardboard I am referring to is the type that suit boxes are made of, not the rigid corrugated cardboard stuff.

Your fairing can be successfully bent by hand to the required curvature in the following manner: Lay the untrimmed aluminum sheet (to be bent) on the floor with a rug or some cardboard under it to protect the metal from scratches. Curve the aluminum sheet into a large C shape with both hands. To avoid the application of too much localized pressure during forming, use a small back board, or a 2 x 4, placed along the top edge of the metal being formed. With the bottom edge of the aluminum pressed against the floor, apply increasing pressure to the top edge to impose the curvature you want.

Who said turtledecks had to be fabric-covered? This one is made of metal.

One end of the fairing will require a sharper bend, therefore, more pressure must be imposed at that end.

While it is difficult enough to make a properly radiused bend by hand in a long narrow strip of aluminum , it is almost impossible to make a bend around a small radius in a piece of metal already tapered and trimmed to size. Therefore, always select a piece of metal wide enough to assure ease of forming. After the part is bent to the contour you want, trim it. The suggested sequence is shown in Figure 29.

The metal, particularly 2024 T3, will have a considerable amount of springback to it and will require more pressure and bending than you might think. Inadvertently overbending the metal a bit is not serious because the part will not be overstressed, as it would in a more severe 90 degree, small-radius bend. Minor adjustments may be necessary to properly fit the fairing to the aircraft. Therefore, it might be wise to trim the fairing to size in several stages.

Don't forget that you must make a left and a right fairing. The curvatures will be opposite for each.

The photos illustrate other kinds of fairings that are easily made of aluminum. The majority of these fairings can more easily be made of aluminum than of fiberglass. While a built up form of some sort must be made for fiberglass lay-up, a simple cardboard pattern is the only preparation necessary for a metal fairing. What could be quicker and more economical than that?

Where the installation is intended to be permanent, rivets may be used. Often, the use of pop rivets will be necessary because of the lack of access for

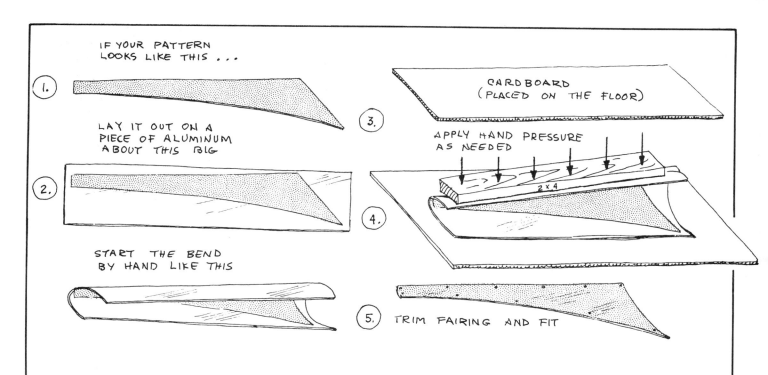

1. IF YOUR PATTERN LOOKS LIKE THIS . . .

2. LAY IT OUT ON A PIECE OF ALUMINUM ABOUT THIS BIG

START THE BEND BY HAND LIKE THIS

3. CARDBOARD (PLACED ON THE FLOOR)

4. APPLY HAND PRESSURE AS NEEDED

2 X 4

5. TRIM FAIRING AND FIT

Figure 29

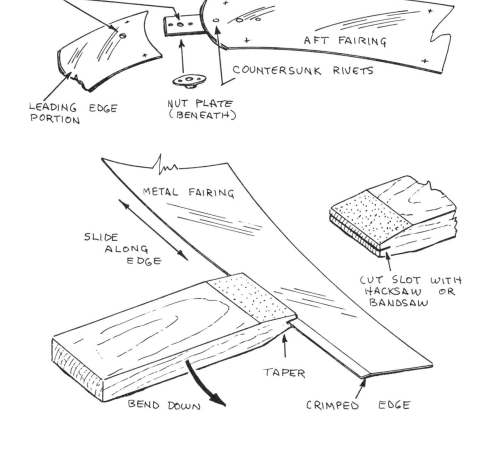

MATCH-DRILL

LEADING EDGE PORTION

NUT PLATE (BENEATH)

AFT FAIRING

COUNTERSUNK RIVETS

METAL FAIRING

SLIDE ALONG EDGE

BEND DOWN

TAPER

CRIMPED EDGE

CUT SLOT WITH HACKSAW OR BANDSAW

Figure 30

EDGE CRIMPER TOOL FOR METAL

bucking standard rivets. When drilling the attachment holes, hold the fairing firmly in place and, as each hole is drilled, insert a cleco fastener or a screw to guard against slippage and misalignment of holes as you work out toward the far end of the fairing.

Avoid the use of too many fasteners. The number required will depend on the location and the shape of the fairing at any particular point. However, an 8- to 10-inch spacing should be about as close as is necessary except for problem areas. Wrap-around wing gap fairings, for instance, may need fasteners only at their trailing edge junctures.

For aerodynamic purposes, you should avoid joints along the upper portion of the wing root fairings. But, this is difficult to avoid doing because it is not at all practical to attempt making a one-piece metal fairing of 2024 T3. It is easy enough, though, to make good flush joints incorporating a metal tab, nut plate and a few countersunk rivets. The two parts of the fairing may then be butt-fitted and secured with a flathead machine screw. This makes an aerodynamically clean joint.

Any metal fairing will fit much better after its

edges are given a slight break (crimped down about 5 degrees). If there is a long straight edge along one edge of the fairing, the crimp may be made with a sheet metal brake but, more likely, all the edges will have been trimmed to a gentle curve and some other means must be used.

You might try crimping metal edges with a homemade creasing device similar to the one shown in Figure 30. A piece of hardwood about 7 inches long and a couple of inches wide is shaped as shown and finished with a bandsaw- or hacksaw-cut slot in its tapered end. The depth of the saw cut determines the width of the crimp. A crimp ¼-inch to 5/16-inch wide looks good for most parts. When using the tool, make only a slight bend on the first pass along the metal's edge, advancing the tool with each downward bend. Always keep part of the bend within the width of device in order to minimize crease marks along the bent edge. I suggest you practice a bit on some scrap metal first.

The areas of an aircraft that lend themselves to improvement are many, and fairings and gap covers are easy to make and install . . . . especially metal ones.

Cutting Spring Steel

Many builders cut down a set of Cessna 150 spring steel gear legs to use in their projects. I cut mine down without using a cutting torch or even getting the gear annealed. What a surprise.

My 12-inch Sears bandsaw already had a used, ½-inch flexible metal cutting blade (18 teeth per inch). Of course the bandsaw is converted for metal cutting through Sears' gear box. A big 12-inch pulley replaces the regular bandsaw pulley. This combination gives me a nice speed for most work.

All that was necessary was to draw my cutting lines with a silver pencil and just feed that heavy old gear into the blade. It is important to keep the blade cutting by feeding the work as needed. You can't rush it. The saw cut

through the 5/8-inch steel in a most gratifying manner — about 1-inch per minute. The whole cutting operation took only 30 minutes. I was amazed. Still am. The cut was very straight and clean.

Also surprising was how simple it was to get a straight, smooth, perfect edge on the cut-off areas merely by running them across my bench disc sander. It had a 10-inch aluminum oxide sanding disc glued on at the time (medium grit).

If I had used a cutting torch (which I don't know how to) there would have been one long job of grinding and smoothing of the cut edges. Remember, the cuts were made with the gear in its normal hardened condition, and it didn't get hot enough to require annealing and subsequent reheat treatment.

Tips on Glue

A few common glues being used in aircraft projects today are Plastic Resin, Resorcinal, Aerolite, and epoxies like T-88 (Chem-Tech), Hughes FPL-16A, and others such as those used by the Varieze, Quickie and KR builders. Each glue is excellent and will allow you to obtain aircraft-quality joints consistently. There are, however, a few characteristics peculiar to each type glue which can lead to inferior joints.

First of all, even for the so-called low-temperature glues, I believe that the temperature of the material being glued and the surrounding air should be at least 70 degrees F. If not, go do something else.

Make the best possible fit of the joint to be glued. Freshly planed surfaces are best. For prepared joints which have been sanded, dust or blow off the sanding dust thoroughly. Always remove the surface glaze on birch plywood by lightly sanding before gluing it.

Follow the manufacturers' mixing and use instructions.

PLASTIC RESIN GLUES

These are the closest to fool-proof glues now available. They are economical too. Just dump some powder into a container, add a little water and stir. Too thin? Add some more powder. If it's too thick, add another few drops of water. You can use it right away. It's nice sticky glue and dries rather quickly in high temperatures. The glue is very brittle and not very effective in ungussetted, cross-grain or end-grain joints. It requires moderate clamping pressure. The glue powder has a high affinity for moisture and, unless the can is kept tightly closed, you may find just a solid lump in the container after a humid period.

RESORCINAL GLUE

Mixing ratios are critical. Follow directions. When measuring out the liquid by volume (teaspoons, for example), make sure each full measure is permitted to drain completely. Otherwise, the measure would not be completely emptied and you would wind up with an excess proportion of powder to liquid. Good clamping pressure is important, as is double spreading on larger surfaces.

AEROLITE

Not so good for gluing on large plywood panels, but it is excellent for small items such as ribs and gussets. It is easy to forget to dab on the catalyst liquid and never realize your ommission. No catalyst, no safe joint! Excess liquid catalyst often discolors the wood and gives it a dry rot appearance. Although this in no way affects the wood quality, it can be a startling experience to an FAA inspector unfamiliar with the characteristics of the glue.

EPOXY

It is difficult to use small quantities of epoxy if you have a ratio of 10 parts glue to one part liquid catalyst. For example, the smaller the amount you mix, the more critical the proportions become. Epoxy glue is excellent for gluing up large areas and installing plywood skins. However, be careful with small batches.

The easiest epoxies to use are those with a mixing ration of 50/50 (equal parts of resin and catalyst); the reason being that most of the gluing jobs just require small batches of glue. Mixing up a lot is wasteful and mighty expensive. Epoxies are weakest in peel-strength. However, aircraft joints are not normally subjected to such stresses, so this shortcoming is of little consequence.

There are many excellent epoxies available for use by homebuilders. The classified section of EAA's SPORT AVIATION magazine is a good source for this material.

TEMPERATURE AND HUMIDITY PROBLEMS

Remember, all glues require that the temperatures be above a certain recommended minimum. For Recorcinol and the Plastic Resin glues, the temperature should be maintained above 70 degrees F for the best results. (Always glue a little test sample for checking later on. Don't forget to date and label it.) Aerolite glues have worked out all right for me in the past with temperatures down to about 60 degrees F . . . . but here again, if the temperature is kept above 70 degrees F, you should have no trouble.

The epoxy glues, in most cases, work-cure all right at somewhat lower temperatures. The best rule, of course, is to follow directions on the container. Who knows better how to use a product than the manufacturer?

If you have to turn on the heat to get the workshop temperature up to safe gluing limits, you can run into other problems. Humidity, or rather the lack of it, can be troublesome. The more heat you need to get the temperature up, the drier the air will become. The wood, if exposed for prolonged periods of time under such conditions, will dry excessively. The ideal moisture content of spruce is about 12 per cent. Plywood panels, if glued to a fuselage frame or wing panels, will expand at some future date when the humidity gets back to more normal levels. Here are two important points to remember.

1. Keep your gluing temperatures above 70 degrees F while the joint dries.

2. Avoid gluing operations on large plywood panels if the humidity is high (uncomfortable) or is very low (dry).

OTHER GLUING PROBLEMS

As I have already pointed out, it is important that minimum temperatures be maintained for the glue being used. Another thing . . . . a heavy layer of glue will not take the place of decent workmanship. Even a glue with excellent gap filling properties cannot do its job properly unless the joint is clean and well fitted. Some glues are extremely critical to proper proportion and measure. Although Recorcinol glue is very good, it is also very unreliable unless adequate clamping pressure is used, in accordance with the instructions on the container.

CONTROL SYSTEMS

Fabricating Control Cables

I marvel at the genius of the old time aircraft builder. His basic concepts have hardly been changed or improved. Whatever improvements there have been, it seems, are mostly in the development of improved designs and sophisticated materials. The cable-operated control system is a good example. It's as popular and as useful today as it ever was, and you can find it in use on the most up-to-date aircraft as well as the oldest antique. It's quite reasonable to say that using aircraft cables to activate your control surfaces gives you the lightest, simplest, safest, most economical, and most effective way of doing the job ever conceived.

The aircraft control cable in general use is known as "extra flexible 7 x 9 preformed carbon steel," or "corrosion-resisting steel cable." The cable is fabricated of 7 strands comprised of 19 wires each. Six of these strands are preformed around the 7th or center strand. This results in a very flexible cable ideally suited for primary control systems. There are, of course, other types of cable such as the 7 x 7 for use in other applications where flexibility is not a requisite.

The standard size cable used in most homebuilts is 1/8-inch for all primary control systems. Although the breaking strength of 1/8-inch aircraft cable is about 2,000 pounds, the highly-desirable corrosion-resistant cable is rated as being slightly weaker than the carbon steel cable. The difference is nothing to worry about.

WHY USE CABLES?

The advantages of cables are many. They are light, strong, and flexible. They do not require line-of-sight routing, and slight deviations to bypass structural obstacles present no problem. The cables can be deflected by simple fairleads and even routed around pulleys to change direction. Try that with a push-pull tube! Since the cable is light in weight, it can be installed over considerable lengths without any intermediate support.

Cable-operated surfaces respond instantly and precisely to cockpit control movements because they are used in pairs and are stretched to the proper tension by turnbuckles. This effectively eliminates all play in the control system. Cable failure is virtually unheard of because cables are not subject to vibration-hardening or crystallization as are push-pull tube controls. Certainly a cable failure, were it to occur, would not happen suddenly. More likely, there would be a prolonged period of deterioration that could be detected during preventative maintenance inspections.

The only disadvantage I've heard concerning cable control systems is an unsubstantiated claim that cable tension must be adjusted frequently because of stretching and temperature changes. As far as the typical homebuilt is concerned, I am inclined to disagree even on this one point. Do you know of any homebuilder going around readjusting his cable tension frequently . . . . or even once in awhile? Mine hasn't been adjusted in years. Admittedly, a minor adjustment may be found necessary during the aircraft's early test stages, but after that, maybe once every 50 years or so. Perhaps the comparatively short length of control cables in homebuilts eliminates that problem.

CABLE FABRICATION HARDWARE

The hardware used to make up an aircraft cable unit includes a variety of swaging terminals, Nicopress sleeves, thimbles, bushings, and shackles. The function of cable terminal hardware, of course, is to provide the means of connecting the cable to a turnbuckle, bell crank, or to some other fitting or linkage. Since you will be using 1/8-inch cable, you should make sure that each of the cable hardware items used is for that same size.

Thimbles are streamline-shaped, grooved loops of thin metal around which cable is bent for making terminal splices. Thimbles serve to reinforce cables and are necessary to prevent severe bending and chafing at points of attachment. Aircraft cable is tough, but without a thimble it can be frayed or cut one wire at a time by friction or by any sharp surface. For this reason, aircraft cables are always formed around a thimble or bushing. **Bushings** are not too common now, although if the eye of the terminal is to be attached to a fitting directly by a bolt, the bushing does make a nice set-up.

Many good mechanics make it a standard practice to clip off the pointed ends of the thimbles with a pair of diagonals. They feel that this makes it much easier to get the Nicopress sleeve up tight against the thimble and results in a more efficient terminal splice. Personal experience has proved it to be very effective and worth the effort.

Shackles are steel loop-like connectors used to attach cables to fittings which are used in places where the attaching point is in the form of a single plate or lug. (Figure 1)

The shackle is ordinarily slipped through the thimble after the cable terminal splice is fabricated. However, you should check before making the terminal splice, that the wide flat part of the shackle is not too wide to slip through the thimble without distorting things. Also be sure that the opening for the fitting is large enough for the thimble to pass through without your having to spread the shackle apart. In some cases, it may be necessary to form the eye with the shackle first slipped into place.

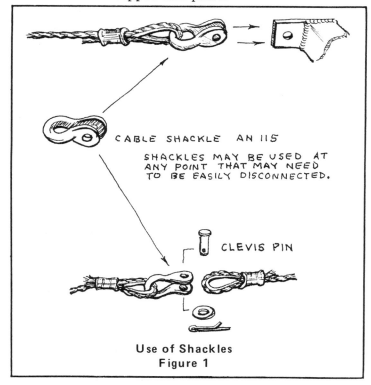

CABLE SHACKLE AN 115

SHACKLES MAY BE USED AT ANY POINT THAT MAY NEED TO BE EASILY DISCONNECTED.

CLEVIS PIN

**Use of Shackles
Figure 1**

FABRICATION OF CABLE UNITS

Before you can put control cable to work for you, a terminal splice must be formed on each end of the cable so that it may be connected to the controls you want activated.

There are two modern cable terminal splices, The Nicopress Oval Sleeve Splice and the Swaged Terminal Splice.

Swaged Terminal Splices: The best splices are those made with swaged terminals. They are beautiful and, when properly manufactured, can develop 100 per cent of the cable's potential.

The swaging process consists of inserting the cut cable into the barrel of a special terminal. Great pressure is then applied by the dies of the swaging machine to shrink the barrel of the fitting so that it grips tightly around the cable. In the process, some of the metal inside the barrel is forced into the stranded crevices of the cable. (Figure 2)

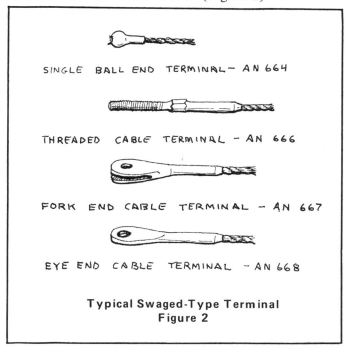

SINGLE BALL END TERMINAL - AN 664

THREADED CABLE TERMINAL - AN 666

FORK END CABLE TERMINAL - AN 667

EYE END CABLE TERMINAL - AN 668

**Typical Swaged-Type Terminal
Figure 2**

Unfortunately, to make a swaged terminal you do need a machine, or at least a swaging tool that is not ordinarily available to most of us.

Some of you folks, however, who live in areas where there are big aircraft plants and other large repair facilities should be able to get your controls swaged at reasonable cost. If so, great! It is the preferred choice.

Even though swaged cable connections are great, they are out of the question for most builders. Your best bet in this case is the Nicopress caper.

Nicopress Oval Sleeve Splice: Thanks to the National Telephone Supply Company, the folks who manufacture the Nicopress cable splice tool, homebuilders around the world now have a simple, effective way of fabricating aircraft cable terminals or splices. Until the Nicopress tool came along it helped if the homebuilder had a little nautical blood in his veins, because the cables had to be spliced in the best of Naval traditions. That splice was known as the "five-tuck" splice. Luckily, unless you are an antique restorer and a purist at heart, there is no need now to learn how to weave a five-tuck splice. That "art" should have, and finally did go the way of the pterodactyl.

Nicopress terminals may be used with complete assurance that the full-rated load of the cable can be developed . . . . provided the cable is first formed around a thimble and the Nicopress sleeve is compressed properly.

NICOPRESS CABLE FABRICATION

Using the Nicopress oval sleeve in the making of control cable units is simple because there are only two critical factors: (1) The completed cable unit must be the right length. (2) Your Nicopress oval sleeve splice must be properly compressed.

Determine Cable Length: To get a better idea of how long a piece of cable you will need, form your terminal on one end first. Drive a nail in one end of your workbench and hook the formed terminal over the nail. Stretch the cable out and measure the required length on the bench allowing an additional 6 inches or so for forming the second terminal.

This second terminal may, as the need dictates, be formed around a turnbuckle eye or a shackle. In either case, your finished length will be determined with the proper fitting installed in the terminal eye. The turnbuckle, if used, should be unscrewed so that some of the threads are showing on either side of the turnbuckle barrel. When the finished cable is installed in the aircraft, its length should be such that when the turnbuckle is tightened, the cable will be properly tensioned with no more than 3 threads showing on either side of the turnbuckle barrel.

Cutting Aircraft Cable: Use a sharp cutter to cut the cable to the approximate length. Remember to allow yourself an extra 6 inches or more cable for forming your terminal splices. Aircraft cable may be cut mechanically but not by torch. When cutting cable, try to obtain a sharp, square cut without greatly distorting the strand group. If you don't have a cable cutter, take some friction or masking tape and wrap a couple of turns of it tightly around the cable at the point where you want to cut it. Lay the cable on a solid metal surface and then, with a cold chisel and a heavy hammer, give it a good whack. This does a beautiful job, and both ends of the cut cable remain neatly wrapped with a bit of tape that that will protect your fingers from getting pricked by the sharp strands.

Making the Nicopress splice: When using the Nicopress tool, make sure you have selected the proper size oval sleeve and thimble and that you use the correct tool groove size to make the required number of presses for the cable size used. (Figure 3)

Slide the copper sleeve onto the cable and loop the short end of the cable back through the sleeve.

Insert a thimble in the loop and push the sleeve up tight against the thimble. Use a pair of vise-grips or a spring clamp to hold the sleeve in place. Check Figure 4 to see how the sleeve fits into the tool for pressing. Make sure you close the handles of the tool completely for each press. You will notice that after pressing, the oval sleeve has become round at the point where it was pressed. For best results,

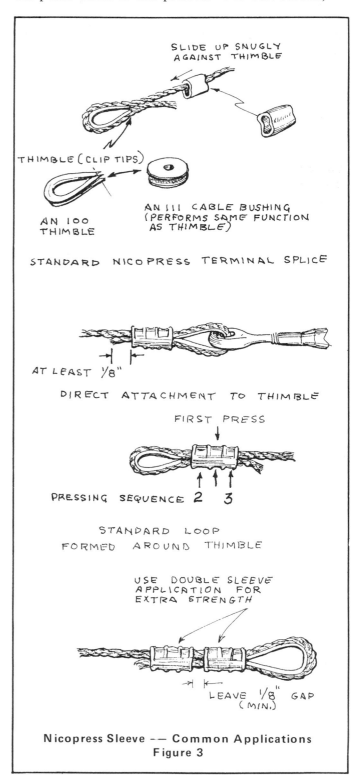

STANDARD NICOPRESS TERMINAL SPLICE

DIRECT ATTACHMENT TO THIMBLE

STANDARD LOOP FORMED AROUND THIMBLE

USE DOUBLE SLEEVE APPLICATION FOR EXTRA STRENGTH

Nicopress Sleeve -- Common Applications Figure 3

make your first press or compression at the center of the sleeve. The second press should be next to the thimble, and the third on the end opposite the thimble. Your splices should be checked at random with the gage provided with the Nicopress tool. You will notice that both the tool and the gage have the sizes identified by a stamped letter imprint. In using the gage, hold it so that it contacts the compressed portion of the sleeve at its major axis. The pressed area of the sleeve should slip into the appropriate gage slot easily. If it does not, the Nicopress tool must be adjusted.

The free end of the cable must project beyond the sleeve after pressing, otherwise the full strength of the splice may never be developed. The excess end can be cut off with a cold chisel as before. For the sake of your sanity, just make mighty sure that you are indeed cutting off the excess end and not the good part.

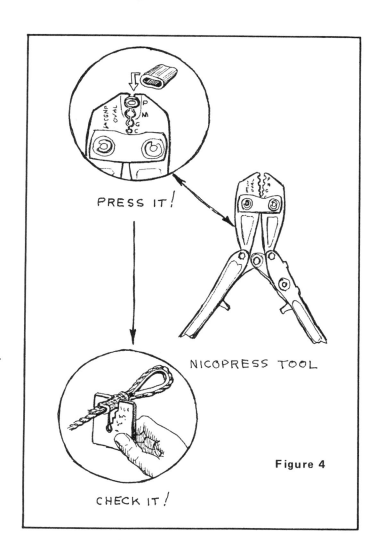

PRESS IT!

NICOPRESS TOOL

CHECK IT!

Figure 4

Cable Size	Sleeve Stock Number		Tool Groove	Number of Presses
	Plain	Plated		
1/16-inch	18-1-C	28-1-C	C	1
3/32-inch	18-2-G	28-2-G	G	1
1/8-inch	18-3-M	28-3-M	M	3
5/32-inch	18-4-P	28-4-P	P	3
3/16-inch	18-6-X8	28-6-X	X	4

NICOPRESS OVAL SLEEVE DATA
(The National Telephone Supply Co.)

Routing Control Cables

In the process of transmitting motion from the cockpit to the fuselage control surfaces, a variety of mechanical linkages come into play. The complexities of the linkages used are often determined by the design complexity of the airplane and its size. Whether the builder uses push-pull rods, torque tubes, or cable-and-pulley arrangements, his objectives are the same, keep it simple, keep it light.

No argument here, is there? Simplicity in the control system reduces the possibility of malfunction and offers the minimum friction. Friction is one of the loads you feel in the controls. It is caused by the combined conglomeration of pulleys, cables, chains, gears, hinges, levers, fairleads, guides, bushings, bearings, and miscellaneous items integral to the system.

The homebuilder's objective is to keep this friction load as low as possible, for in order to "feel" the air loads, the friction load must be less than the air loads.

Of course, we begin with the determination to run our control cables or tubes as direct as possible. Oh sure! Just try to route the control cables or push-pull tubes along a straight path and you will quickly see that there are obstacles in the way that prevent a line-of-sight hook-up from the control surface to the cockpit control. To get around such obstacles (formers, bulkheads, ribs, spars, seats, etc.) it is necessary to install fairleads or guides for minor deflections of the control cables; pulleys or bell cranks are used for major changes of direction.

Those of you who are building some of the popular designs have been endowed with a detailed set of plans, and will have no problem with the proper routing of your own control system, as the designer (bless him) has already worked that out for you. Just stick to the plans and marvel how simple it really can be. The plans will show where to use pulleys and where to use fairleads. Not only that, but they will indicate the size, type and exact placements. Unfortunately, many plans omit precise information and may only show a rudder cable drawn in on a fuselage side view, which gives you no exact clue as to its route. Even where the side view routing is clear

enough, it is not at all indicative of the surprises that might be in store for you when you try to visualize the installation as viewed from above. Anybody developing his own design knows full well how the "simple" problems have a way of turning out to be the most difficult to resolve.

By now you may be getting mental images of your own control system routing problems. If so, fine. Let's think about the rudder cable hook-up and routing as a typical control system installation problem.

CABLE ROUTING

There are texts that illustrate how easy it is to install rudder cables. They show that the cable is attached to the rudder horn on the right hand side of the rudder and runs directly from the rudder horn to the lug on the right rudder pedal. The left control cable is connected to the left side in a similar manner at each end. Figure 5 shows the usual textbook solution as compared to the real-life installation.

The basic goal in routing control cables is to install them with a minimum of deflections and in such a manner that they do not contact the structure at any point enroute.

The first point at which structural interference is apt to be noticed is where the rudder cable enters the fuselage. It may be necessary to deflect the cables here slightly with fairleads, or considerably, by using pulleys. The second major area of interference encountered in most projects is the routing of the cables around the seat area in the cockpit. Some low-wing jobs have the additional problem of routing the rudder cables around the spar, or through it.

ESTABLISH THE BEST ROUTING

Before the fuselage is covered or skinned, a dry run for the cable routing is a worthwhile exercise. Use temporary wires stretched from the rudder pedal attachment lugs to the rudder horns. Determine the amount of deflection required in order for the cables to clear all structural members in the cockpit area and elsewhere.

The proper way to determine how much deflec-

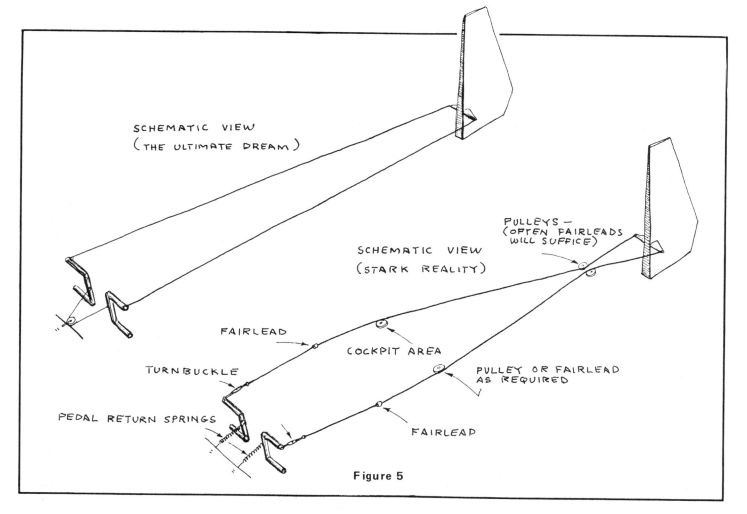

SCHEMATIC VIEW
(THE ULTIMATE DREAM)

SCHEMATIC VIEW
(STARK REALITY)

PULLEYS –
(OFTEN FAIRLEADS
WILL SUFFICE)

FAIRLEAD

COCKPIT AREA

TURNBUCKLE

PULLEY OR FAIRLEAD
AS REQUIRED

PEDAL RETURN SPRINGS

FAIRLEAD

Figure 5

tion will be needed is to insert small wood wedges between the cable and the structure to hold the exact amount of deflection needed at the minimum number of points that will give you the results you want. Double check this newly established routing, as error can creep in and the finished installation may still have some interference. Install guides or fairleads at the locations marked.

Carefully note the exact point where the cables enter the fuselage. Measure and dimension this location on a crude sketch for future reference. After the fuselage has been covered, it will be necessary to slit a slot for the entry of the cable into the fuselage. If you have to guess where to make the slot at that time, I'll bet you miss the entry point by a country mile and end up with a very large hole for a very little bitty cable.

FAIRLEADS AND GUIDES

It is essential that control cables do not contact the aircraft's structure anywhere. Such contact would probably result in the frictional wearing away of the structural member or the fraying of the cables. Of course, fairleads and guides are intended to prevent such difficulties. As I have already pointed out,

fairleads are used only to effect minor cable deflections. In practice, fairleads should not be used to deflect cables more than 5 degrees. This amount of deflection would be about 7/16-inch in 5 inches. Not much is it? I've seen a number of homebuilts where the deflection is more severe than that, and I'll bet, in most of those birds, broken strands in the cables showed up by the time their second annual inspection rolled around. Deflections of more than a few degrees are always best handled by pulleys.

A good fairlead (or guide) material is not necessarily one that has a lubricant-like characteristic, but one that will wear and not damage the cable. The traditional material for fairleads has been micarta. Other materials, however, such as teflon, nylon, copper tubing and phenolic plastics receive considerable use also. A micarta strip 1½-inch x 1/8-inch is handy to have around for guide material. Some builders prefer ¼-inch thick material. Regardless, make fairleads and guides as small as is practical for the job to be done.

Figure 8 shows suggested forms. Make yours to fit the location it must service and the shape of the guide will take care of itself.

Something not to be overlooked is the possible

future need to remove your cables. Some fairlead designs will not permit this as the holes are too small for the cable terminal to pass through. If you can, always make guides and fairleads so that they permit easy removal of the cables. Otherwise, you may have to cut the cables to get them out someday.

If you have no particular inclination to make your own fairleads, store-bought varieties are available but you will have to shop around to find them.

PULLEYS

Whenever a pulley is used, a rigid bracket installation must be worked out to insure continued proper alignment and secure attachment. Be very careful because the mere fact that you need a pulley in a particular location is indicative of a considerable loading on the pulley. This is due to the constant tension of the cable and the rather severe change of direction common to such installations. So, wherever large changes in direction are required, the pulleys or levers must be mounted to some rigid part of the structure. Any place a pulley is used, the pulley attachment bracket must also have some sort of a cable guard to prevent the cable from slipping off or jamming when in its slackened position. These cable guards can be very simple. (Figure 6)

Be careful of pulley pull-off or misalignment. Give close attention to the alignment of the cable with the pulley. You want some standards? How about this? A maximum misalignment tolerance of 1 degree (with the control held in a neutral setting)

is acceptable, provided no more than 2 degrees misalignment shows up when the control has been actuated to its extreme position of movement. Misalignment of cable on a pulley increases the risk of the cable jumping the track, and imposes a severe friction and wear condition on the pulley.

Pulleys with built-in anti-friction bearings (rather than the simple sleeved-bushing type) are the best. And, while on generalities, here is an old rule (there are a million of them) . . . . the pulley diameter should be at least 20 times larger than the diameter of the control cable. That means the smallest recommended pulley would be about 2½-inches in diameter whenever a 1/8-inch cable is used. But I really don't think much of that rule as it doesn't take into consideration the number of degrees of direction change imposed on a cable. For example, I would suggest that at least a 3½-inch pulley be used to change the direction 90 degrees. I know darn well that there are dozens of builders using 2½-inch pulleys to do that kind of a job. However, I believe that some of them wonder how come their controls are so stiff. Can you imagine how much more system friction is built into the controls of a high-wing job that utilizes about a half-dozen 2½-inch pulleys for the routing of its aileron cables through a series of 90-degree bends?

Remember, the larger pulleys will help keep the flight control system friction down to a minimum and reduce the wear and fraying of the cables.

By the way, one reason for a heavy control system feel is excessive control cable tension. Loosen them up . . . . they don't have to twang. If you can

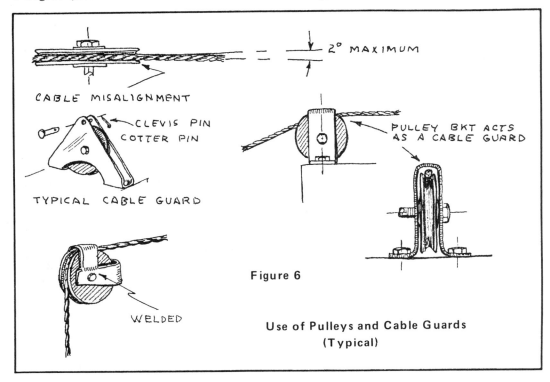

CABLE MISALIGNMENT

2° MAXIMUM

CLEVIS PIN
COTTER PIN

TYPICAL CABLE GUARD

PULLEY BKT ACTS
AS A CABLE GUARD

WELDED

Figure 6

Use of Pulleys and Cable Guards
(Typical)

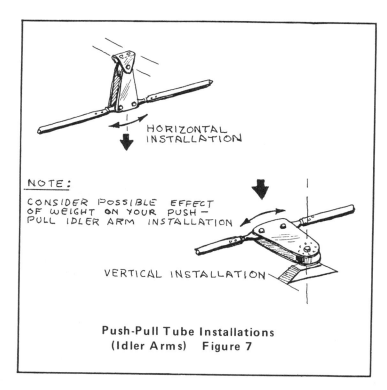

Push-Pull Tube Installations
(Idler Arms)   Figure 7

make them twang and vibrate they are too tight.

PUSH–PULL TUBES

Even with our marvelous technology, we still have to accept the fact that push-pull tubes will be subjected to much less stress (and distress) from the effects of their own weight and vibration if idler arms are mounted vertically rather than horizontally. Although idler arms tend to complicate a control system, they do serve to eliminate the need for an ex-

cessively long tube as might be used to activate the elevator or stabilator. (Figure 7)

Those installations where a long push-pull tube is used should be checked to see if some support is needed to hold down vibration in the tube. One method of reducing the tendency of a long tube to vibrate and flex is by installing a roller guide at the tube's midway point. However, do a little checking before you install such a guide. Control stick movements cause the attachment points at the control horns and levers to swing through small arcs. This action, in turn, causes the interconnected push-pull tube to rise and fall as well as move to-and-fro. You can see then that if a rigid roller-type guide were installed at the half-way point, a slight bending moment would be imposed on the long push-pull tube when activated. In some cases this could be a serious problem while in others the deflection is slight and noticible only when the control is moved to its extreme positions.

Cutting holes in the primary structure to permit passage of the control cables or push-pull tubes should not be undertaken without serious evaluation of the alternatives open to you. I make particular reference to cutting passageways through spars and bulkheads. It doesn't hurt to remind builders frequently to follow the designer's recommendations. If you are the designer, it wouldn't hurt to recheck your own figures just in case somebody asks, how come?

Push-pull tube installations may be plagued with excess play in the system. Not only is this annoying to a pilot, but it is also a factor that could

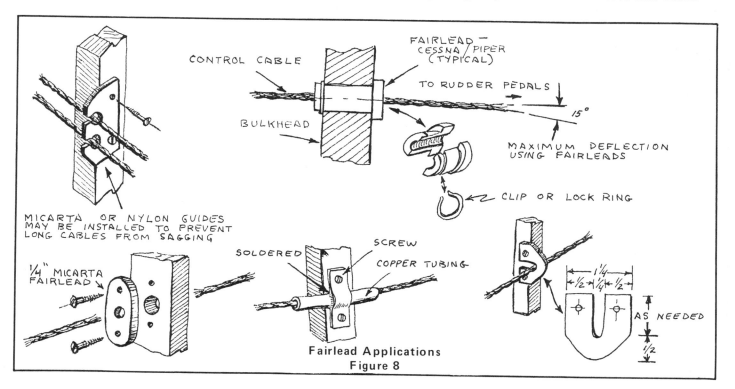

Fairlead Applications
Figure 8

127

contribute to control surface flutter in flight. To avoid play in your airplane controls, you must work to close tolerances in all bolt holes, fittings and brackets. The physical connection of the rod-end bearings to the various levers should be done with well fitting bolts. You may not believe it, but out of a random handful of AN-4 bolts you may find one that fits pretty snug and another that will be loose. Anyhow, work at eliminating all the play . . . . it is important.

JAMMED CONTROLS

Jammed controls are always a possibility due to some foreign object (usually in the cockpit area) wedging itself against the cable at a fairlead, pulley bracket, control stick attachment, or passageway through a bulkhead. Another common source of jamming can develop behind the rudder control pedals. Check out the possible trouble spots and protect those points against the danger. An unused seat buckle can jam the control stick not far away, by dropping down between the torque tube and the seat. The panicky pilot doesn't have the time to do a lot of checking around in an emergency.

Don't ever lose sight of the fact that any mechanical installation must be accessible for inspection, maintenance and possible replacement. This is a particularly important requirement for the control system.

Trim Tab Installations

A lot of people have conceived a lot of clever ways to relieve the pilot of much of the work of continuously holding control pressures during long flights. This labor-saving magic can be built into any homebuilt aircraft simply by adding some form of trim system.

We all know that the homebuilder who is constructing a small, light, low-powered plane for putt-putting around the local pea patch is not going to bother himself with trim devices as long as his center of gravity (c.g.) is within limits.

Those of us with larger or faster aircraft, however, can't dismiss the problem of trim as easily as that because the effects of changing flight conditions are more apparent, more obnoxious.

Constant changes in the c.g. caused by different power settings, airspeeds, and fuel consumption, all point to the need for a means of trimming or adjusting longitudinal balance in flight. Suddenly, the persistent requirement for holding considerable control pressures gets to be very tiring.

Homebuilts have a reputation of being rather sensitive to conditions affecting their c.g. to the point that there are those who claim they have to retrim after a sneeze . . . . probably an exaggeration. The real reason most builders install trim tabs, especially cockpit-controllable trim tabs, is because they are basically good pilots and appreciate the finer things in life. (Listen for the drum roll and a flourish of trumpets.)

As a builder, you have several options to choose from in the trim device department:

1. Fixed tabs (ground adjustable)
2. Cockpit-controllable trim tabs
3. Bungee/spring trim systems
4. Anti-Servo trim (cockpit-controllable)
5. Stabilizer jacks (adjustable stabilizers)
6. Movable tail section (like Mooney aircraft)
7. Adjustable, automatic flap trim systems

FIXED TRIM TABS (GROUND ADJUSTABLE)

Fixed trim tabs are most often bent strips of aluminum fastened to the trailing edges of control surfaces with sheet metal screws or rivets. While this is fine for wood and all-metal structures, steel tube and fabric construction does not lend itself to fixed tab installation unless some provision is made for its attachment prior to covering. The reason of course is that it would not be prudent to drill holes in the small trailing edge tubing just to attach a fixed tab. Certainly, not without first reinforcing that area.

Although you may not have been looking for that sort of thing, you have probably noticed at some time or other, that some trim tabs are bent (deflected) severely. As a casual observer, you might have thought the airplane simply needed a lot of corrective trim. However, it is more probably an indication that the trim tab is too small.

How big should a trim tab be? Who can say? Why not start with one about 3 inches x 7 inches (made of 2024 T-3 aluminum about .032-inch thick). If that size tab can accomplish the job of trimming without an excessive deflection, fine. If not, try a larger one.

Fixed tabs are attached to the bottom side of the aileron or elevator trailing edges for appearance' sake more than anything else. As for rudders, the side you select is also optional except, perhaps, for the consideration illustrated in Figure 9.

Remember, bending the tab in one direction causes the control surface to be deflected aerodyanically in the opposite direction. The plane then reacts directionally to the aircraft's deflected control surface.

After installation, you will probably have to make several test flights to obtain the trim results you want, as ground-adjustable tabs are, at best, a bend-and-try operation.

Bend the tabs by increments until the aircraft is trimmed to maintain a level attitude at its normal cruise power setting (without the necessity of manually holding continuous control pressures).

Be careful when bending a tab attached to a control surface as you may twist it off. To lessen this risk, clamp small boards on either side of the control surface and ask someone to grip the trailing edge area as you rebend the trim tab. It is usually better to remove the tab, if you can, before bending it.

In the final analysis, fixed trim tabs can trim the

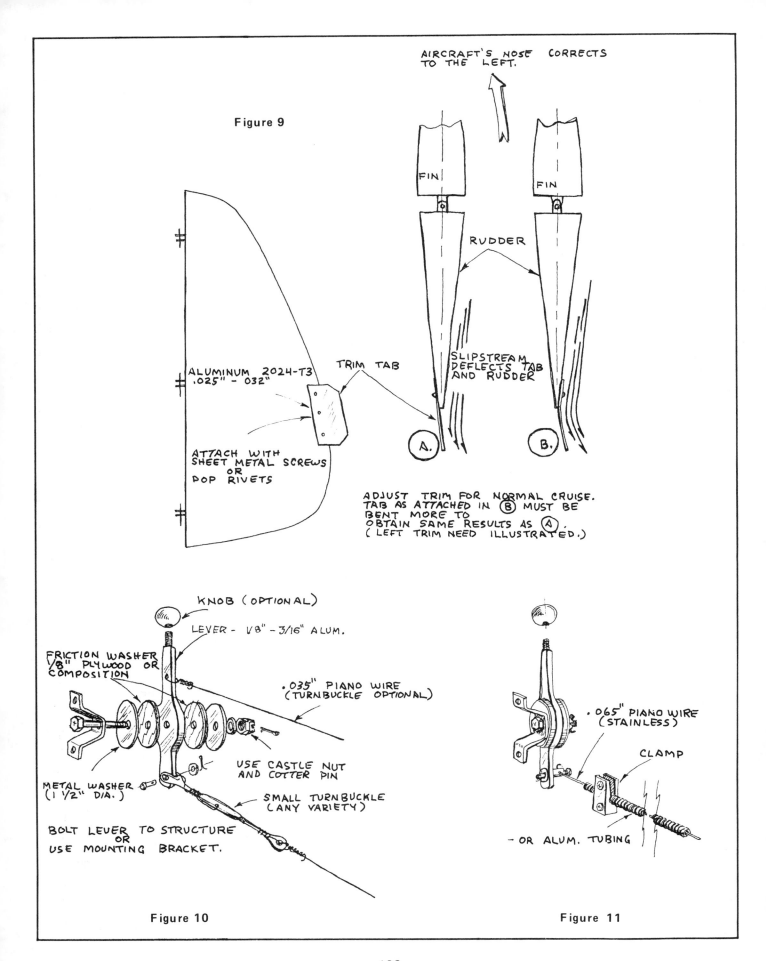

AIRCRAFT'S NOSE CORRECTS TO THE LEFT.

Figure 9

FIN

FIN

RUDDER

ALUMINUM 2024-T3 .025" - 032"

TRIM TAB

ATTACH WITH SHEET METAL SCREWS OR POP RIVETS

SLIPSTREAM DEFLECTS TAB AND RUDDER

A.

B.

ADJUST TRIM FOR NORMAL CRUISE. TAB AS ATTACHED IN (B) MUST BE BENT MORE TO OBTAIN SAME RESULTS AS (A). (LEFT TRIM NEED ILLUSTRATED.)

KNOB (OPTIONAL)

LEVER - 1/8" - 3/16" ALUM.

FRICTION WASHER 1/8" PLYWOOD OR COMPOSITION

.035" PIANO WIRE (TURNBUCKLE OPTIONAL)

METAL WASHER (1 1/2" DIA.)

USE CASTLE NUT AND COTTER PIN

SMALL TURNBUCKLE (ANY VARIETY)

BOLT LEVER TO STRUCTURE OR USE MOUNTING BRACKET.

.065" PIANO WIRE (STAINLESS)

CLAMP

- OR ALUM. TUBING

Figure 10

Figure 11

130

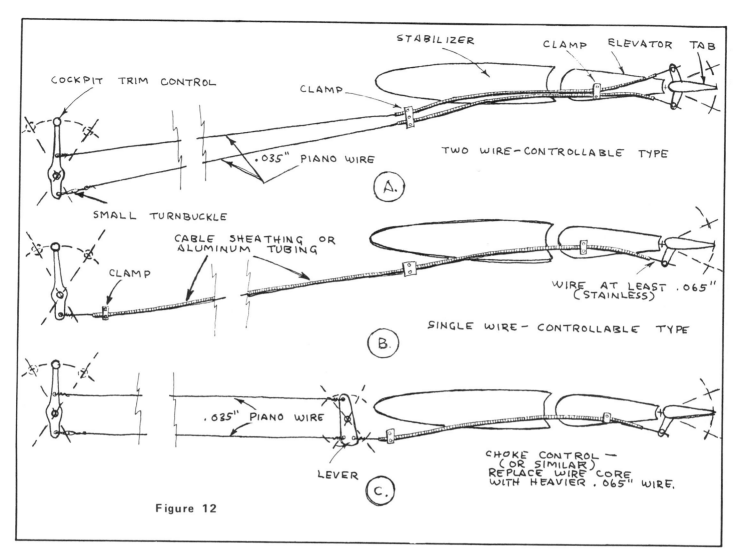

Figure 12

aircraft for one flight condition only. Add a passenger, consume fuel, change the power setting or cruise speed, and the aircraft's trim degenerates.

You can say this much in defense of the fixed trim tabs. They can always be added after the airplane is built and flown, and they are a darn sight better than no trim at all.

CONTROLLABLE TRIM TABS

Controllable trim tabs have all of the characteristics inherent in the ground-adjustable variety plus the beneficial aspects of being adjustable in flight from the cockpit. (Figures 10 and 11)

In some aircraft, the controllable elevator trim system considerably complicates the control system by adding an unbelievable number of components and a complex routing of cables from the tab to where they terminate in the cockpit in an equally complex assembly of sprockets, chains, pulleys, brackets, wheels, levers or cranks, friction devices and irreversable gears. To illustrate the point, one 4-place plane I inspected had 37 separate components, including 12 pulleys (priced any pulleys lately?). This parts tabulation did not include the numerous bolts, nuts and washers used to hold that trim system creation together. Is all this necessary for the operation of a simple slab trim tab affixed to the elevator?

Fortunately, most homebuilders find ways to obtain effective controllable elevator trim without such complexity and expense. See Figure 12 for reassurance that this is, indeed, possible.

One difficulty in installing controllable trim tabs, particularly on elevators, is in installing the control linkage so that the position of the trim tab remains in the same relative angle to the control surface, no matter how much the elevator is moved. This, of course, creates a bit of a challenge as the control linkage must transfer its action from a movable control surface (elevator in this example) to a stationary structure (stabilizer/fuselage). The simplest way to accomplish this is to use a flexible sheathed push-pull wire running from the tab, on the movable surface to the stablizer. This permits you to cross at some point close to the elevator hinge axis rather than exactly through it as would be necessary with any other nonflexing mechanical linkage.

The sheathed portion of the push-pull wire does not have to run all the way to the cockpit except in a single wire installation. Since the conduit sheathing of the ordinary push-pull control is heavy, its use in long lengths is to be avoided. Some builders prefer to switch to aluminum tubing for the long run to the cockpit.

The cockpit trim control may be a wheel, lever, crank or switch. Whatever it is, it should have an irreversible characteristic, or at least have sufficient friction built in to prevent the creeping of the control in flight once it has been set.

Mechanical linkage should provide positive control without slack or sloppiness and without excessive sensitivity to tiny movements of the trim.

Make a determined effort to eliminate play in the linkage and tab connections as such a condition invites flutter.

AUTOMATIC FLAP TRIM

Recently, a major aircraft manufacturer proudly announced that one of their models would have an automatic trimming feature integral to the flap operation. That is, when the flaps are deployed, the automatic trim would relieve control pressures involved by compensating for the pitching tendency that the use of flaps produces. Heck . . . . homebuilts like the Emeraudes have had this provision incorporated (and simply, too) for the past 20 years. Emeraudes,

for example, have two separate trim tabs that are attached to the trailing edges of the elevators. The tab on the left side is a conventional trim tab, actuated by wires running to a cockpit lever. This controllable trim tab takes care of inflight nose-heavy or tail-heavy conditions caused by the using of fuel, changes in power settings, changes in airspeed, and passenger and baggage variations.

The other tab, on the right elevator, works only in one direction. It is connected by a piano wire to the flap control arm or bell crank. As flaps are deployed, the wire simultaneously pulls the trim tab down, causing the elevator to respond correctly to the sudden nose-heavy imbalance produced by dropping flaps.

As the flaps are raised, a spring-loaded wire simultaneously pulls the tab back to its neutral position. (Figure 13) It is a dandy device and can be installed very easily in any flap-equipped homebuilt.

Trim tabs built into the elevators, rudder, or ailerons, are a bit more difficult to construct than the externally affixed tabs as in the Emeraude design. However, either design works equally well. It could be though, that tabs built into the control surfaces might have to be made a bit larger to achieve the same degree of trim effectiveness as those add-on types.

WHICH WAY DOES IT GO?

Make sure the trim tab moves in the correct direction when you move the cockpit lever, crank, or wheel. A nose-down trim indication inside the cockpit, for example, corresponds to an "up-tab" position on the elevator surface. Correct?

If you want the nose to turn to the right, the

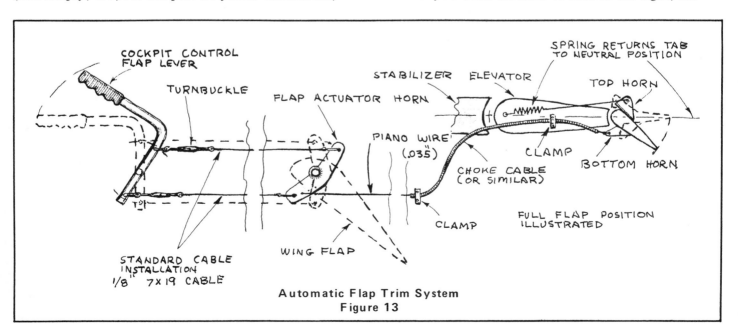

Automatic Flap Trim System
Figure 13

rudder tab must be deflected to the left. Right? (Sorry, couldn't resist.)

How about a right wing-heavy condition where there is only one fixed tab mounted on the left wing? Do you bend the tab down? Right again!

Remember, a deflected tab, with the help of the airstream, forces the control surface in the opposite direction. The tab-influenced control surface causes the aircraft to respond to it as though the rotated surface were actuated by the pilot.

Cockpit trim controls are labeled to indicate correct movement for "nose-down," "nose-up," etc. However, you may not consider this as important a need when only an elevator trim lever is mounted parallel to the longitudinal axis, and the direction of movement is obvious. If a trim control is mounted overhead or elsewhere, and if its direction of move-ment or rotation is in doubt, it should be marked, as it may rotate in a direction contrary to what another pilot might expect.

Except possibly for a lever-type trim, which by its design virtually shouts out its trim position, other types of trim control, such as wheels and cranks do need a positive indicator that affords some clue as to their exact relative position with that of the remote slab.

COCKPIT CHECKLIST

"Trim Tabs" or "Set Trim" should be added to your printed cockpit check list (you do have one, of course?). The bigger and faster the airplane, the more important this reminder, since forgetting to reset the trim could be an unexpected invitation to a traumatic takeoff.

What to Do About Adverse Yaw

Most of us have flown airplanes that require a lot of rudder input. Of course, those of you who are aerobatic pilots probably wouldn't have it any other way. A lot of us more sedate pilots, on the other hand prefer an airplane that does not demand much rudder effort . . . . an "aileron airplane" if you will. (The antithesis, I suppose, would be called a "rudder airplane.")

It is not at all uncommon that some airplanes do require unusual rudder pressures in order to make properly-coordinated turns. Undoubtedly, this difficulty in coordinating a turn with some aircraft may be due to an inherent adverse yawing tendency. Adverse yaw, oddly enough, is not a function of the rudder, but rather an aerodynamic condition directly attributable to aileron design.

About the first thing we ever learn about ailerons is that they impose a rolling movement about the aircraft's longitudinal axis. Also, the aileron that is deflected downward creates additional lift, while the opposite aileron produces less lift. This, of course, is good as it induces the desired bank in the airplane. Unfortunately though, there is a drawback to this ideal condition. The down aileron, while providing this welcome lift, also has produced quite a bit of drag, and this is bad-bad, because the added drag of this aileron causes the nose of the aircraft to slew towards that side. This direction is opposite to the turn being executed. To put it another way, while you are trying to bank and turn the airplane to the right, for example, the nose wants to swing to the left, just the opposite of your intended direction of turn. This uncoordinated, dynamically-induced action is adverse yaw. Because of it, every time you initiate a turn, additional rudder pressures must be used to get the ball in your turn indicator out of hiding and back in the center where it belongs.

To some pilots such rudder action gives them the impression of an uncoordinated effort, or at least an unnatural one.

What can you do about it besides the extra rudder compensation? Well, there are at least two good ways of minimizing or eliminating the effects of adverse yaw. Naturally, the best time to do something about adverse yaw is while the aircraft is still on the drawing board or while it is still under construction. However, it is never too late to make a slight modification in the control system if the yaw condition in your homebuilt is an annoying characteristic to you. Of course, if you've never flown the type of plane you are building, how would you know? Well, just take my word for it, unless your aircraft plans call for differential aileron control, your plane probably suffers from too much adverse yaw.

DIFFERENTIAL AILERON ACTION

You can modify your control system to provide a differential aileron action to minimize the effects of adverse yaw. This differential action allows the ailerons to deflect up more degrees than down. This differential action is mechanically produced by a bell crank. The arrangement effectively nullifies the tendency of the aircraft's nose to swing unnaturally in the direction of the down aileron.

In some homebuilt aircraft it may be possible to obtain a differential aileron action by slightly modifying a portion of the aileron control linkage.

This modification, ordinarily, will not entail work more complex than replacing a couple of pulleys with a bell crank and adding a short push-pull tube to connect the newly installed bell crank to the aileron horn. No control cable changes from the bell crank to the cockpit control stick would be necessary.

What makes the system work is the design of the bell crank, which imparts a differential movement to the aileron control surface. Figure 14 illustrates the principle used in obtaining this differential movement. Notice the one arm of the bell crank is not at a 90-degree angle, but is offset approximately 28 to 38 degrees. This offset angle will provide the desired relationship of movement in most installations. The total amount of aileron travel is also affected by the dimension between the aileron hinge axis and the aileron horn push-pull tube connection. A simple full-size plywood and string mock-up should be constructed, if necessary, to work out the desired aileron travel.

FRISE AILERONS

Another way of eliminating the effects of an

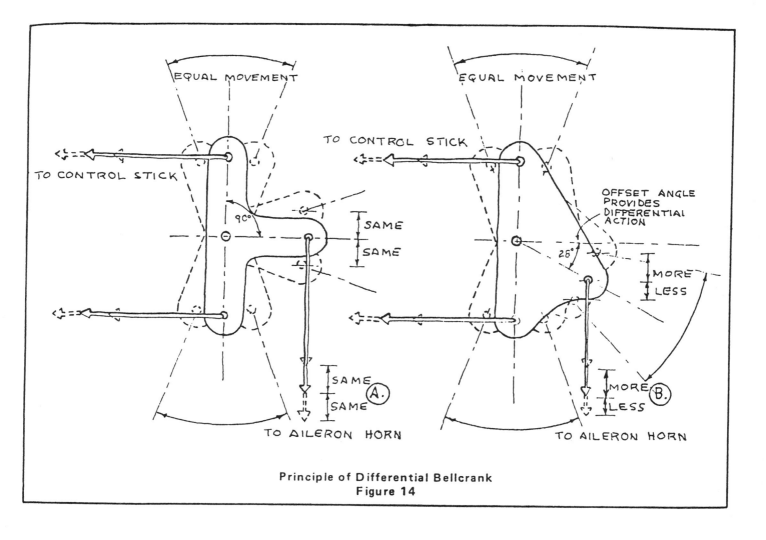

Principle of Differential Bellcrank
Figure 14

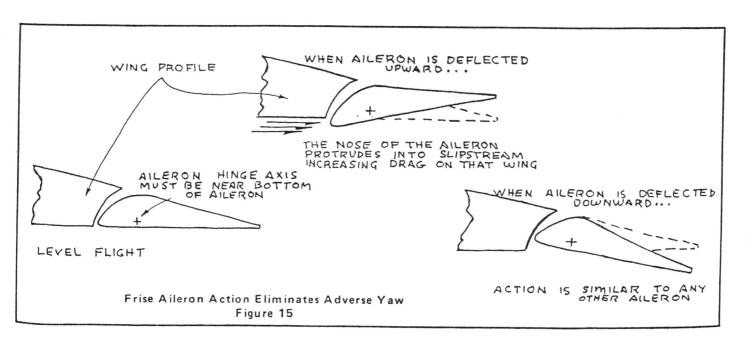

Frise Aileron Action Eliminates Adverse Yaw
Figure 15

135

adverse yaw tendency is by deliberately causing an increase in drag on the wing with the up-raised aileron. This will nullify the natural increase in drag of the other aileron. The way to obtain this result is through the use of Frise ailerons. (Figure 15)

A Frise aileron is designed and hinged in such a manner that when the aileron is deflected upward, its leading edge protrudes below the wing's lower surface, causing an increase in drag on the wing.

In order to employ the principle of the Frise aileron, it is best to provide for it during construction.

You will note that the key to its effectiveness is in the low location of the aileron's hinge axis, well behind the leading edge of the aileron. This configuration could be difficult to duplicate in a modification on a completed wing.

It is worthy of note that some designs employ a combination of both the differential aileron concept and the Frise aileron to achieve a control system that is easily coordinated in flight without the requirement for heavy pressures and awkward movements of rudder or aileron controls. (Figure 16)

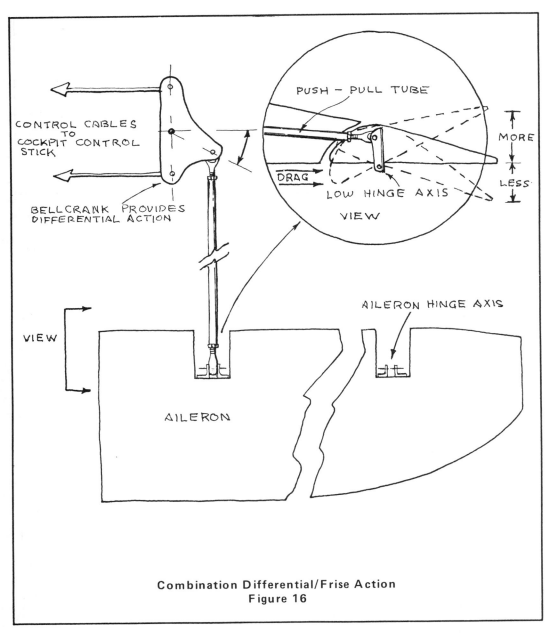

Combination Differential/Frise Action
Figure 16

Spoilers for Glidepath Control

Spoilers have always fascinated me, ever since the time Uncle Sam 'invited' me to take glider pilot training (1943) in CA4-A Cargo Gliders. I remember how I marveled over the fact that, by deploying spoilers incrementally, I could accurately land that big glider, stopping it within a 3-foot-square yellow flag placed on the ground. I remember too, I did well just to get one of Uncle's 'Vultee Vibrators' (that's an airplane, son) down within a couple of hundred feet of where I aimed it.

In the big gliders we used the spoiler control just as we would a throttle. Retracting the spoilers had the same effect as applying the throttle in an airplane. Conversely, as soon as the spoilers were deployed, the effect was similar to chopping the throttle and simultaneously dumping full flaps in a conventional airplane.

Many years have since passed, and it wasn't until recently that spoilers again intruded into my awareness. I must conclude that there is indeed a lot of interest now in spoilers, except among homebuilders. NASA is interested and has published many papers and documents reporting on their research, studied conclusions, and wind tunnel tests. The general aviation industry, although not exactly stampeding toward the implementation of spoilers on storeboughts, nevertheless, has something to show on their part. Mitsubishi's well known MU-2, for example, is a production airplane featuring spoilers. Other major aircraft manufacturers have no spoiler-equipped production planes and are not revealing future plans. But airplane modification specialists such as Horton and Robertson have been doing some amazing things with production line airplanes to improve their low-speed flight capabilities. The Robertson Company is into spoilers in a big way, making good use of NASA's research, supplemented by their own. Their most notable success, as far as the aviation public is aware, is with the Seneca and the Cherokee Six.

I, for one, have never seen a homebuilt with spoilers installed. Still, each year these eyes eagerly scan the countless homebuilts on the line at Oshkosh and on the far-flung airstrips of Texas. Alas, no spoiler installations do I see. Of course, sailplanes, even homebuilt ones, have been using spoilers for years.

But powered homebuilts? No sir!

Maybe this lack of interest by EAA builders in years past has been due to the scarcity of information on the subject. But things do change, and thanks to helpful and informed people, additional spoiler information has been accumulated.

First, I would like to point out that the concept of using spoilers is not a new idea or fad. The principle was first proposed in Europe in the mid-1930s when Germany was displaying tremendous interest in sailplane and glider training.

Incidentally, speed brakes, air brakes, and similar devices spoil the airflow and generate drag, but they are not exactly the same as spoilers. Flaps generate drag too, but there the resemblance to spoilers ends.

FLAPS

Flaps are common devices and most of us are quite familiar with them. However, it should be understood that flaps are installed primarily to enable an aircraft to fly more slowly. They do this by increasing the wing's lift, although there is some increase in drag as well. Dropping flaps creates a positive camber or an increase in the curvature of the upper surface of the wing. This results in a net increase in the lifting effect imparted to the air flow. In aircraft where Fowler flaps are installed, their deployment also effects an increase in wing area. This is in addition to the previously mentioned camber change common to all flap operations. As a result, Fowler flaps have been known to provide the greatest increase in lift coefficient, by about 100 per cent. This, with a flap chord of only 30 per cent of the wing chord.

Dropping flaps usually results in a momentary but noticeable increase in lift. If your speed is a bit high, the aircraft tends to gain altitude .... not much, true, but the resulting initial direction of flight is opposite of what you want. Simultaneously, a slight increase in drag is felt. Furthermore, the lowering of flaps invariably affects trim, and there is a very pronounced nose-down pitching moment. We therefore can conclude that flaps not only provide some drag, but, more significantly, they create added lift and permit slightly lower airspeeds for approach and landing. (Figure 17)

SPOILERS

Spoilers are aerodynamic fences, located in each wing, which a pilot may extend at will. These fences might be better described as fairly long plates or slats inset in the surface of each wing. When the pilot extends these spoilers to an upright position more or less perpendicular to the wing surface, the flow of air over that portion of the wing is disturbed, or you might say, spoiled. In this respect spoilers differ markedly from flaps. Spoilers are used to destroy some of the wing's lift . . . . not increase it.

Therefore, deploying spoilers, unlike flaps, causes an immediate loss in lift, similar in effect to an instantaneous reduction in effective wing area. As a result, the aircraft immediately starts to sink at a rate related to the amount of spoilers deployed.

When the spoilers are released (retracted), there is an immediate restoration of wing lift without any appreciable change in pitch attitude. This trait makes them a natural for glidepath control.

Recall if you will, what happens when you do the same thing with flaps. Raise flaps and you get an instant loss of lift and that sinking feeling, right? In a like situation, the spoilers would give the impression that the airplane has leveled off and darted ahead as though you gave it a blast of the throttle. This characteristic, fully exploited with spoilers which can be deployed or released incrementally, should

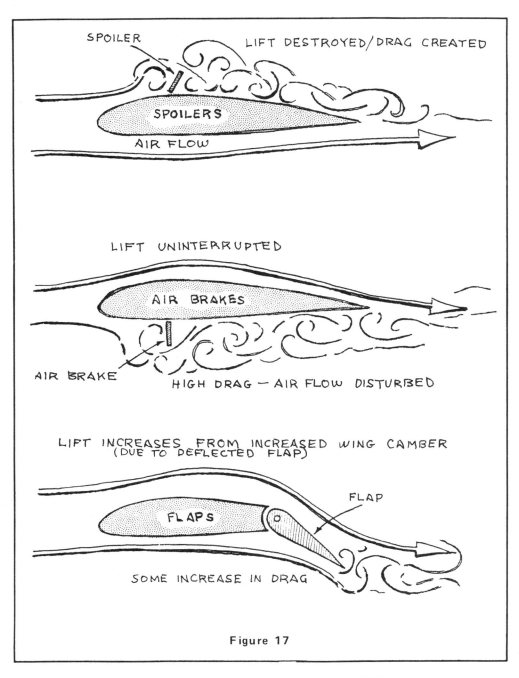

SPOILER
LIFT DESTROYED/DRAG CREATED
SPOILERS
AIR FLOW

LIFT UNINTERRUPTED
AIR BRAKES
AIR BRAKE
HIGH DRAG — AIR FLOW DISTURBED

LIFT INCREASES FROM INCREASED WING CAMBER
(DUE TO DEFLECTED FLAP)
FLAP
FLAPS
SOME INCREASE IN DRAG

Figure 17

make an excellent final approach glidepath control package for any high-performance homebuilt.

Incidentally, spoilers may be utilized for two different functions.

1. They may be deployed *collectively*, as in sailplanes where they serve to provide a rate of sink control only.
2. They may be operated *differentially*, as in aileron use to provide roll control.

In this article I will explore the *collective* use of spoilers as an improved method of descent rate control.

AIR BRAKES (SPEED BRAKES, DIVE BRAKES)

Yes, there is a similarity between spoilers and air brakes (alternate terms are speed brakes and dive brakes) in that both devices, when installed in the wings, are in the form of narrow slat-like devices which cause an immediate increase in drag when deployed. In both instances, too, these slat-like devices retract flush with the wing surface when released and are not at all noticeable unless you are looking for them.

Speed brakes, dive brakes, and air brakes are just different terms for the same type of device . . . . one designed to provide plenty of drag, suddenly!

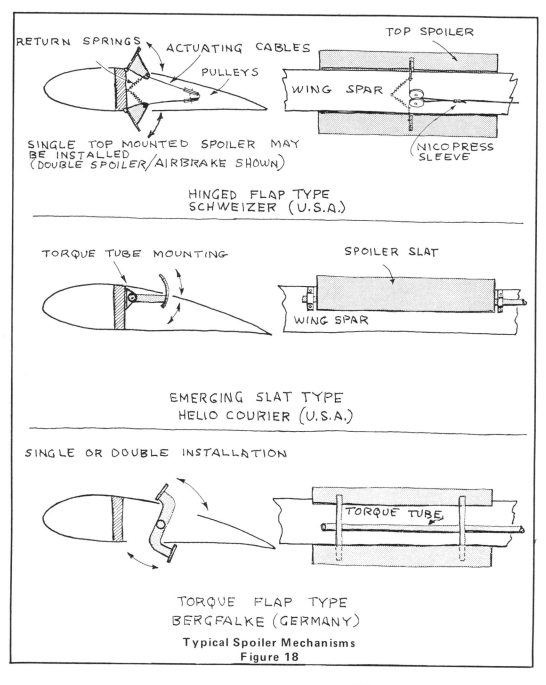

Typical Spoiler Mechanisms
Figure 18

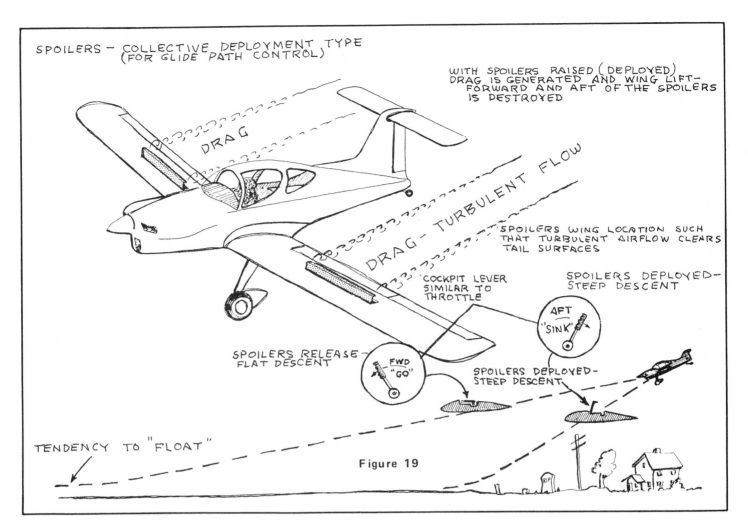

SPOILERS — COLLECTIVE DEPLOYMENT TYPE
(FOR GLIDE PATH CONTROL)

WITH SPOILERS RAISED (DEPLOYED)
DRAG IS GENERATED AND WING LIFT—
FORWARD AND AFT OF THE SPOILERS
IS DESTROYED

DRAG

DRAG - TURBULENT FLOW

SPOILERS WING LOCATION SUCH
THAT TURBULENT AIRFLOW CLEARS
TAIL SURFACES

COCKPIT LEVER
SIMILAR TO
THROTTLE

SPOILERS DEPLOYED—
STEEP DESCENT

AFT
"SINK"

SPOILERS RELEASE—
FLAT DESCENT

FWD
"GO"

SPOILERS DEPLOYED—
STEEP DESCENT

TENDENCY TO "FLOAT"

RIP

Figure 19

Air brakes may be located almost anywhere, on the fuselage sides, on the underbelly, or on the wings. However, when located on the wings, there is the additional effect of a loss of some of the wing's lift upon activation. When installed in wings, air brakes are usually arranged with one plate installed on the upper wing surface and one on the lower surface. They differ from spoilers in that they are normally constructed to rise vertically out of the wing. When installed in fuselage areas, the air brakes may be hinged on their forward edge in the standard method employed for spoilers. It is interesting to note that the bottom of the air brake slab is above and well clear of the wing surface when fully deployed in order to obtain the maximum drag effect from the brake.

There is another way to differentiate spoilers from air brakes in wing installations . . . . spoilers are typically installed only on the upper side of the wing. At best, the difference between spoilers and air brakes is nebulous. If a guy tells you he has speed brakes installed . . . . he has speed brakes! (Figure 18)

GETTING DOWN TO THE NITTY GRITTY

The problem with the use of spoilers in approach path control as I see it is the introduction of a third control. After you commit one hand to the throttle and the other to the control stick, you find you have run out of hands. Of course, you can always briefly detail one hand for the deployment of the flaps and/or the spoilers. The flaps will require no further attention but the spoilers will if you intend to use them to control your approach. However, during a spoiler-controlled approach, the manipulation of the throttle should not be necessary. Chances are you will be carrying slightly more rpms than for a conventional throttle/elevator jockeying kind of approach.

It would seem that a separate throttle-like lever on the power control pedestal, mechanically connected to the spoilers would simplify cockpit functions. This lever should be easy to move and have low friction forces, yet it should stay at whatever position it is placed.

Also to be considered in the design and installation of spoilers is the tendency of spoilers to produce turbulence. When spoilers are deployed, they can cause tail or wing buffeting. This, in turn, can reduce control effectiveness and induce flutter. Spoilers should, therefore, be in such a spanwise location that neither the ailerons nor the tail surfaces lie in their wake. This is not easy to arrange in an aircraft with a comparatively short wing span. Determining the best chord-wise position for spoilers poses another problem as well, because a change in the pitching moment can result on deployment. And yet these and other aerodynamic considerations may have to be subordinated to structural realities. It is understandable, therefore, why most spoilers are mounted to a spar or installed immediately aft of the main or rear spars.

I would question the merit of installing spoilers on any aircraft with a short wing span and steep glide characteristics . . . . particularly in low-powered aircraft. Spoilers in such aircraft would merely serve to steepen an already breathtaking sink rate.

There is some logic however, to installing spoilers on clean, high-performance aircraft to serve in much the same capacity as speed brakes or dive brakes, permitting large altitude changes at comfortable airspeeds. In addition, these spoilers could be used for glidepath control purposes. (Figure 19)

Remember, deployment of spoilers causes an initial and immediate change in flight path . . . . and in the proper direction. This, if you'll think about it, is opposite to the reaction obtained when flaps are dropped. Therefore, an important benefit realized from spoilers is that they provide a final approach flight path control response that is both intuitive and immediate.

It is appalling that so many accidents happen during some phase of landing. Too many of these are the result of overshooting or undershooting the available landing strip. This could well be an indication that just about all pilots tend to make mistakes at one time or another in their glidepath control. Pilots of homebuilts, particularly during early testing stages, are vulnerable. Whatever the reason, the present system of controlling aircraft in approaches to landing leaves a heck of a lot to skill . . . . some luck and . . . . cooperative elements. It might be that the development of spoilers can ensure more approach precision.

Sidewinder's speed brake permits steep descents without excessive speed and reduces aircraft's tendency to float during landing approaches.

Spoilers for Roll Control

Ailerons have been around for almost as long as man has been flying . . . . long before we EAA'ers came on the scene. That they are used so extensively in existing aircraft designs is not because of their aerodynamic merit, but rather because of their structural convenience. Installation of ailerons is uncomplicated and their control principle and action is obvious even to the neophyte.

Spoilers, on the other hand, are considered odd and relatively new to the aviation scene, and they sometimes require complex operating mechanisms.

Actually, spoilers are really not as new as some people think because NASA (formerly NACA) has been experimenting with different forms of spoilers, and reporting on these experiments since the early 1930s. Spoilers have been used for both glidepath control, as described in the previous article, and for lateral or roll control, as discussed in this article.

When used for roll control, the spoilers are located in the same general area of the wing as the ailerons are, or would be. We usually don't think about it but ailerons are like flaps in that they are attached to the rear portion of the wing. Unlike flaps, however, ailerons are hinged to move upward as well as downward. Spoilers, on the other hand, will deflect upwards only. Otherwise they are neutral (streamlined with the airflow). Another difference, when used for lateral or roll control, only one spoiler at a time is actuated, while ailerons always move simultaneously, but in opposite directions. For example, to cause a spoiler-equipped airplane to bank to the left, the control stick is moved to the left. The left spoiler will then rise proportionately to the movement of the stick, and will cause a reduction of lift on that wing. The reduction of lift caused by the disturbed air results in the spoiled wing being lowered. Since the opposite wing's lift is unspoiled, it rises. A beneficial byproduct of this action is the positive yaw imparted to the airplane. As a result, the aircraft banks and turns naturally in the intended direction. There is no adverse yaw as when ailerons are used.(Figure 20)

PECULIARITIES OF SPOILERS

One recurring observation gleaned from the old NACA reports is that some spoilers produce an ap-

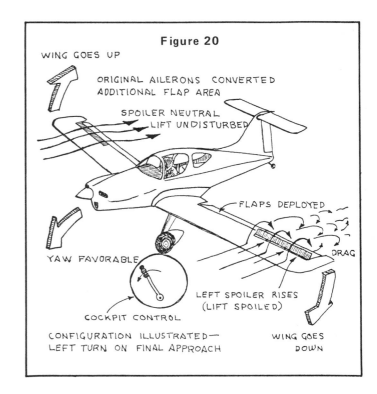

Figure 20

WING GOES UP

ORIGINAL AILERONS CONVERTED ADDITIONAL FLAP AREA

SPOILER NEUTRAL LIFT UNDISTURBED

FLAPS DEPLOYED

DRAG

YAW FAVORABLE

LEFT SPOILER RISES (LIFT SPOILED)

COCKPIT CONTROL

CONFIGURATION ILLUSTRATED— LEFT TURN ON FINAL APPROACH

WING GOES DOWN

preciable time delay (a control lag) between the movement of the spoiler control surface and the development of the resulting rolling movement. In general, one could only conclude that some spoilers were ineffective in producing a rolling moment until they were raised a considerable degree above the wing surface. Many spoilers do require an initial 1 per cent to 3 per cent deployment out of the wing before the pilot notices control response in the airplane. Apparently then, one oddity an experimenter might encounter with his spoiler installation in flight is excessive lag in making roll corrections, particularly with small projections of the spoiler. This could cause an inexperienced (or unsuspecting) pilot to overcontrol . . . . most annoying if not dangerous. Another strangeness, I learned, is that when returning the spoiler control to neutral, the response of the aircraft was more rapid than when the control stick was moved from neutral to make the initial correction.

And still another peculiarity that impresses me is that the aerodynamic characteristics of the spoilers improves as the location of these gadgets is moved toward the trailing edge of the wing.

Here is another interesting characteristic of the spoiler/flap installations. Lateral control (roll) response is generally greatly improved with the lowering of flaps. Spoilers used in conjunction with slotted flaps (Fowler) are more effective than those used with plain or split-flap configurations. Of course, these generalities only describe spoiler behavior in a very broad sense and may not be characteristic of a particular design and installation.

THOUGHTS ON CONVERTING TO SPOILERS

Conversion to spoilers and full-span flaps is an intriguing thought. This should be quite feasible for many rectangular-wing designs .... especially those equipped with Fowler-type flaps. The inboard ends of the ailerons for example, could be joined to the flaps so that the entire trailing edge becomes, in effect, a full-span flap. It might, however, be necessary to rework the flap actuating mechanism to enable it to handle the added loads of a vastly increased flap area. Otherwise, to actuate those flaps you would have to have the brawn of a Russian weight lifter.

Structurally speaking, it is fortunate that spoilers are most effective when located well to the rear of the wing. This location permits a solid mounting for the spoiler hinges. Furthermore, when the spoiler is

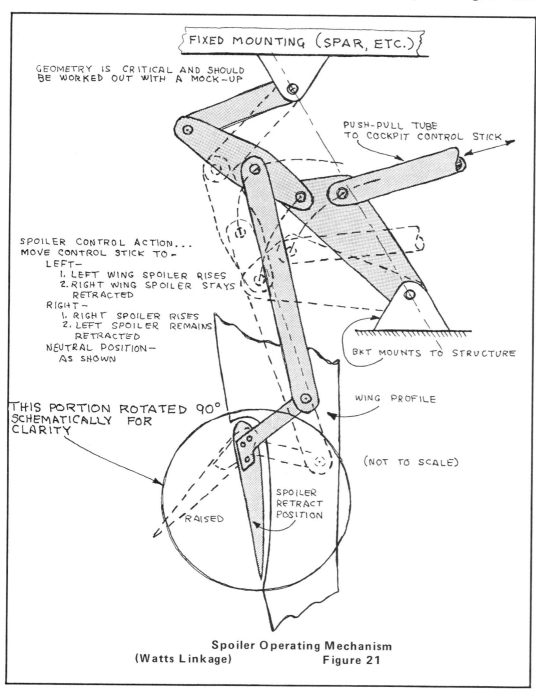

Spoiler Operating Mechanism
(Watts Linkage)   Figure 21

in its retracted position, it becomes a very effective gap seal between the wing and the flap.

Spoilers tend to have a large aerodynamic hinge moment which requires large actuation forces. Worse yet is the fact that they often require complex actuating mechanisms. (Figures 21, 23 and 24)

What is needed is a technique for actuating the spoilers with acceptable (small) forces through a simple control mechanism. An idea of how complex these control systems can become is illustrated in Figure 23. It shows the mechanism devised years ago to provide for the assymetrical raising of the spoilers (roll control) and the dropping of ailerons, as well as deployment of the flaps. About the only thing missing is a means of raising both spoilers collectively (for glidepath control) while retaining their asymmetrical action for lateral control. To achieve all these actions would certainly challenge the greatest of EAA's mechanical and engineering geniuses.

In their ultimate development, spoilers could take the place of the ailerons. The aileron drooping requirement would then be eliminated and the ail-

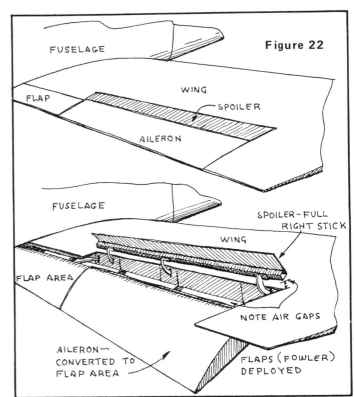

Figure 22

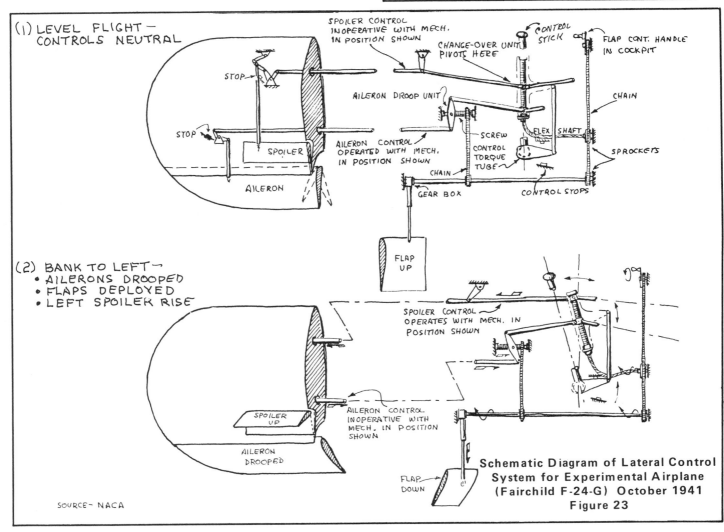

(1) LEVEL FLIGHT — CONTROLS NEUTRAL

(2) BANK TO LEFT —
• AILERONS DROOPED
• FLAPS DEPLOYED
• LEFT SPOILER RISE

SOURCE - NACA

Schematic Diagram of Lateral Control System for Experimental Airplane (Fairchild F-24-G) October 1941
Figure 23

erons could be changed into additional flaps.

In early attempts to employ spoilers for roll control, they were used to supplement the ailerons. The Robertson Company, on the other hand, seems quite successful in using spoilers to completely replace the ailerons in its recent conversions. After all, why have both ailerons and spoilers? It would be redundant.

In Figure 22 you will note that the raised spoiler has an air gap under it. It seems that many of the spoilers, when in their deflected or raised position, can cause a small oscillation of the wing. These oscillations persist until the spoiler is released to its neutral position. Apparently the condition is due to the disturbed flow over the wing behind the spoiler. Providing an air gap between the wing surface and the

raised spoiler seems to overcome this tendency. However this means that the simple method of hinging the leading edge of the spoiler with a piano hinge is not likely to give as good results as the type of hinging illustrated in Figure 22. It is possible that making cut-out areas along the bottom of the spoiler would also work as well. The NACA experiments found that spoilers built like a garden rake turned upside down were immune to the odd oscillations, and in many respects, were more effective than the plain slab spoiler.

Spoilers could be added to a number of home-built designs for experimentation without too much difficulty. However, such an undertaking should be approached with caution. The addition and testing of a spoiler installation without the removal of the ailerons might afford greater safety in making these ex-

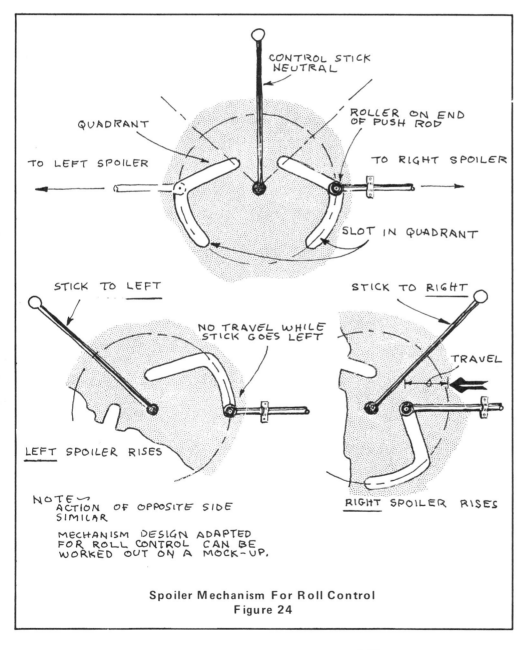

Spoiler Mechanism For Roll Control
Figure 24

145

periments. Only when a particular spoiler modification has proved itself would the removal of the ailerons, or conversion of them to additional flaps be prudent.

As you may have concluded by now, the sophisticated use of spoilers requires a relatively complex mechanism. It would therefore be unlikely that greater use of spoilers will be forthcoming until someone devises the kind of installation that would provide for a simple mechanical mixing system of control which permits a selective, balanced deployment of the spoilers for both roll control and glidepath control.

SUGGESTED REFERENCES

Andrisani, Gentry, Jr. and Stickle: Wing Tunnel Study of Slot Spoilers for Direct Lift Control. NASA TN D6627

Baker: The Development of a New Lateral Control Arrangement. NACA 1104/294 October 1941

Ashkenas: The Development of a Lateral Control System for Use with Large Span Flaps. NACA TN 1015 January 1946

Wenzinger and Rogallo: Wind Tunnel Investigation of Spoiler, Deflector, and Slot Lateral Control Devices on Wings with Full Span Split and Slotted Flaps. Report No. 706

Laitone: An Investigation of the High Speed Lateral Control Characteristics of a Spoiler. NACA 1104/355 March 1944

Lowery and Liddell: Wind Tunnel Investigation of a Tapered Wing with a Plug Type Spoiler Slot Aileron and Full Span Slotted Flaps. NACA July 1942

Verstynen and Andrisani: Full Scale Wing Tunnel Investigation of Effects of Slot Spoilers on the Aerodynamic Characteristics of a Light Twin-Engine Airplane. NASA TN D-7315 September 1973

Lowry: Data On Spoiler Type Ailerons NACA RM L53I24a

Hoerner and Borst: Fluid Dynamic Lift

FIBERGLASS TIPS

5

Getting Acquainted with Fiberglass

There must be as many ways of working fiberglass as there are builders. Still, one thing is certain, no matter what method is used, or how well everything really turns out, the undertaking is still guaranteed to be one messy operation. Don't let the built-in messiness or a lack of experience with fiberglass intimidate you, however, because anyone can turn out a good functional fiberglass cowling or fairing if he is willing to work at it. Besides, no matter how uncertain you may be at the start, you will develop a knack for working with fiberglass very quickly.

Anyone planning to work fiberglass for the first time certainly should study the instructions (if any are available) very carefully. The process of making fiberglass components is not complicated but it is one that must be carefully controlled.

In the event you have to buy your Polyester resin and hardener from a local boat shop, don't be surprised if they dust off an old plastic container, fill it from a big 55-gallon drum, and hand it to you without any directions for its use. If this is the case, it would be a good idea to ask in what proportion the hardener or catalyst should be mixed for that type of resin. Be prepared to hear a "recipe" like some a GI Mess Sergeant might pass on. You know..."Well, let's see...to a gallon of resin use just about all of this little jigger of hardener." From such guidance it might be hard to determine the exact amount of hardener for just a small batch of resin except thru trial and error.

In the absence of any other formula, I suggest as a starting point when mixing small amounts of resin, that you use 8 drops of hardener for each ounce of resin. Sometimes this will be too much; at other times, too little, so adjust this ratio to suit working temperatures. Knowing how much hardener to use is critical in working successfully with fiberglass. If this sort of thing is new to you, you'll find it hard to believe that so few drops of catalyst can actually set things off.

There are two basic types of Polyester resin.

Make sure you purchase the type you need. One is a bonding or laminating type used to obtain a good bond to a wood surface, for example. This type (nonwax bearing) cures with a tacky surface. It cannot be sanded without clogging the sandpaper on the first pass. To obtain a nice hard surface you need a finishing resin (wax bearing). It can be sanded. If you do use the bonding or laminating type of resin, you should top it off with a final coat of finishing resin.

You can always save time and money by working within proven guidelines. Some of the more important ones are summarized as rules for your convenience:

Rule I: Always weigh the amount of resin (a household scale is all right), then add the exact amount of hardener for the quantity to be mixed. Don't guess!

The rule is simple enough but some comments may be helpful. First, don't forget to 'zero' your weighing scale when you place the empty container on it. Secondly, understand that temperature has a big influence on how the resin behaves and how quickly it cures.

If the temperature is much over 75 to 85 degrees F, you'll find yourself rushed. With the hotter temperatures you will experience too rapid a curing, and maybe hot fingers from trying to hold on to the container of a runaway, quick-curing resin. When temperatures hit 90 degrees F and above, find something else to do. Conversely, when the temperature is on the low side, say 65 degrees F and below, the stuff becomes very unpredictable and is in no hurry to cure at all. Sometimes, the net result is a tacky, sticky surface for a prolonged period of time. Roughly speaking, using a temperature of 70 degrees F as a standard, it will require twice as much catalyst or hardener at 40 degrees F and only half as much at a temperature of 90 degrees F. So, record your tested ratios, temperatures, and working times on a scrap of paper and pin it up in your work area so you don't forget them.

You'll notice that the rule says "...the exact amount of hardener." If you put in an extra few drops for good measure, you may regret wasting the unused portion of the resin that sets up before you can use it. Some Polyester resins start turning a greenish hue when the curing process nears its gelling state...when it does, ol' friend, you have but a few minutes before even the brush becomes immobilized in the gelled resin (slight exaggeration). Anyhow, it's a good idea to have a plentiful supply of containers and inexpensive brushes for replacement.

Just as worthy of note is the thorough stirring of the two ingredients. Stir the mix for at least one full minute. After all, when you realize that the few drops of hardener must be thoroughly diffused with the resin, it is easy to see the importance of proper mixing. Be forewarned ...insufficient mixing can cause spotty curing of the resin.

Rule II: Have everything ready! Everything!

The glass cloth should be precut to size, allowing a generous margin for misalignment. Be careful; the cloth, if pulled or stretched in one direction, narrows proportionately. The structure to be covered should be clean and dusted. You should have the right size brush or roller at hand, plenty of wiping rags or paper towels, and, as a mess chaser, at least a gallon of acetone or lacquer thinner for clean-up. A strategically located clock for timing yourself would be reassuring. You'll have but about 30 minutes working time. This is why being absolutely prepared is so important, If the resin starts to set up before you use it all up, say goodbye to the can, the brush and the remaining resin. Nothing will stop the hardening process and nothing will dissolve the hardened resin.

Rule III: Ignore all distractions and interruptions . . . . especially phone calls.

Your 30 minutes of work time will scoot by before you realize it.

Rule IV: Don't work in direct sunlight.

The hot surfaces of the structure being worked, coupled with higher temperatures (over 90 degrees F), stack the odds against doing a decent job.

Rule V: Avoid working during periods of high humidity.

It affects the curing unpredictably.

Rule VI: Avoid excessive brushing at the time gelling begins.

The resin is not like paint. Apply it generously with a full brush and allow it to flow out without overbrushing. Continued brushing of the resin after it loses its inclination to flow freely will only make a mess and upset the gelling process.

Rule VII: Never use Polyester resin over epoxy resin.

It will not stick or endure very well in use. You can, however, use epoxy over Polyester. Actually, you can use epoxy over almost anything because epoxy sticks like a leech. Of course, it won't stick to a waxy or oily surface, but everybody knows that. Never apply additional coats of Polyester resin over a Polyester surface that has already cured.....not without a thorough sanding of the surface first.

Rule VIII: In most cases 3 layers of cloth is sufficient.

This is especially true if an extra layer or more of material is applied to localized points needing reinforcement.

Rule IX: Don't use old resin that has thickened.

It will have very poor penetration and adhesion qualities.

MOLDS, FORMS, PATTERNS AND THE LIKE

There are two common methods used to build fiberglass parts. Oddly enough, both of them require the construction of the same sort of form as a basis. So, it doesn't matter whether you intend to lay up the fiberglass on a male mold or form it in a female mold, there is no way out. You will have to figure out how to best build simple molds or forms for making the fiberglass fairings, cowlings, and other parts.

The female mold. The first step requires the construction of the original sculpted mold, form, plug, or whatever you want to call it.

Over this heavily waxed mold, build up a plaster or fiberglass shell (female mold) of sufficient thickness to retain its shape rigidly after removal from the master form or plug. This female form is then smoothed and sanded to a fine finish as it will be used for the forming of all desired copies of the fiberglass part. The original mold or plug is usually discarded after the female form is made. Female molds are used by professional fiberglass craftsmen and by others who intend to make numerous identical fiberglass components. Although the technique requires considerable work and expense in preparing the female mold, the fiberglass parts can be layed-up inside the form and turned out with minimum effort and very little finishing work.

The male mold. This is the one-mold concept. Here the original form is used as a male plug and the fiberglass layers are formed right over it. This is the most economical way to go. It does require a good eye and skilled hands as considerable external shaping and smoothing must take place to finish each fiberglass component made on the male form. For this reason the male mold method is usually a one-shot deal. Actually, unless you intend to go into the business, what difference to you whether you spend your time putting a good finish in a female mold or on the layed-up surface of the fiberglass component that you intend to use? The initial amount of labor required for one fiberglass part will be about the same for either method. By not building a female form though, you can save enough to buy a nice instrument for your panel.

BUILDING FORMS AND MOLDS

Just about every EAA type knows something about building a mold for a fiberglass cowl. He knows how the engine has to be wrapped with rags and hardware cloth (or screen wire) to form a rough foundation for the plaster that follows. What is difficult to describe is the unbelievable mess generated, and the tremendous amount of labor expended, in shaping and smoothing the plastered form. Naturally, everyone keeps looking for a simple way to do the job. However, as usual, not all ways find favor with all builders, and each builder tends to pick the method he thinks will be the easiest for him to use. Here are some common approaches.

STYROFOAM MOLDS AND FORMS

It is a snap to make nice forms using Styro-foam (or one of the other expanded foam products) because they are easily shaped and sanded. They are also light and easily handled. Unfortunately, Polyester resin dissolves Styrofoam like water going through sugar. Because of this characteristic, builders usually do one of two things. They use epoxy resins in laying up their fiberglass as epoxy has no effect on the foam form. The other precaution often used is to protect the Styrofoam mold with a thin layer of plaster or some other similar coating compatible with the Styrofoam.

When you build your foam form, remember to make it slightly smaller than the finished dimensions so that you can add a protective layer of plaster to it.

As the foam is quite light, some builders leave the Styrofoam form in place after the fiberglass has cured and permit it to become part of the structure. Of course, this is not done with cowlings, but it is with wing tips and some other fairings. There is one problem with that — it does add weight to the airplane. On second thought, using the foam as a permanent base may permit you to use fewer layers of cloth, and that would offset some of the weight.

METAL FORMS

Fiberglass cloth can be formed over simple metal forms (aluminum or galvanized sheet) specially constructed or secured in place on the aircraft. Such a structure serves as a male form. Remember, however, after curing, it must be hand finished by sanding its surfaces in a skillful manner.

As it is with all fiberglass forms and molds, a heavy waxing of the form is needed to ensure easy separation of the completed fiberglass part. Even household floor wax will work on simple forms. Don't polish or rub the wax after applying it as you will remove most of it.

Wherever fiberglass is to be layed directly in place on the aircraft, protect the structure from the wax and the resin with masking tape and paper or plastic sheet. If you get any wax on your structure, paint will not stick to it later on.

WOOD FORMS OR PATTERNS

Wood forms are an excellent base for forming plastic (fiberglass) parts. Any soft wood such as white pine carves and shapes nicely. Even a form for something as large as wheel pants can be carved from laminated layers. You old ship

BEFORE YOU BUY...

When faced with the hard, tedious, and messy sessions during the making of the cowling, it's no wonder some builders begin to look for ways of getting out of such an enlightening experience. The obvious impulse...buy a ready made cowling and a set of wheel pants.

This is great for those building a well known design, provided the design of the available product is suitable and personally appealing. Usually, the price is reasonable and not much more than it would cost a nonexpert builder to purchase the raw materials, make the molds, and muddle through an unbelievably messy, time-consuming job. After all, making your own fiberglass cowls can do nothing for you but help develop your self control...and who needs that?

A word of caution to those who intend to buy a ready made cowling or any other fiberglass component. Unless you are buying from an established and experienced fiberglass producer for the homebuilt trade, be careful. Some of the cowlings being sold are made by gents like yourself who decided to make the more expensive female mold for their particular design. They then try to turn out additional replicas of the cowling to sell to other builders to help recoup some expenses. While most such cowlings are pretty nice, some of them are much too heavy. Some of them lack the absolutely smooth surface and contoured lines that a careful craftsman is able to achieve only after much labor of love. Know what you are getting. Certainly, don't overlook the possibility that you may have to make some modifications to a purchased cowling to get it to fit your airplane.

Imperfections in a fiberglass cowling will be most noticeable when the sun strikes its surface in the early morning and late afternoon hours. On the other hand, this same sun emphasizes perfection of workmanship as illustrated in the photo below.

The sun will reflect the degree of perfection achieved in your fiberglass components.

Fiberglass Your Bird

Building an all-wood airplane? Why not fiberglass it? Hold on now mates, I'm not talking about the usual boat glass-fiber-cloth that weighs 8 to 10 ounces per square yard. That makes for a lead sled, certainly. There is a very very lightweight glass cloth available through many hobby shops that can give the aircraft builder another material for experimentation.

THE VERY LIGHT GLASS CLOTH

In 1962 I first came upon this glass-fiber cloth in a small hobby shop in Lincoln, Nebraska, and right there I decided it would be just the thing for my first Emeraude's plywood-covered stabilizer and fin rather than the customary lightweight fabric. The glass cloth came in a small plastic package costing a dollar. It was labeled as being 28 inches x 38 inches in size. The manufacturer is well known in model airplane circles as the Sig Mfg. Co., Montezuma, Iowa. At that time I figured that by covering the tail pieces with this glass-fiber material I shouldn't pick up more than 2 or 3 pounds. Surely that wouldn't be much more than a fabric covering with its numerous build-up and finishing coats.

Now, more than a decade later, I have taken another look at the results with the realization there here was a super lightweight material and finish that has defied the ravages (melodramatic expression) of time. Those tail surfaces look like fine pieces of porcelain . . . . they're as beautiful today as they were when I doted over them 10 years ago. I recall, I spent many hours sanding some crummy fiberglass resin that did not seem to want to harden and kept gumming up the files and sandpaper. I also had to use scrapers and lacquer thinner in my attempt to get down to the good dry material. Now I know that, in my innocence, I had used a resin (laminating) which cured with a sticky, tacky surface, making sanding an impossible chore.

One learns things about fiberglass work, and today the commercially available "Finish Resin" just suits me fine. It resists running, cures pre-dictably, and sands beautifully.

A local hobby shop informed me that they could get the lightweight glass cloth in rolls 38 inches wide and up to 200 yards long. The price has not changed much through the years. Since it will take about 30 yards of cloth, a reasonable discount can sometimes be negotiated. It seems that there are 2 weights of this glass cloth. The extra-lightweight and the regular. The extra-lightweight stuff weighs (according to my Japanese fish scale) about 25.5 grams per square yard, and the regular cloth, about 36.75 grams per square yard. To put that into American-ese, I think that it comes to 9/10-ounce per square yard for the extra-lightweight glass cloth. Compare this with the usual 8–10-ounce boat glass cloth.

According to my screwdriver and hammer calculations, the weight of the resin on the finished surface can be held down to about 1 ounce per square foot. If this is so, then by using the extra-lightweight cloth, a person should be able to cover a typical homebuilt with an increase in weight of only 22 to 25 pounds. This compares favorably with any fabric covering on an airplane, which could weigh as much after all the various build-up coats of dope are applied.

GETTING READY, SURFACE PREPARATION

Quite important that you do this right. To achieve a good bond, you must have a clean, dry wood surface free from wax, varnish, paint, or oil of any kind. Any obvious imperfections in the wood surface should be filled with plastic wood or a Polyester putty. Don't bother with small staple holes or nail holes, as the resin will fill those in nicely. Go over all the surfaces one more time lightly with sandpaper, being especially attentive to all edges and corners. After you dust things off, you are ready for the application of the glass cloth and resin. Cut your glass cloth to the approximate length needed for the job and then roll it up around a piece of broom handle or tubing for easier handling. (Figure 3)

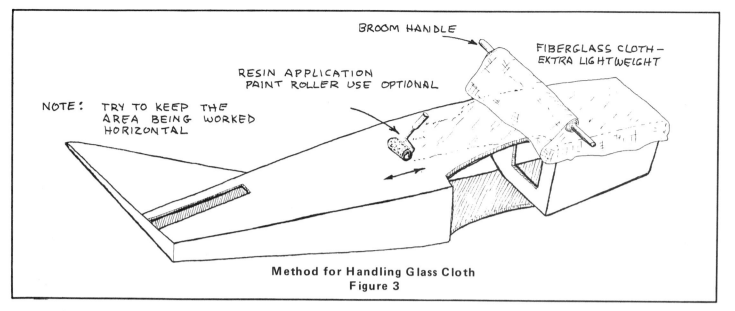

RESIN APPLICATION
PAINT ROLLER USE OPTIONAL

BROOM HANDLE

FIBERGLASS CLOTH –
EXTRA LIGHTWEIGHT

NOTE: TRY TO KEEP THE AREA BEING WORKED HORIZONTAL

Method for Handling Glass Cloth
Figure 3

LAYING IT ON

I know that brushes do not last long when working with glass cloth because sooner or later, you will miscalculate and allow the resin to harden on the brush while you are preoccupied with something else. Nevertheless, you should use a fairly good brush . . . one that won't shed bristles all over your work. In applying the resin and cloth to larger areas like the wing surface or the fuselage side, you will find that a 3-inch brush will be just fine. Certainly, using one smaller than 2 inches is too slow for the quick-curing resin mixture.

If you are so inclined you can use a paint roller to apply your resin to the plywood and then to roll the cloth down. This works very well on large surfaces and virtually eliminates the sliding and creeping of the glass cloth. You can mix more resin and cover more area with this method than with a brush before the resin starts to set up. Even though the resin ordinarily is mixed to give you about 30 minutes work time, my own experience painfully reminds me that it can set up in as short a time as 10 minutes, 2 minutes of which were spent in mixing the stuff. A reminder: Do not work in the direct sunlight!

Mix no more than 3 or 4 ounces at a time if you are working with a brush. This amount should be sufficient for one side of a fin or stabilizer, etc. Measure out your catalyst or hardener carefully and jot down the ratio of resin to the hardener so that you can later remember what it was when you adjust your formula to control the rate of gelling. I use 8 to 10 drops of hardener per ounce of resin for small batches.

While a quart of resin will not cover much over 14 square feet when used with heavy fiberglass cloth, you can easily cover about 42 square feet using the extra-lightweight glass cloth.

Brush the resin on generously over about a 3- to 5-foot area of the structure. Start at one end of the resin-wetted area and unroll your cloth brushing it down smoothly until the weave disappears from view. Make your brush strokes gently and work from the center outward, else the cloth will tend to slide in the direction of the brushing. Make sure that it does not slip so much that the opposite end winds up short of the space you want covered. This is a good place to use your hands and fingers, as the cloth may tend to develop creases or wrinkles. Smooth it out by hand or with a small rubber squeegee. After things look pretty good prepare another 3 or 4 feet and continue the process until you have covered the entire length. If you are working with smaller pieces of glass cloth, lap each of the joints about 2 inches. Trim the excess edges with scissors and brush them down with resin.

CAUTION: **You may be allergic to epoxy resin. I suggest you use disposable rubber gloves or other devices to prevent skin irritation.**

Do not continue to brush fussily over an area once you have the glass cloth down smoothly, even if you see some uneven brush marks showing. Let well enough alone. Excess brushing at the time the resin is gelling can prevent it from curing thoroughly. In short, do not overbrush. After the resin has gelled, however, brush on another coat of resin. This se-

157

cond coat of resin will help considerably in leveling the covered surface for your smoothing and sanding operations. When the extra resin coat has cured, you can start the smoothing operation or go on and finish covering the other sides of the structure.

SMOOTHING THE SURFACES

The cured surface will have ripples and brush marks hardened into it. This is to be expected, and if you can muster enough nerve to knock down the high spots with a sanding disc slipped onto your electric hand drill, you will make your life much easier. Use a medium or even coarse grit aluminum oxide disc and simply go to work. I guarantee that in about 30 minutes you will develop a high degree of skill in dressing the glassed surface. A good procedure is to work a large area (about 1 square foot) uniformly. Do not get too preoccupied with one small particular spot. By working a gradually expanding area at one time, you will get a more even job. It also will be very helpful in preventing accidental sanding through the glass cloth into the bare wood surface beneath .... too often, that is. It will happen, but don't let that upset you. Remember that this is a protective weatherproof coating over the plywood and not a structural covering. As a protective film all you need is the thinnest possible layer of glass and resin over the wood. It is therefore, most effective to sand the resin down to where the slightest hint of the cloth's weave begins to show. How do you judge how much sanding to do? Easy enough. The low spots will show up as very shiny spaces or spots, while the areas that have been sanded

Fiberglassed fuselage and center section sanded and ready for primer. White areas on tail and canopy are test dabs of the primer.

will have a dull whitish sheen to them. You should continue disc sanding lightly over large areas until you have worked the surface down to where most of the shiny spots have disappeared. Your glass-covered surface is now almost perfectly true, level and smooth. After you have completed the entire structure to this point, put your electric disc sander away and switch to a hand-held sanding block or an orbital electric sander. A regular sanding block is good, but I prefer a hunk of balsa wood with a radiused corner on one edge and a square corner on the other. Continue with your hand sanding, working over rather large areas in all directions. Wipe the sanding dust away frequently to check how close you are getting to the cloth or to the elimination of the tiny low spots. Without a doubt you will have sanded through the glass fibers in a number of places. If these places are small, just mix up some resin and brush over them. If the area is as large as a couple of inches or so, it would be best to dab on another piece of fiberglass cloth, overlapping the offending space by a couple of inches. After the resin has gelled brush on another layer over the patch and any other place necessary. You have now reached the fussy stage and can spend many happy hours resanding the offending spots.

If you don't remove as much of the cured resin as possible in your sanding process, you will only be leaving useless weight on your airplane. An excess layer of resin over the entire airplane can easily add pounds to the aircraft. A good check and a sensible approach is to weigh the structure being coated before applying the fiberglass and then again after the rough sanding work is completed. If you have picked up much more than 1.2 ounces per square foot of surface, go back and do some selective sanding. Be very careful sanding on edges or corners of the structure (do this by hand) or you will sand through before you realize it. Remember this glass cloth is mighty thin. Nevertheless, it should add significantly to the overall strength of the structure and will certainly reduce the tendency of the plywood to swell and shrink during changes in humidity.

PRIME & PAINT

It is now time to wipe the whole structure down thoroughly with a clean cloth. The chances are that after you have done so, you will still find a number of tiny shiny spots that you overlooked. These you can forget about unless you are an unrelenting perfectionist. In that case amigo, back to the sanding block. You will notice that all mention of sanding has been with coarse or maybe medium grit sandpaper.

Now, here is where some of us will part company. Some builders will want to switch to finer grit sandpaper or even to wet or dry sandpaper and really put a smooth finish on the fiberglass coating. This is exactly what I did 10 years ago on an all-wood stabilizer and fin, and the results have been excellent. The primer stuck to it well and so has the finish. Why challenge success? Laziness. On my latest project, I cut down the amount of work by eliminating all the ultra-smooth sanding and just put on my primer next. Then I worked the prime coat down as needed for the ultra-smooth finish. Actually, the fiberglassed surface sanded with medium grit sandpaper is pretty smooth anyway.

Finishing the fiberglassed bird proceeds normmally from this point. It depends on what kind of finish you intend to use. Just this bit of advice: Decide on the brand of paint you intend to use and select the primer recommended for that brand.

Your completed bird will look like a big polished gem cut out of a solid hunk of precious stone. Maybe it will last as long too!

Fiberglass Fairings

We go to the trouble of making fairings because we believe airplanes should have them, and they make airplanes look better. But fairings have the function of reducing drag as well as being nicely curved covers that look good.

Fairing design on homebuilts has always been more a matter of eyeball-engineering and craftsmanship than the exercise of an exact aerodynamic science. Chances are if fairings have a pleasing free-flowing appearance, they are also aerodynamically efficient. Fairings need not be elaborate. Often a sealing strip or a rubber channeling strip fitted along the juncture of the structure will suffice for elegance and aerodynamics. Sometimes even a piece of tape does adequately in areas not ordinarily visible to those curious, erect-walking Homo sapiens known to frequent airports, and to point out tiny flaws in other Homo sapiens' aircraft.

Unless you have detailed plans or a fist full of computerized figures and formulae for calculating the aerodynamic efficiency of your fairings, you will probably rely on your instinct or try duplicating the type of fairings you have seen and liked on other aircraft. Nothing wrong with that certainly, but wouldn't you like something more practical to rely on than instinct? Here's a simple rule that won't subject you to a morass of theoretical aerodynamic vagaries.

Rule: To reduce aircraft drag, install fairings at the junctures of any two surfaces joining at angles of less than 90 degrees to each other.

Take a long look at Figure 4. It could well influence your thinking on fairings from here on. Whenever a wing surface and a fuselage surface form a 90-degree or greater angle, no fairing is required. Nor would one, if installed, do much to reduce the drag in that area. This concept applies to other components as well.

A stabilizer joining the fuselage at a 90-degree or greater angle, likewise, needs no fairing, nor would a landing gear leg joining its wing or fuselage attachment points at a 90-degree angle.

Why not do a little research to establish the

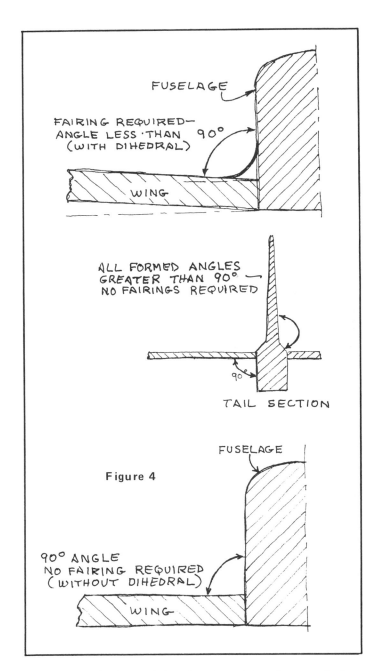

Figure 4

accuracy of the rule? At the risk of your being distracted for a few pleasant hours, I would suggest you get out your old aviation magazines and look at pictures of different airplanes, military jets and other high-performance aircraft included. Notice how various designs accommodate the problem. Notice, particularly, how wings are mated to fuselages, and the same thing with the fins and stabilizers and landing gears.

Convinced? Generally speaking, where a 90-degree angle is formed, many modern-day aircraft probably will not have noticeable fairings. In sharp contrast, you may have noticed that the old time designers really went for large fairings in a big way.

Of course, this is not to say you won't at times see long, smoothly contoured fairings on newer aircraft, seemingly contrary to your new-found rule. Other things could have influenced such a deviation. For example, fairings often make it easier to conceal structural protrusions or the large openings sometimes necessary for structural assembly or disassembly, or for inspection purposes. Furthermore, highly tapered and curved fuselage sections in the area of the wing trailing edge usually create a need for generous fairings at these locations. As a result, you will sometimes see airplanes equipped with partial fairings over the aft two-thirds of the wing only, as certain designs dictate unusual treatment.

Typically, low-wing aircraft have about 5 degrees of dihedral. If that dihedral starts at the fuselage, the angle formed between the fuselage surface and the top of the wing will be less than 90 degrees, and, according to our rule, a fairing should be installed. Otherwise surfaces joining at a 90-degree or greater angle simply need to have some sort of a gap seal. Gaps and openings located anywhere on the aircraft's surface contribute to drag and should be covered, taped over or otherwise sealed.

METAL VS FIBERGLASS FAIRINGS

Metal fairings are almost, without exception, lighter than similar fairings made of fiberglass. Whenever compound curves are not required, install metal fairings. You will find them easier and quicker to make than the fiberglass fairings. Besides, even the finishing of fiberglass formed over male molds takes a lot more work and time than similar pieces made of metal. No, there is no doubt, metal fairings are consistently lighter, longer-lasting, and much quicker to make.

Fiberglass fairings, on the other hand, have some advantages. One is that they provide the builder with all sorts of solutions for difficult areas. Fiberglass can be made to any shape, and it is most effective in components requiring compound curvatures. Parts made of fiberglass are tough and strong for their weight. Besides, the materials are usually available locally, while

aluminum of the proper type may not be.

Another quality, fiberglass wing fairings and tail fairings can often be permanently and invisibly bonded into plywood and composite structures. Of course, fiberglass also has its more obnoxious characteristics. It is a messy, itchy process at best. It requires the fabrication, preparation and use of some sort of a form over which the glass layers are placed and wetted down with resin. It continues to shrink imperceptibly for a few days after it is made. And it is prone to crazing, and sometimes to warpage, after prolonged exposure to the sun and elements.

GENERAL CONSIDERATIONS

There are three basic fiberglass fairing installations, permanent, semi-permanent, and those that are removable.

1. **Permanent fairings.** The easiest to make wing root fairings are the permanently integrated composite fiberglass or Dynel covered fairings. They also yield the neatest looking installations. Unfortunately, their use is limited to plywood-covered and composite structures because the fairing's fiberglass layers are bonded directly to a preshaped foam underbody, joining everything permanently to the aircraft. Properly done you can't tell where the fairing ends and the aircraft's structure begins. Of course, these fairings can be made later and then bonded with epoxy to the aircraft without any foam underbody. However, additional layers of glass are needed for rigidity so there is no advantage either way.

2. **Semi-permanent fairings.** These are fairings attached to metal, wood, and composite or fiberglass structures with pop rivets and sometimes with sheet metal screws. The fairings normally are not considered removable, but I suppose they could be should circumstances dictate.

3. **Removable fairings.** Removable fairings include all those attached with sheet metal screws, clips, or machine screws. The recommended method of attachment is with strategically located machine screws and nut plates wherever access permits. These are the most frequently used type among the homebuilders.

Fabric-covered fuselages are usually still uncovered at the time you want to make the fairings, so it will be necessary to provide some sort of temporary backing against which your mold can be built. Use pieces of scrap plywood fitted to the fuselage sides from the fairing strip down. Another excellent substitute backing material is a sheet of formica. Remember, the backing is only temporary, so just tape, tack, or stabilize it in such a way that it can be easily removed later.

Generally speaking, you can use either Polyester resin or epoxy resin when laying up your fiberglass fairings. Do not, however, use Polyester over unprotected foam without first testing it on some scraps to see if the fumes and resin will destroy or damage the foam.

Epoxy resin can be used just about anywhere as it will not damage any of the commonly used foams.

Fiberglass parts ordinarily do not have to be made to exacting specifications because they are usually add-on accessories like wing fairings, cowling, wing tips, etc.

It is important to emphasize that fiberglass parts shrink during the curing process and continue to do so for several days thereafter. The drilling of holes for attachment should be delayed until the fairings have cured for about a week after removal from the mold.

CONSTRUCTION DETAILS

The first chore in constructing a fairing is to make a foam or plaster mold. Since the mold must be shaped and smoothed in place on the aircraft to obtain the correct shape, the wings and fuselage must be protected during the process. Adequate protection is assured by taping waxed paper to the fuselage sides and to the wing root. Figures 5 and 6 show an alternate method.

Next, the top and bottom contour lines of the fairing's limits should be outlined with masking tape to serve as a guide while the foam is being shaped. You will learn that it's no easy task to affix masking tape in a nice smooth curve. Just keep after it until the effect pleases you.

The third step is to fit and secure partially preshaped pieces of foam directly to the protective wax paper. Keep the foam within the outlines of the masking tape.

Liquid Nails is a good adhesive to use, and one that will not destroy the foam. It is economical to use and may be obtained from most building and supply outlets and discount stores. It was originally developed to be used as a wall adhesive for attaching plywood room panels. The adhesive comes in a tube very much like caulking compound and is used with a caulking gun. Very handy. The wall adhesive works quite well and holds the foam securely to the protective wax paper for shaping while in place. Liquid Nails

has potential for other nonstructural aircraft uses.

Now, you are ready to undertake the rough shaping of the foam base. Try using a flexed hand-held hacksaw blade, coarse file, large wood rasp, or just about anything else that is abrasive and will work for you. As the contouring is refined, switch to a piece of coarse sandpaper for the final finishing.

That black emery-cloth-like sandpaper used to finish floors is excellent for this purpose. At this stage you should check the contours for low and high spots. Do this with a long strip of wood (about ¼-inch square) held flexed against the foam mold. Squint under the strip of wood and look for light areas, an indication of low spots. An additional sanding of the high areas will easily correct this. At the leading edge the strip of wood will be too stiff to use so try a narrow strip of cardboard cut from a manila folder. Hold this around the curved leading edge and the low spots will be easy to locate.

After you are satisfied with the general appearance and shape of the foam mold, overlay

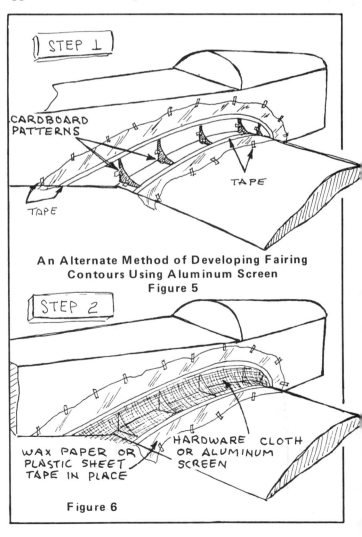

An Alternate Method of Developing Fairing Contours Using Aluminum Screen
Figure 5

Figure 6

Newly made fiberglass fairing is trimmed and tried in place after removing plaster form and protective plastic.

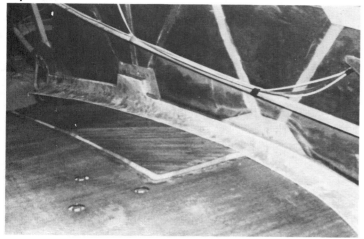

Here foam fairing form is being overlaid with a layer of Durham's Water Putty. Note protective plastic sheet.

Once this was a nice fairing. A couple of additional layers of glass cloth would have prevented this. No, it is not on a homebuilt.

it with a ¼-inch layer of Patching Plaster. You will find that Patching Plaster is much easier to work than Durhams Water Putty or Plaster of Paris (Hydrocal). The greatest thing about it is its sanding ease. Plaster of Paris, by comparison, is a rather hostile substance, uncooperative and sometimes difficult to sand and finish because of hard spots.

The reason for the plaster layer over the foam is to ensure the easy release of the completed fiberglass fairing from the mold and to protect the foam from the effects of Polyester resin, if you want to use it. (Alternatively, you could cover the foam mold with scotch tape, masking tape or an adhesive foil, although the results may not be as predictable.)

After the plaster layer has dried it must be sanded to its final contour. Passing your fingers up and down the plaster mold will reveal to your senses the existence of larger dips and lumps in the mold, but not the tiny ones that will look so big later on.

A wonderful gadget for locating all high spots is the smudge stick (something I just made up). Any flexible batten (wood strip) about ½-inch x 1/8-inch x 18 inches long will do. Rub colored chalk heavily all over one wide surface of the batten. Now you have a smudge stick. To actuate it, place the smudge stick on the surface of the mold, smudged side down and rub it all around over the plaster surface. All of the chalk-smudged areas showing on the plaster are high spots. Sand them down, rechalk your smudge stick and do the rubbing exercise again. Do this until the entire plaster mold smudges evenly . . . . an indication that there are no more low spots.

Your mold should now look like a nice white fairing. Seal the plaster mold with a couple of coats of shellac or any quick-drying paint. When the sealant is dry, wax the completed form heavily with a paste floor wax. A brush or spray coat of mold release will make removal of the fiberglass shell easier.

This might be a good time to make a few templates from stiff cardboard or metal for 3 or 4 selected points along the mold so that you can again duplicate the foam and plaster base for the other wing. You are finally ready to make the fairing. But all of the work is not over yet. You are aware, of course, when working from a male mold, that a lot of itchy surface sanding of the fairing still remains after it cures.

It would be nice to make a female mold from which to pull all the finished fiberglass fairings you want with no further finishing required. However, just for one fairing it is not worth the cost. No matter, there is still plenty of sanding and finishing work involved with either method. So go ahead.

Coat the foam plaster mold with resin and lay on about three layers of 6-8 ounce glass cloth in rapid succession, staggering the joints in the different layers. Additional layers may be desirable for added stiffness or where the fairing may be subject to abuse.

After the resin has cured, the unpleasant task of smoothing must be undertaken. Use a disc sander in a hand-held electric drill for leveling rough areas of the fairing and those caused by lapped joints. The glass surface is very hard, and is difficult to sand, therefore, a coarse file is better for the initial heavy smoothing work. If the surface is fairly smooth and true, a sharp plane blade, gripped vertically between your thumbs and first two fingers, can be used to remove surface glaze. Continue the scraping or shaving action until all of the glaze spots disappear. At this point that smudge stick can be pressed into service again. Incidentally, the smudge stick is a useful finishing tool for all composite sanding and finishing work. It is especially useful in working cowlings and truing large composite surfaces.

Signs of the glass fibers will show in the sanded surface. I finish my fiberglass parts by giving them a brush coat of epoxy resin. Following this treatment, wet-sand the entire surface until the glaze is removed. The surfaces are now ready for a good surface primer, or, as some call it, a sanding primer.

COCKPITS AND CABINS

Cockpit Mock-up and How to Use It

While you are waiting that interminable four to six weeks for your first shipment of materials to arrive, you can start on your project. For that matter, you can start on it before any materials are even ordered. After all, why waste time just waiting? Why not get started with your project by building a cockpit mock-up from scrap materials? You probably have pieces of wood, plywood scraps, nails, some kind of glue, masking tape and cardboard around the homestead. All of these things, and just about anything else that can be cut, bent, glued or nailed could be handy for putting together a cockpit mock-up.

WHY A MOCK—UP?

Why waste your time on something like that? Here's why. Most designers attempt to provide adequate cockpit space for the average man, but how many of us are really average? If you are taller or shorter than 5 feet, 9 inches, or weigh more or less than 170 pounds, it is quite possible that the design you intend to build, or are building, will have a cockpit accommodation and arrangement that is something less than the optimum for you. You may find after you have built your fuselage, installed everything, and climbed in for the first time, that the cockpit is awkwardly arranged. You may be cramped for leg room and the control stick and seat may feel all wrong.

You should use a mock-up as a testbed for resolving such difficulties and to help keep you from making building errors. See Figure 1.

You should use it to check the fit of all components and assemblies, without the risk of damage or abuse to your project. It will help prevent those unwelcome extra installation holes that may be drilled and redrilled in the wrong places. As each fitting, assembly or component is completed for the airplane, install it first in the mock-up. If everything checks out, remove it and duplicate the installation procedure and details in the airplane.

I'm convinced that homebuilders would make greater use of a mock-up as a building aid if they had practical suggestions for its use. The following cockpit areas are those most likely to require some degree of modification from the plans to suit your particular requirements.

POSITIONING THE SEAT

Only by sitting in the airplane or in a mock-up of the cockpit can you really determine the most comfortable location and position for the seat and for the rudder pedals. Don't be surprised if it is not that shown on the plans. There is, after all, a lot of difference between one builder and another.

Until the seat location is established, it will be risky to proceed with the rest of the cockpit layout, as the location of just about everything else is affected by the pilot's seated position and his reach.

The vertical position of the seat affects headroom, as does the angle formed by the seat back. Most seat backs should be tilted approximately 15 degrees for "conventional" designs and somewhat more (about 30 degrees) in the new generation aircraft such as the Taylor Imp, VariEze, the Bede 5 and the Quickie. As the seat back slope is increased, an increase in headroom results. Unfortunately, there will be almost a proportionate increase in the leg room required. This is an important relationship which must be taken into account. In addition, the semi-reclined seating almost certainly requires a headrest support and a contoured seat. (Figure 2)

The size of many homebuilt cockpits borders on the absolute minimum. In these designs, moving the seat an inch or two in any direction represents just about all of the optional range of adjustment at your disposal.

The conventional low-wing designs often have a large front spar cutting across the cockpit area and the usual practice is to plunk a flat board on it and proudly proclaim it "The Seat." Obviously, such a seat cannot be moved, but its sitting comfort could be improved. Steel tube fuselages, on the other hand, ordinarily have a few pieces of tubing welded across the structure for a seat. This arrangement, likewise, might be too high, or too low, or too something else not suited to your personal custom-built physiognomy.

LOCATING THE RUDDER PEDALS

Undoubtedly, you will find it better to work out the location of the rudder pedals and the seat concurrently.

Of all the design features shown on the plans, the location of the rudder pedals may be the one thing not right for you. This means some adjustment will have to be made by moving the rudder pedals fore or aft. Some slight adjustment may be obtained by tilting the pedals. However, the pedal angle selected must permit easy brake application and yet not be such that inadvertent braking or brake drag would result.

If you find it necessary to relocate the rudder pedals from the position shown on the plans, be prepared for complications. At the very least, additional structural cross members or reinforcements will be required for the new position of the rudder pedals. You will find that it is far better to mess around with changes like this on the mock-up than on the real bird since the mock-up permits easy access to the area. Also, work out mechanical stops for the rudder pedals in the mock-up. The simpler the solution the better.

Another thing, the mock-up installation will show immediately if there is sufficient space behind the rudder pedals for hydraulic brake cylinders. As a matter of fact, the brake lines can be fabricated to the exact lengths required and their routing determined all at the same time.

POSITIONING THE CONTROL STICK

Sit in the seat of the mock-up (or airplane) and see where your hand rests naturally in your lap. That should be the stick's neutral position. Simple? Not so simple because there is more to consider. Will the cockpit width at that point, the position of the longerons, and other cockpit protrusions permit you to move the control stick in all direcitons to the degree needed? If the control stick is too far from the seat, its movement may be hampered by the instrument panel or by the pilot's knees. Actually, most homebuilts really suffer from the opposite difficulty. The control stick is usually too close to the seat. Remember that as the control stick is pulled back its left and right movement becomes more and more restructed by your legs.

Be sure the control stick has sufficient clearance from the bottom of the instrument panel. You don't want to leave part of your knuckles implanted in the panel during a forgetful moment. However, don't cut the control stick too short either because that could make the airplane very sensitive to small stick movements, which automatically result in big actions.

THE INSTRUMENT PANEL

The instrument panel should be far enough away from your face so that you can scan all of the instruments easily. The panel should not be closer than 24

to 25 inches from the seat back. See Figure 1.

Some designs leave very little space between the instrument panel and the gas tank. Check to see that all of your instruments will have a sufficient amount of space for hook-up.

A poker-faced friend told me of an old cabin job he knew about—a Bellanca I think it was—that had a compass mounted behind the pilot. He read it with a mirror. I still don't know if he was kidding, but the yarn is believable enough since it is often difficult to find a suitable compass location that is also relatively free of magnetic influences.

Here is a trap to guard against in a single-seater. A center console or an extension of the instrument panel to the floor solves the panel shortage problems but creates others. This "leg spreader" will force you to keep your knees apart in flight. The inability to grasp the stick with your knees while flying puts your poor man's auto pilot out of commission. Also, the inability to move your legs around freely could affect long range comfort. If you are planning on such an installation, try it in the mock-up first.

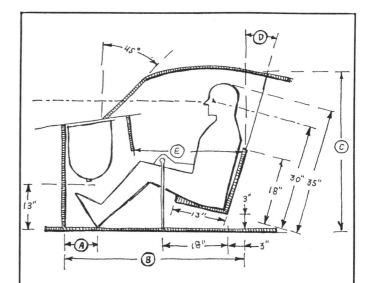

Comparative Dimensions
(Representative Conventional Homebuilts)

AIRCRAFT	A	B	C	D	E
ACRO SPORT	20.5"	87.7"	NA	13°	31.0"
CA-61	9.0"	54.5"	NA	0°	24.5"
EMERAUDE	4.5"	52.0"	44.5"	9°	28.0"
JODEL D-11	4.0"	49.5"	46.0"	9°	31.0"
SCOOTER	8.5"	56.0"	41.2"	8°	27.0"
T-18	5.0*	54.0	44.0"	15°	33.0"
T-40	10.0"	53.2"	44.0"	15°	28.5"
VP-1	8.0"	55.0"	NA	0°	24.0"

NOTE: DIMENSIONS VARY WITH THE BUILDER. CHECK PLANS FOR EXACT MEASUREMENTS.

* FIREWALL SLANT PROVIDES EXTRA CLEARANCE

Figure 1

ENTRY AND EXIT

Can you imagine what a shock it would be for a builder to learn, after he has completed most of his fuselage, that he cannot even get into it, or that it is too cramped for comfort? A dry run to check this little uncertainty is mandatory . . . . and made-to-order for a simple cockpit mock-up. While you are studying the matter of entry and exit, check into these potential problem areas too:

——Will your knees go under that instrument panel? Knees bend the wrong way for getting into cockpits you know.

——What will you be able to hang onto, stand on, or sit on while getting into and out of the airplane?

——How about the passenger? Passengers are not normally familiar with structural limitations and could unknowingly damage the airplane or themselves if provision is not provided for a dignified, easy entry and exit. A built-in hand hold is valuable and the mock-up can help you determine what can be done about it. Incidentally, many cabin type aircraft do lend themselves to the addition of a small but very handy hand hold which can be welded inside the cockpit at the top of the windshield bow.

——How about exiting under emergency conditions? What provisions can you incorporate?

——If a sliding canopy is used, how can you best fit it and seal it against wind noise? Do you want a means of locking it? Will you expect to fly it partially open? These are typical problems which are better worked out on the mock-up.

THE FUEL TANK INSTALLATION

Installing a fuel tank properly is difficult. Securing it in place can turn into a complex operation, so it is well worth trying to simplify the installation with the mock-up. Don't lose sight of the fact that one day the tank might have to be removed for repair or replacement. Will there be a way to do this without tearing the cockpit apart? Prove to yourself whether you will be able to reach the fuel shut-off.

Fuel lines can be prefabricated and their routing determined before final installation in the airplane.

You may, at this time, discover that it is almost impossible to run the throttle cable from your panel, around the tank and through the firewall, without some pretty sharp bends. This is also likely to be true of the tachometer cable. Because of this revelation, you might decide it more convenient to build your tank with a hole smack dab through it as a passageway for some of the controls and the tachometer cable. A practical solution for a common problem.

WHERE TO PUT THE THROTTLE

Some builder/pilots, of single-seaters especially, like to locate the throttle fighter style, on the left side of the fuselage. This is great but be careful. It may be mounted in the wrong place. This is first discovered when the pilot finds he can't pull the throttle all the way back because his elbow hits the seat back.

Throttle sensitivity can be avoided by working out the linkage so that there is at least sufficient movement to create the impression there is plenty of power. Moving a throttle a mere inch to go from idle to max rpm is not good.

ELIMINATING VISIBILITY PROBLEMS

Your eyes can see more, assuming the instrument panel is not too close, if there are no large frames and braces cluttering up your normal line of vision. Sometimes raising or lowering the seat as little

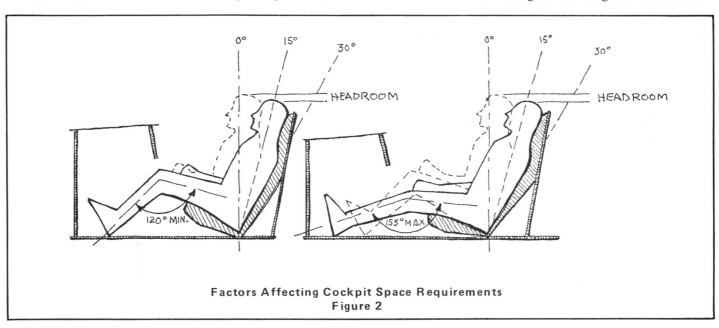

Factors Affecting Cockpit Space Requirements
Figure 2

170

as one inch can improve the situation considerably.

Good visibility from the cockpit should never be sacrificed for the sake of esthetics. Your entire windshield and window installation should first be made on the mock-up and then vision-checked from inside for things like distortion, unobstructed visibility up, down, and at least 180 degrees horizontally with some extra plexiglas areas to accommodate peripheral vision.

SUGGESTIONS FOR MOCK−UP CONSTRUCTION

Whatever the type of construction features for your aircraft, the mock-up can be most easily constructed around four longerons. Cross members or bulkheads cut from ¼-inch plywood can be used to tie the frame together. Use small plywood gussets glued and stapled to the frame, or metal tabs and angles, wherever needed as reinforcement for the joints. Mock-ups simulating all-metal construction will probably require a partial skin covering (cardboard or plywood) to provide the necessary rigidity to the assembled bulkheads and longerons.

A mock-up must be constructed as accurately as possible from the dimensions given in the plans. It is not necessary, however, to use aircraft quality materials or to construct the complete fuselage mock-up if storage is a problem. A mock-up to be used for cockpit layout needs to consist only of the firewall or nose bulkhead and all of the primary structure up to and including the seat back or baggage compartment bulkhead.

Keep the mock-up in your work area, if possible, and use it frequently. It will turn out to be a great morale booster and a confidence builder because those things that look so hard and complicated to do will fall into place easily when you do your problem-solving and experimenting on a structure built from scraps and costing only a few dollars.

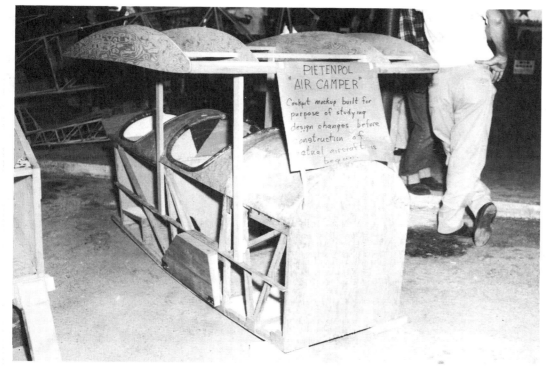

Can you get into the front cockpit? A mock-up can give you the answer.

The Shoulder Harness

At an altitude of 200 feet, soon after take-off, the engine lost power. The biplane was observed gliding in a shallow left turn until it disappeared from view behind a knoll. The aircraft impacted in a soybean field, in level attitude hard enough to fail both main gears, and slid to a stop in approximately 45 to 50 feet.

The seat belt held, but with no shoulder harness to restrain his upper torso, the pilot's head struck the top of the instrument panel, displacing it forward.

An extruded aluminum section, illustrated in Figure 3, used to support the top of the instrument panel and secure the coaming, pierced the pilot's head, causing a fatal injury.

If this extruded aluminum section had not been in this location, the pilot probably would have ended up with nothing worse than a headache.

IMMEDIATE ACTION IS RECOMMENDED

There was no reason for the spear-like extrusion or angle reinforcement to be positioned as shown in the drawing. If such a reinforcement is installed in your aircraft, it should be removed, or at least modified so that it does not extend beyond the fuel tank. This kind of reinforcement is more likely to be found in biplanes as presence of center section brace wires, in some designs, makes the installation of the instrument panel hood in one piece very difficult, if not impossible. Nevertheless, I would suggest that perhaps no reinforcement at all is needed here. That metal hood or coaming merely has a fairing and streamlining function in most cases.

By using nut plates, even a two-piece coaming could be installed with no need for a reinforcement strip.

Equally dangerous are protruding knobs, switches and ignition keys in the central portion of the instrument panels of single-seaters. In the case of two-seater aircraft, you should avoid the placement of such protrusions in the areas directly in front of either the pilot or the passenger.

REMEMBER THE PLEDGE?

The critical need for the installation and use

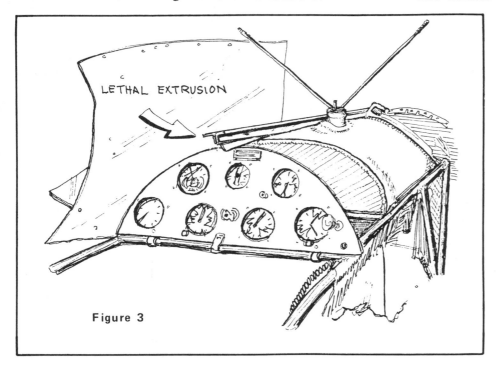

LETHAL EXTRUSION

Figure 3

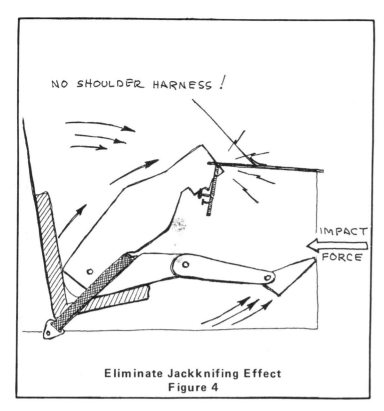

NO SHOULDER HARNESS !

IMPACT FORCE

Eliminate Jackknifing Effect
Figure 4

of pilot and passenger restraint systems in sport aircraft has been recognized and supported by the EAA for more than a quarter of a century. EAA membership applications have long contained the Shoulder Harness Pledge.

"I _____ hereby promise to install and wear shoulder harness and safety belts in my private built aircraft to protect myself, passenger and the good name of the association. Air Force and Navy tests have proven that a 20-G harness will eliminate 90 per cent of aircraft accident injuries."

The necessity for pilot and passenger restraints is well documented with numerous examples of serious or fatal injuries sustained in potentially survivable accidents. Potentially survivable accidents are those in which the surrounding cockpit or cabin structure remains intact without serious deformations, and where the level of impact forces is below expected human tolerances.

Time and again it is proven that one of the prime factors contributing to head injuries is the widespread reliance on only a seat belt to restrain the body. A seat belt alone cannot provide the needed protection.

The installation and proper use of a shoulder harness will, however, help eliminate the jacknifing action of the body in event of sudden impact forces. (Figure 4)

SELECTING ATTACHMENT POINTS

Each builder should make a critical analysis of his aircraft to establish the best location for the seat belt and shoulder harness attachment points. If the belt is to be attached to the seat, the structural integrity should carry through to the aircraft structure.

If the aircraft is being built from plans, the seat belt attachments and shoulder harness attachments will probably have been worked out and detailed on the plans. Unfortunately, a few of the aircraft designs have what I consider to be inferior shoulder harness installations . . . . my own Emeraude, for example.

This basic fault is as common to all-wood aircraft as it is to the tube and rag types. The particular deficiency I have in mind is the use of the unreinforced seat back or fuselage cross member as an attachment or loop-over point for the shoulder harness. This method does provide some protection, but not much. Such structural members will fail long before the belts themselves fail. The completed installation might give you a nice moral feeling but very little protection. Aircraft with such installations should perhaps have a section of 1/8-inch flexible control cable running aft to some solid point on the aircraft as an additional restraining point. This would serve to increase the strength of the restraint system considerably.

The builder should also be careful not to weaken the basic structure of his aircraft by drilling holes through unreinforced portions of his longerons just to find a good place for the belt and harness attachments.

Not only must the points of attachment be strong enough to develop the full potential of the restraining belts, but the attachment ends of the belts must present and maintain certain relative positions or angles as they pass over the lap and shoulders.

The shoulder harness must also be positioned in such a way as to permit limited freedom to accommodate normal body movements of the pilot and passenger without head-neck contact or interference with vision.

Typical good and poor restraint configurations are illustrated in Figures 5 and 6.

The installation of shoulder harnesses is really uncomplicated and at worst would require but little change or modification of the structure.

Undoubtedly the four-place aircraft cause the greatest difficulty when it comes to finding a suitable attachment location for the shoulder har-

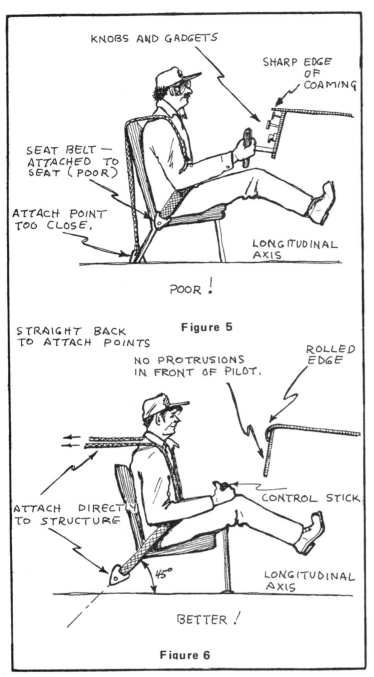

KNOBS AND GADGETS

SHARP EDGE OF COAMING

SEAT BELT — ATTACHED TO SEAT (POOR)

ATTACH POINT TOO CLOSE.

LONGITUDINAL AXIS

POOR !

Figure 5

STRAIGHT BACK TO ATTACH POINTS

NO PROTRUSIONS IN FRONT OF PILOT.

ROLLED EDGE

ATTACH DIRECTLY TO STRUCTURE

CONTROL STICK

45°

LONGITUDINAL AXIS

BETTER !

Figure 6

them? What sort of condition are they in now? The sun is pretty rough on most material, especially fabrics. Take a good look, for after all, when sudden stoppage of an aircraft occurs, the difference between little or no injury and disaster often hinges on the condition of the belts and their attachment to the aircraft structure. Replacement of your seat belts and harnesses is recommended when:

1. Frayed belt edges have become apparent.
2. There are indications that the stitching is deteriorating.
3. The buckle serrations have become worn to the point where slippage is possible.
4. The belt shows other signs of deterioration.

THINK ABOUT IT . . .

It is natural enough for many builders to overrate the protective benefits of the safety belt and as a result underrate the value of the shoulder harness and the need for building crashworthiness into the cockpit and cabin installations. I'd say these gents are dead wrong and no pun intended. I still recall early military training reports which the Air Force used to convince us of the value of these safety precautions. Later, studies by the Cornell University Medical College in New York, the FAA and others, all strengthen the case for adequate body restraints and improved cockpit design to reduce bodily injury in survivable accidents.

All this is not new . . . . in a report during the 1950s, the Cornell Medical College Study Group found that almost 80 per cent of the survivors of light aircraft accidents, in which seat belts were the only restraints used, sustained head injuries.

Any time you have the situation where the head is injured three times as often as parts of the body which are adjacent to the safety belt, it is mighty hard not to believe that some sort of restraints should be provided for the upper torso. The simplest means for this sort of protection is a shoulder harness. Not just any shoulder harness but one that is sufficiently strong, properly anchored, and used. Take another look at Figure 3. It also makes a good case for the use of crash helmets, doesn't it?

ness belts. Part of this is due to the likelihood that the front seat harness might unduly restrict the vision of the rear seat passengers. This sort of inconvenience can be minimized, however, by making use of suitable attachment points located in the upper-side areas of the fuselage structure.

A GOOD INSTALLATION CAN STILL BE BAD

All right, so your seat belt and shoulder harness installation is a pretty good one and should be effective. Well, if you are over that hurdle this might also be a good time to think about the physical condition of your belts and harnesses. Were they new when you installed

Sitting Pretty

Visualize in your mind's eye, if you will, European designs such as the Emeraude, Jodel, Druine Turbulent, Minicab, Tempete, Sirocco, and even the Mignet Flying Flea series. Beautiful little machines, n'est ce pas? Each the essence of functional simplicity.

Of course, these aircraft and their designers on the other side of the great pond do not reign supreme in this respect. We find such Old Country descendents as Messrs. Pietenpol, Bowers, and Evans also stoutly preserving the same fine all-wood design tradition of stark simplicity with numbing effectiveness.

What am I talking about? Seats, that's what! Oh no, not just any seats but those hard plywood slabs internationally accepted as standard equipment by so many builders of wood aircraft.

There is really a surprising similarity of design among wood aircraft when it comes to the seats. While the individual upholstery treatment is often beautiful and imaginative in design, underneath it all is that plywood slab seat with the built-in aft bulkhead doubling as the seat back.

And what's wrong with plywood seats, you say? Nothing much, really. They are simple and strong. They do the job they are required to do . . . . it's just that the comfort factor producing that "numbing effectiveness" is not worthy of otherwise superb aircraft. Well, actually what they are, are real "Butt Busters."

For a long time I wasn't at all aware that seats were the cause of any problem to homebuilders or that the problem was so wide spread, (sorry about that) until a recent Oshkosh Convention. It was there, during one of the many impromptu parking area chit-chats that I learned a surprising number of builders considered their airplanes uncomfortable to sit in after the first hour of flight. One gent summed it up fairly well when he said that he realized that his flat plywood seat would be hard and uncomfortable so he installed a nice, fat 4-inch foam rubber cush--ion. He just couldn't understand why he still had the problem.

One can only conclude that the plywood seats were initially designed using that flat bottomed "Cockpit Man" to check dimensions and cockpit layout, and were never upgraded to people specs.

Figure 7 shows the difference in weight distribution. The human pelvis apparently isn't designed for sitting. (I say that's why people get tired sitting and loafing rather than moving about working on their projects.) The lower the seat in the cockpit, the greater the load that is concentrated on your derriere.

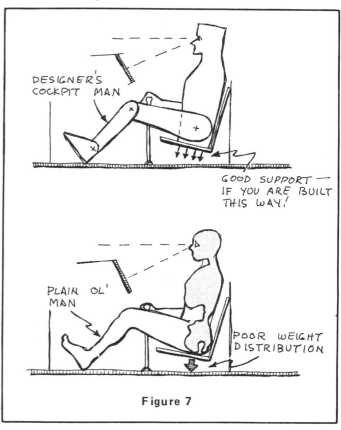

Figure 7

If most of your flights will be comparatively short, local hops of less than one hour, you will probably be content to stick with the original plywood seat and settle for the 60-minute Spartan-like ride that it affords.

Regular cross-country flying is something else though. I see no reason why a beautifully built airplane with the sleekness of an airborne Cadillac should have the seating accommodations of an upholstered buckboard.

We all know why the plywood seat is used so widely. It is the simplest and most basic of solutions. Two pieces of plywood, one for the seat, and one for the back. Any other design or arrangement will take a greater number of pieces to construct .... more work .... more weight.

Still it is human nature to want to have things better, basing improvements on past experiences.

If your airplane is already in service and you want to do something about that seat, you can, and without major surgery.

I'll bet the first thought that comes to your mind is to remove that old plywood seat bottom and throw it away. Better reconsider. You may be the owner of a low-wing all-wood cantilever design where the seat forms a part of the integral structure of the wing center section and, in effect, helps keep your wing tips separated, an excellent static condition to maintain. If there is any question in your mind, leave the built-in seat in place!

You can, nevertheless, improve seating comfort by building up and lengthening, if possible, a contoured seat bottom to better distribute the weight of the seated pilot. In reality, almost any amount of curvature in the seat bottom helps. Although such a built-up contour can be made of any of a number of materials, I believe that laminated polyvinyl chloride foam sheets, shaped as shown in Figure 8, would be the best choice.

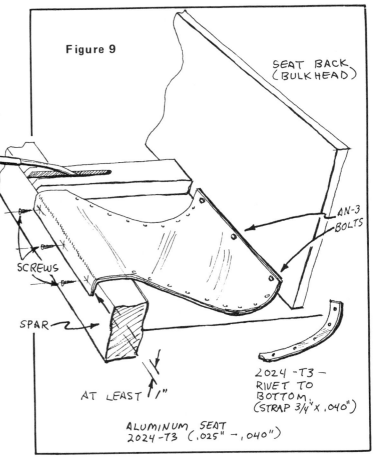

Figure 9

SEAT BACK
(BULKHEAD)

AN-3 BOLTS

SCREWS

SPAR

AT LEAST 1"

2024-T3 — RIVET TO BOTTOM,
(STRAP 3/4" x .040")

ALUMINUM SEAT
2024-T3 (.025" – .040")

The foam glues easily with almost any glue. A layer of epoxy fiberglass cloth seals everything into a lightweight rugged structure. Some foams are dissolved by Polyester resin so try a test sample if you want to use it instead of epoxy resin. No other changes would be necessary. In most instances, you may even be able to slip your original cushion in place and find that it adapts to the new seat form quite readily. Voila! A comfortable new seat.

Alternatively, you might prefer the cure for my own end's numbing experiences. It is shown in Figure 9 and is made of aluminum sheet.

The conversion required some scrap aluminum but no major construction. In my case, it did not result in any weight increase as it was possible to throw away the original heavy, removable plywood seat bottoms. The advantage of the sheet metal seat is that it flexes and adapts to my body contours (I was going to say curves but thought better of it), distributing the load most comfortably.

Another advantage is that this seat design permits me to stand on the spar while getting in and out of the airplane without doing any damage to the seat.

Many of the older store-bought airplanes had

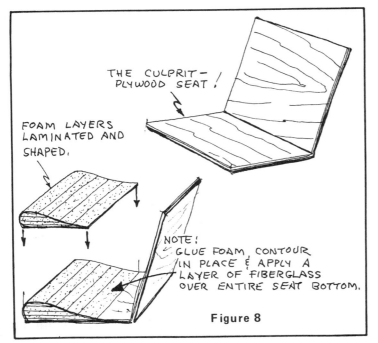

THE CULPRIT—
PLYWOOD SEAT!

FOAM LAYERS
LAMINATED AND
SHAPED.

NOTE!
GLUE FOAM CONTOUR
IN PLACE & APPLY A
LAYER OF FIBERGLASS
OVER ENTIRE SEAT BOTTOM.

Figure 8

comfortable yet simple seats, even though their cushions were quite thin by present day standards. Their success resulted from the canvas sling-like webbing supported by a simple welded frame as is so commonly found in welded steel-tube fuselages. (Figure 10) Woven seat bottoms of nylon rope or straps work equally well, the main requirement being that the seat bottom not be flat, and that it be permitted to flex and to adapt to the pressures imposed on it by the weight of the occupant. If body weight can be distributed over a larger area, the comfort factor will be greatly enhanced. This apparently is the theory behind the bed of nails routine used by Hindu Fakirs.

So really, all it takes to improve your seating accomodations is to substitute a curved (and lengthened, if space permits) seat bottom for the flat plywood set-up. Those of you still building on your project would be wise to give some thought now towards building your seat for comfort.

Nothing much can be said for the use of foam rubber cushions other than they are cheap and easy to make. Well, they can look good too. For body support and crash safety, however, foam rubber cushions rate about as high as wet noodles under compression. It is far better to use a crushable material such as polyvinyl chloride foam. It has good body and will exhibit excellent resistance to crushing. When suddenly loaded with tremendous G forces, as in a crash, the hard foam absorbs considerable energy as its fibers crush under the impact.

If your airplane is still in its early stages of

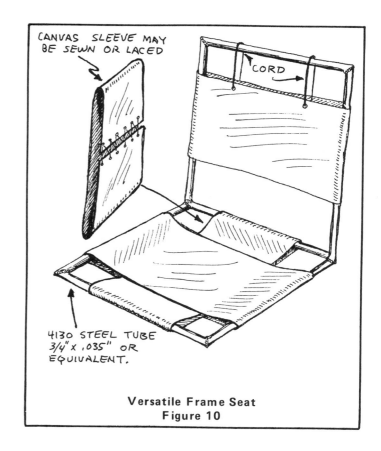

CANVAS SLEEVE MAY BE SEWN OR LACED

CORD

4130 STEEL TUBE 3/4" x .035" OR EQUIVALENT.

Versatile Frame Seat
Figure 10

construction, you could design and build up an all-foam/fiberglass contoured seat, or you might be interested in building a real honest-to-goodness professional-type seat for yourself.

To sum it all up, your sitting comfort is improved more by the contour and length of a seat which permits an even weight distribution than it is by the softness of a thick foam rubber cushion over a flat hard surface.

Push-Pull Controls

It isn't always easy for builders to find the answers they need from time to time as they progress with their projects. Most plans available to the homebuilder do not go into detailed particulars regarding engine installation, instrumentation, and electrical and fuel systems. Yet, before the airplane can be flown, all of these systems must be fabricated and installed by the builder.

Most mechanics look on the installation of these systems as a rather simple task. Quite true, however, when the builder has to build or fabricate all of the component parts or try to figure how to adapt some available stock item, the so-called simple job gets complicated fast. With me, as with a lot of other folks, the "simple" jobs are the ones that usually lead to compounded difficulties and frustrations. So, in spite of the risk of oversimplification, let's explore in detail a simple problem . . . . the installation and use of flexible push-pull controls. (Figure 11)

FLEXIBLE PUSH-PULL CONTROLS

These controls are used for a variety of cockpit operations. The controls are light in weight, simple and economical. They can do an effective job of activating a unit or a system without complicated linkage. It is well to remember that the fewer the parts in any control system, the more fail-proof it is likely to be.

The typical push-pull control is obtainable from a number of outlets. Automobile parts stores stock a good variety as a rule. As inexpensive as these controls are to buy, it would be foolish to buy something inferior. Some of the cheaper units are very poorly made. In some cases, the handle might pull off or the control wire is of such poor quality metal that it lacks the necessary degree of stiffness and is highly prone to rusting. Quite often, it costs very little more to go first class. Why not shop around and compare before you buy?

Just what units would we ordinarily operate with push-pull controls? To name a few: carburetor heat, mixture control, cabin heat control, ventilators (fresh air controls), cowling shutters, etc.

Naturally, not all aircraft designs will require all of the controls mentioned, but the considerations affecting their installation and use are equally applicable whether one control unit or a number are called for.

LOCATION OF PUSH-PULL CONTROLS

This problem usually starts in the cockpit. Where should the control knob be located? The normal impulse, I guess, is to put it in the panel wherever there is space, and where it looks good. In my opinion, however, all of the push-pull controls should not be neatly aligned in one impressive group installation. Why? Too big a risk that the wrong control will be selected and operated in flight.

Take the carburetor heat control as an example. With the small 4-cylinder engines most of us are using, carburetor heat is important. The location of the control is likewise important.

Most pilots will agree that it (carb heat) should be located close to the throttle . . . fingertip close. On the other hand, its location should not be such that it might easily be confused with the mixture control.

DIRECTION OF CONTROL ACTIVATION

There is a proverb among old timers in aviation that "in case of emergency, everything goes forward." Whether or not you subscribe to that generalization, it is true that most aircraft controls and their direction of operation are standardized to a remarkable degree. It would be wise to follow accepted practice in this respect. The normal position (cold air) for the carburetor heat control, in flight, is with the control knob pushed forward (or "IN"). To get hot air to the carburetor, the control is pulled "OUT". If you have any doubts as to the direction any particular control should be normally activated, check it out on other aircraft. Notice, too, how the control is labeled.

INSTALLATION CONSIDERATIONS

After the proper size hole is drilled in your

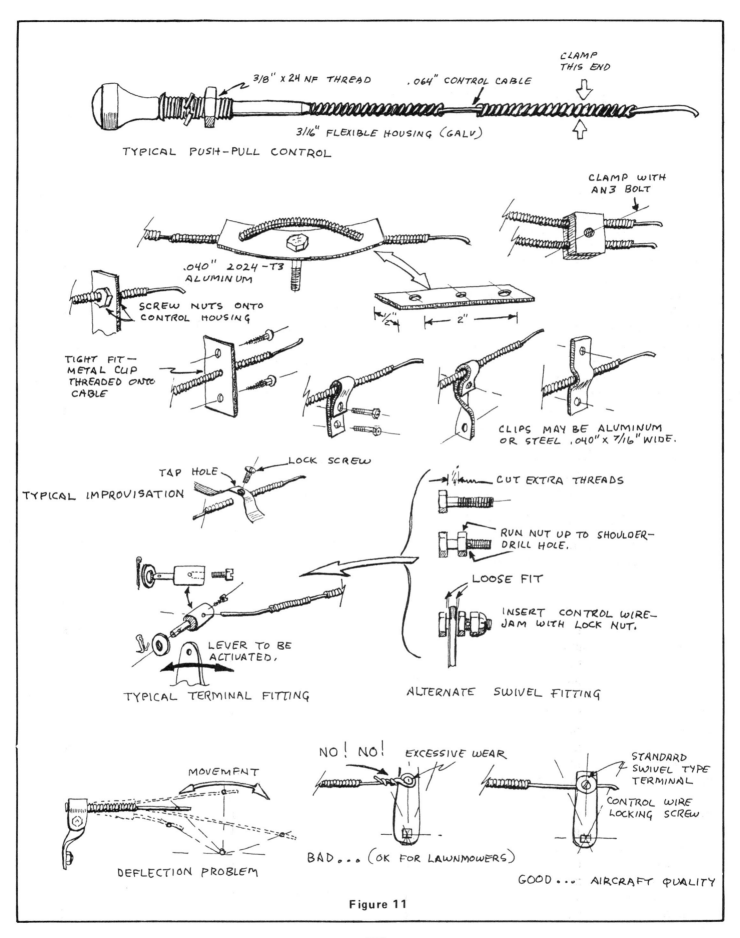

Figure 11

instrument panel for the installation of a push-pull control, its best routing must be determined. This is not always easy as something else always seems to be in the way. Avoid sharp bends and changes of direction as they tend to increase friction and make the control more difficult to operate. Plan carefully so that when you do punch a hole in the firewall for one of these controls, it will be nicely aligned with the control lever of the unit to be operated. Those building a VW-powered aircraft or one which does not use a tubular engine mount will find that the alignment of the push-pull control wires are more critical because of the short distances from the firewall to the units being controlled. Where the firewall consists merely of a thin sheet of metal, always use a rubber grommet to protect the flexible control housing from the sharp edges of the metal hole.

If there is a relatively long unsupported stretch of the push-pull control housing running through the cockpit area under the panel, secure it at some point midway so that it doesn't sag and flop all over the place. Incidentally, it is poor practice to run electrical wires and flexible push-pull controls through the same hole in the firewall. Vibration of the flexible wire housing of the control may wear away the insulation on your electrical wiring. Serious consequences will follow. Bundle your electrical wires separately, before you route them through the firewall.

ENGINE COMPARTMENT HOOK—UP

Once the push-pull wire and its flexible housing is routed through the firewall you are ready to hook it up. Two important functions remain. First, the flexible housing must be clamped to some stationary object near the unit to be controlled. Secondly, the control wire must be secured to the lever to be activated or operated.

A few ideas for making your own control wire clips are illustrated. These clips need not be large or made of heavy material.

In the event you have a severe deflection problem, as illustrated in one of the sketches, it would be best to locate your clamp further back along the flexible housing. This allows the free end to flex a bit more without causing binding of the control wire.

Other than that, a good point for the anchoring clamps would be within a couple of inches of the end of the housing.

If the control housing is too long it can be

IF CONTROL IS ALREADY INSTALLED — POP RIVET TWO ANGLE PLATES ON EACH SIDE OF CONTROL.

IF INSTALLED WITH CONTROL — MAKE A "U" PIECE OF ALUMINUM AND INSTALL UNDER CABLE KNOB.

Mixture Control Guard
Figure 12

cut off as needed. Excess lengths should not be coiled up in the engine compartment. (Always keep the problem of unnecessary weight in the back of your mind.)

The excess housing can be easily cut with a pair of diagonals or a small cold chisel. A note of caution ... before cutting the excess housing, pull the control wire out far enough so that you do not cut it too. (Of course you wouldn't do that, but one has to be careful when doing the simple thing.)

The final step in the installation is the physical hook-up of the control wire to the lever to be activated. This is usually accomplished with the aid of a swivel-type terminal fitting.

It is unacceptable to merely poke the control wire through the hole on the lever and to twist it around itself. This treatment can make stresses in the stiff wire. There is also a high degree of frictional wear in such a set-up.

It is best to use a free-swiveling terminal to hook up the control. These are standard parts, and some types may even be obtained from your favorite motorcycle shop. Some units operated by push-pull controls, such as carburetors for VW installations, already have these terminal connectors built into the levers. In other cases, where you must construct your own carburetor heat box, for example, you can make your own.

The alternate homemade, freely swiveling terminal, as shown, is used by a large number of experienced mechanics. It makes use of an AN-3 bolt and is easy to make. Extra threads are cut leaving just enough shank to the bolt so that after the first nut is screwed on, it will not bind the control lever. Drill a hole for the control wire, as shown, and assemble by jamming the control wire between the two nuts. It works fine and eliminates or at least minimizes the puzzlement of having to solve one of those simple problems.

Last, but most important — make sure full operation of the control lever is obtainable without binding.

Throttle

The throttle is the most frequently used engine control and its installation should be designed and executed for absolute reliability. (No place here for a Mickey Mouse rig.)

A regular knob throttle control (like in the Cesana 150) with an adjustable friction device is perhaps the best, simple set-up.

Some people like a fighter-style lever and that is all right too, if you make it so that it doesn't creep on you. . . . and you don't get the action reversed. Remember, we want full throttle when the control is moved forward, or firewalled as they say in the action magazines.

A regular "choke" type control with a small wire running through its housing out to the carburetor is not very reliable. This type of control is not recommended for throttles as it has no provision for adjusting friction, and the wire attachment to the carburetor

makes for a flimsy hook up.

The throttle must move very smoothly from the idle range to maximum power. Check this out both in the cockpit and at the carburetor.

If you use a standard aircraft throttle cable, the carburetor end will be threaded and a regular self-aligning rod-end bearing can be screwed on the end for attachment to the carburetor lever. This makes for a very neat and reliable installation. Remember to clamp or secure the outer housing of the throttle cable at some point close to the carburetor.

Plan the routing of the throttle cable or linkage to avoid sharp bends. The planning is necessary, otherwise you will be drilling all kinds of holes in the firewall only to find that they are in the wrong place.

If you decide to make a throttle lever, avoid complicated link-

age. The fewer the parts and pieces in the system, the less likely it will malfunction or fail completely.

At the cockpit end locate the throttle knob or lever where it is comfortable to reach. In single-engine single-seat aircraft, I like for the throttle to be on the left side, however, since it is your airplane and you may be either left or right-handed, suit your own habit.

For two-seat side-by-side aircraft with dual controls, the obvious location would be in the center of the panel so either pilot may reach it.

Those of you building a two-seater with tandem seating, you have extra problems if you go the dual control route. The best advice is for you to keep your linkage uncomplicated. And it is highly recommended that you work out your installation on a mock-up.

Cabin and Cockpit Heat

Apparently the luxury of having cabin heat is mistakenly limited to enclosed-cockpit and cabin-type aircraft. But, why can't you have cabin (cockpit) heat in any open-cockpit Flybaby, Miniplane, Acrosport, or whatever? When your feet are warm, somehow the knife-edge of chill in a cold, drafty cockpit seems not so cutting. Goose pimples recede and blood begins to flow again. So what if the warm air scoots right out the cockpit past your ruddy nose. Your feet are warm aren't they? Your cheeks are carressed by an occasional waft of tropical breeze. What more could you ask?

Think about it for a moment. Why not have cabin heat for any kind of homebuilt? The heat source is already there in the engine compartment . . . and all that heat going to waste. What's needed is some way to entrap it and move it through the cockpit in the amount you want, and when you want it.

The time to think about cabin heat is when you are installing the engine firewall. Although you could modify the firewall after the aircraft is completed and flying, such a modification is not one to be undertaken without a good reserve of choice expletives to draw upon, particularly if your engine compartment is crowded. However, with an engine installation that has plenty of space between the engine and the firewall to accept a heat control box, the undertaking should be uncomplicated. Nevertheless, the best time to provide for the year-around comfort option is when you are building the airplane.

Wood aircraft with built-up plywood firewall bulkheads might need some internal blocking around the hot air inlet cut-out area to accommodate the heat box attachment fasteners. Additionally, the hot air inlet hole should be slightly larger than the minimum size required so that the wood edges can be protected from the heat by a layer of asbestos and/or a metal shield insert.

Metal firewalls, or those employing a single layer of plywood can usually be fitted with the heat box without much more preparation than cutting the hole for the air inlet and securing the heat control box to the firewall with rivets or machine screws.

NOTE: All plywood firewalls, whether of the laminated built-up type, or of the single plywood-web type should be overlaid and insulated with a 1/16-inch sheet of asbestos and a layer of .016-inch stainless steel or galvanized sheet.

The cabin heat inlet must have about 5 inches of unobstructed space directly in front of it and should be positioned where it will disperse the hot air to the greatest advantage, preferably around the feet. You undoubtedly will consider the fact that hot air tends to rise. A hot air outlet about head level in the cabin would, therefore, not be effective except for those who aspire to being hot-headed pilots with cold feet. A lousy combination.

Builders of conventional designs, that is, those with the engine up front, have the easiest time, not only for engine hook-up, but also in providing cabin heat. It is easy to see why. Pusher designs with the engine buried in the aft fuselage area, or with an overhead mounting above the wing, require many feet of expensive ducting, and possibly some applied ingenuity before that remotely heated air, salvaged from around the engine's exhaust pipes, can be conducted through snake-like ducts to the cabin. Regardless of the installation problems presented though, cabin heat is well worth having in any homebuilt.

HOW IT WORKS

The heart of a typical light plane heating system consists of a heat control box (buy, scrounge or make one) that is fastened to the firewall directly over a 2-inch hole cut into the firewall.

As with most accessories and components a homebuilder must fabricate, it is far easier and quicker to adapt a serviceable unit from some other aircraft than it is to make your own unit.

Most cabin heat control boxes are quite similar. A typical installation is illustrated in

Figure 13. These boxes are small rectangular welded units with inlets located on any two of their five available sides. Sometimes a heat box can be better installed by inverting it, or rotating it 90 degrees to permit easier attachment of the ducting.

If you have to make your own control box, decide beforehand which side will provide the best location for the hot air inlet. This advance planning will permit you to mount the box so that you will have sufficient space for the attachment of the flexible ducting. At the same time, consider routing the ducting via the shortest possible distance between the heat muff and the cabin heat control box inlet.

The amount of heat entering the cabin is controlled by a flapper valve in the heat control box. The valve is operated by a flexible sheathed control wire (Bowden wire) terminating at some appropriate location in the cabin or on the instrument panel. Its knob, or an adjacent plate should be marked "CABIN HEAT — PULL."

In the engine compartment, an outlet from the heat control box accepts one end of a 2-inch flexible duct (high temperature resistant) secured with a standard 2-inch steel hose clamp. The other end of the duct is connected to a heat muff, shroud, or as some builders call it, a heat exchanger. This muff is a stainless steel or an aluminum wrap-around that surrounds one or more of the engine exhaust pipes. Heat radiating from the exhaust pipes results in the hot air that eventually enters the cabin when the heat valve is pulled to the open position.

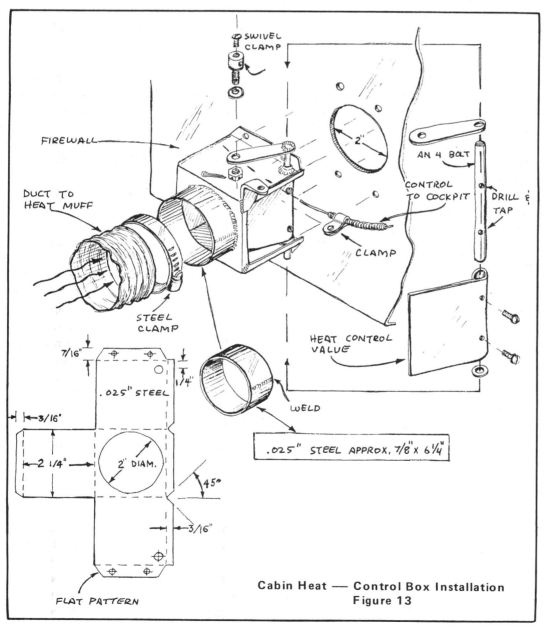

Cabin Heat — Control Box Installation
Figure 13

To induce a positive flow of hot air into the cabin, another duct is ordinarily connected from an outside flow of air to the upper portion of the heat muff.

A more uniform dispersal of heat throughout the cockpit area can be obtained by making and installing a deflector for the incoming hot air. (Figure 14) When properly spaced away from the firewall and centered over the firewall opening, it will effectively deflect the air toward both sides of the cockpit area.

There is an unusual amount of drafty cold air moving about the typical cabin, unnoticed in the summer, but certainly unwelcome in the winter. The sources of cold air may, depending upon the peculiarities of a particular design, be through the slots, openings and gaps accommodating flap handles, controls, and door openings, or from under the seat.

Systematic elimination of each draft source will serve to increase the heater's effectiveness as well as aid in making the airplane noticeably quieter.

BYPASS FOR HOT AIR .... ESSENTIAL

A few cabin heat control boxes I've seen do not provide for an overboard dump arrangement for unused hot air when the cabin heat valve is closed. This is bad! That is, if the hot air is not being used to heat the cabin area, the heat control box should permit the hot air to dump overboard. If this cannot take place, the hot air is trapped in the ducts where it remains backed up to the shrouded exhaust pipes, interfering with the natural heat dissipation of the cylinders and exhaust pipes.

Without an automatic overboard dump feature for the hot air, the risk is great that the cylinder(s) served by the exhaust pipes providing the heat could get excessively hot. This could lead to expensive engine damage.

CABIN HEATERS NEED ATTENTION TOO

. Because of the mechanical nature of the cabin heater installation, it can malfunction in spite of the fact that it always seems to work. To ensure your personal safety, the heat exchanger (heat muff) should be removed periodically and the exhaust pipes inspected for cracks or signs of failure. In addition, any time the odor of exhaust fumes is detected in the cabin, the cabin heat should be shut off. You should immediately suspect that carbon monoxide is leaking into the cabin and attempt to get some fresh air circulating until you can get on the ground to check the system.

The most frequent in-use heat system problem is excessive wear and possible failure in the area of the flapper valve shaft. It would be well to take care in fabricating this part, and perhaps to add bronze bushings to increase its useful life.

The feature I like best about the typical light aircraft heating system is that there is no waiting and shivering until the engine warms up. The heater begins to put out almost as soon as the engine is running. Wish my car would do that.

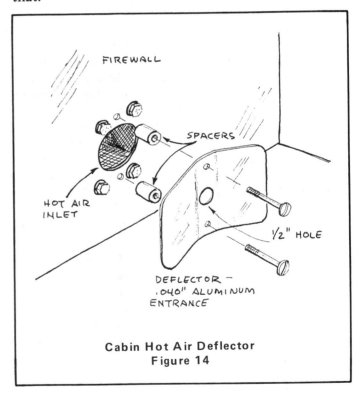

**Cabin Hot Air Deflector
Figure 14**

Cockpit Compartment Ventilation

Take a leisurely stroll down the flight line of any airport. You will observe that the aircraft manufacturers have widely divergent ideas regarding ventilation systems for their products. You will see airplanes with a hodgepodge of protruding scoops, shutters, doors, flaps, submerged ducts and just plain ol' holes in the nose, wings and elsewhere.

One thing is certain. When you're ready to devise some form of ventilation system for your own project, you won't have to worry about standard aircraft practices . . . . there aren't any.

Admittedly, a good ventilation system is not essential to the aircraft's performance, but is certainly important to the pilot's. A pilot needs air for cockpit cooling and, of course, for breathing. This means the air must be clean and unfouled by exhaust fumes. It should also be controllable to the extent that the pilot can easily adjust the flow to suit his comfort needs.

Cabin ventilation seems to be most effective when the pilot can feel the gentle flow of air around his head. Oh, you can get drafty uncontrolled air into the cabin easy enough. As a matter of fact, some homebuilts have plenty of breezes leaking through the cockpit area, but that condition isn't usually accepted in the better circles as a cabin ventilation system.

Bubble canopies can and do produce a fierce cockpit environment under the relentless glare and heat of the sun. Akin to being in an airborne sauna. Under such conditions, the waft of a cooling breeze can be equated, in my mind, only to the environmentally perfect, though legendary Shangri-La.

LOCATING AIR INLETS

Finding suitable locations for the ram air inlets is the first requirement in meeting your ventilation needs. Unless inlet locations are shown on your plans, it will be up to you to find a spot for them where they will not suck in exhaust fumes from unanticipated turbulent airflow. It is also desirable to locate them where they will not pick up a lot of wind and engine noise.

Furthermore, you must avoid cutting into structural members simply to provide a vent opening. A low, up-front fuselage location seems to be favored by many aircraft builders, but this is the very type of location which frequently produces all of the undesired characteristics mentioned.

In quite a few instances, the aircraft's only ventilation is obtained through small vents inserted in the cabin windows. In a similar vein, a small hinged side window is installed, usually on the pilot's side, which may be opened during ground operations.

There are those who obtain ram air for cabin cooling from the engine compartment or the nose of the aircraft through an inlet in the front engine baffles. One drawback to this pick-up point is the rather long (and expensive) ducting that is required to conduct the air all the way back to the cabin.

Other locations utilized successfully include Cessna's air inlets in the leading edges of the wings (near the root section), and scoops mounted on top of the fuselage near the aft end of the aircraft. For aerodynamic reasons, location of an air scoop on top of a wing is not good practice.

Ostensibly, just about any location on the aircraft can be considered as a potential pick-up point for cabin cooling or ventilation.

Keep these thoughts in mind however. Vent openings on the bottom of the fuselage may have more disadvantages than advantages because they ingest copious amounts of oil spray, exhaust fumes and dirt.

The more distant the air inlet source is from the cabin, the longer the ducting and the heavier the ventilation system becomes.

Not to be overlooked are other supplemental means of obtaining welcome cabin cooling. During ground operations especially, a provision for holding the door partially open is very effective. Similarly, aircraft equipped with sliding canopies should have a positive stop or latch to hold them in a partially open position . . . . say about 2 inches

Plastic vent snaps into a 2-inch hole. Can be located anywhere. It can be rotated to regulate amount of air entering cockpit.

NASA air inlet. Effective and quiet when properly designed. Should have an internal shutter to shut off air when not needed.

Clam-shell door needs sufficient friction to prevent its creeping from a partially open position. Effective but noisy.

Plain old air scoop. Very effective, but very noisy if located in cabin area.

Air pick-up for a cabin ventilation is located in air inlet baffle. Requires long ducting to cabin. Should have a screen over it to keep out varmints and bugs.

Cessna cabin ventilation inlets are located in the wing roots and are ducted to the cabin.

minimum. In flight, though, the wind noise generated by a partially open canopy is awful. Therefore, even if your canopy will be of the sliding variety, and the airplane can be flown with it partially open, do not consider that feature as meeting your ventilation needs. Some supplemental cabin ventilation will still be necessary.

SUBMERGED AIR INTAKES (NASA DUCTS)

Low drag, submerged air intake ducts are used on quite a few high-performance aircraft as well as on some homebuilts. Unless you are usually lucky, you cannot just cut out an inlet opening that looks something like what you have seen on other aircraft and expect to obtain a good flow of air through it.

NASA has found that there is a very definite technology applicable to the design and construction of these inlets. Actually, the design dates back to World War II and the period up to the early 1950s when most of the data was being developed.

These indented vents must be built to a precise shape and installed in a suitable location or air may not want to enter. When that happens, a small barrier has to be attached over the opening. For all practical purposes, it then becomes a conventional air scoop with all its inherent drag characteristics.

Use the geometry shown in Figure 15 for constructing submerged inlets and you should obtain cabin air in sufficient quantities without the extra

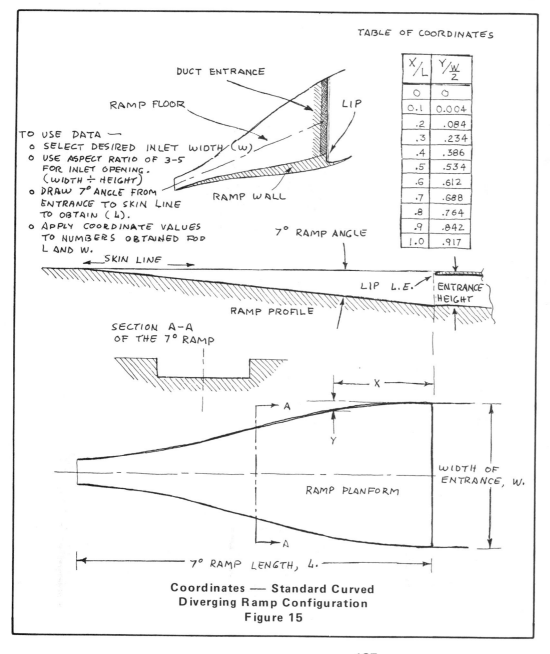

TABLE OF COORDINATES

X/L	$Y/\frac{W}{2}$
0	0
0.1	0.004
.2	.084
.3	.234
.4	.386
.5	.534
.6	.612
.7	.688
.8	.764
.9	.842
1.0	.917

TO USE DATA —
o SELECT DESIRED INLET WIDTH (W)
o USE ASPECT RATIO OF 3-5 FOR INLET OPENING. (WIDTH ÷ HEIGHT)
o DRAW 7° ANGLE FROM ENTRANCE TO SKIN LINE TO OBTAIN (L).
o APPLY COORDINATE VALUES TO NUMBERS OBTAINED FOR L AND W.

Coordinates — Standard Curved Diverging Ramp Configuration
Figure 15

drag that scoop-type vents impose.

Stay as close as you can to the geometrical proportions illustrated because they all affect the duct's efficiency. Do not change the width-to-depth ratio of the duct, nor the lip shape. The ramp angle and the ramp divergence (ratio of ramp width to width of the duct entrance) is likewise critical, as is the ramp planform shape.

Of the three basic inlet shapes (planforms) investigated by NASA for use with submerged ducts, the divergent walls planform shown in Figure 16C proves to be the most efficient. You may have observed that the parallel walls configuration (Figure 16B) is used on Mooney aircraft. The least effective planform, the converging walls shape, is rarely used.

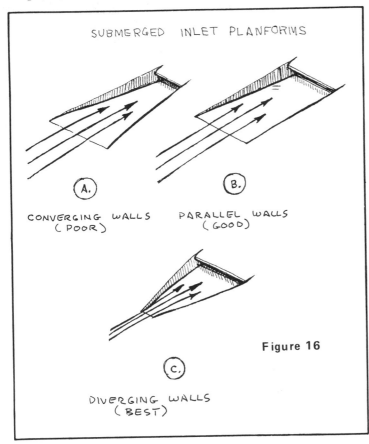

SUBMERGED INLET PLANFORMS

A. CONVERGING WALLS (POOR)

B. PARALLEL WALLS (GOOD)

C. DIVERGING WALLS (BEST)

Figure 16

CONSTRUCTION & INSTALLATION NOTES

There are some commercially available manufactured cabin ventilators and vents designed for mounting in plexiglass windows. Each of these require the cutting of a rather large hole in the window or fuselage skin. The mounting requirements are quite simple though, and will be obvious for the type ventilators purchased. No construction problems should be encountered except possibly, in cutting a 2-inch to 3-inch hole in a plexiglass window without cracking it. Be especially careful if you use a hand-held drill. (**Do not attempt to use a circle cutter or saw in a hand-held drill.**)

Those snap-in plastic vents are the easiest to install and are the most economical to obtain. Naturally, this type of vent should be located where you can reach it in flight because it must be rotated to regulate the amount of air being scooped up.

Small, mechanically operated doors or shutters which swing out into the slipstream forming a natural air scoop are quite effective, popular, and easily constructed. Unless there is sufficient friction in the control linkage for this type of ventilator, the slipstream will force it to the fully open position and make intermediate openings impossible. In other words, you will get full ram air or none at all.

Controllable ram air ventilators as well as fixed scoops must project into the slipstream beyond the boundary layer of air to be effective.

In some installations, a comparatively large can-like plenum chamber is incorporated in the ducting. The idea is to help reduce noise. Fast-moving air is very noisy, but on entering a plenum chamber, the air expands and slows, and wind noise diminishes.

Upholstering around ventilator ducts requires additional framing or trim to provide a means for attaching the upholstery or panel material. It is just a small detail but one which you should anticipate beforehand.

In an installation where the air must be conveyed some distance to a cabin outlet, 2-inch diameter aircraft ducting is used. However, it is possible to construct special ducting of aluminum or plastic or fiberglass to fit odd space requirements.

Using regular aircraft ducting is undoubtedly the lightest and easiest means of conducting air to the location you want. It is also a simple matter to insert a filter screen into the ducting to keep out uninvited animal and insect life. Use a 4-inch diameter piece of aluminum screen shaped and poked into the ducting for this purpose. For that matter, all ventilator openings should have a screen across them at some point in the system. Any insects, but especially hornets and wasps, are never welcome in a cockpit.

WHAT ABOUT AN OUTLET?

What small yet important detail is often overlooked when installing a ventilation system? The correct reply, an outlet. The flow of cooling air can always be improved markedly by providing an outlet for the air somewhere behind the pilot. This is considered an essential fix for bubble canopy installations and will be seen with increasing frequency in homebuilts. Small openings are cut into the canopy at a point near the turtle deck and a controllable vent is installed with a piano hinge. A short section of teleflex cable (sheathed wire used to open and close the vent) is conducted to a point where the pilot can reach it.

From a practical point of view, it is not always necessary or advisable to have an air outlet in a canopy or top of a fuselage or wing. Improperly located, it can unexpectedly work as an inlet. Airflow sometimes is unpredictable. Ordinarily an outlet may be built into the aft bulkhead, where it would dump air directly into the aft fuselage areas. In most cases, that air has a ready exit through the rudder cable openings, stabilizer attachments, etc.

This controllable vent is on a bubble canopy equipped T-18. Some say it's an air inlet, others say, an air outlet . . . . so, a vent it is, of some sort.

CANOPIES/WINDSHIELDS

Working With Acrylics

As homebuilders generally make no distinction between the various trade names for acrylic plastics, neither will I. Therefore, when I use the Trademark name-word "plexiglass," the reference will be equally applicable to all trade-name products such as Lucite, Acrylite, Plexiglas, and acrylic sheet material.

Not only is plexiglass excellent for aircraft windshields and windows, but it also rates pretty high in transparency. It is even more transparent than plate glass. In addition, it is remarkably resistant to weathering and to chemicals. It also has characteristics which permit radio waves to pass through without any apparent loss of signal strength.

Acrylic sheet weighs less than half as much as glass or aluminum, and it can be sawed, drilled, bent, stretched and worked with ordinary workshop tools. All of these are good enough reasons for the homebuilder to rejoice in having such a versatile material at his disposal. Still, it does have some characteristics that give no cause for dancing in the streets.

Acrylic plastics do scratch easily and are adversely affected by some liquids. Aromatic solvents like benzene and toluene, carbon tetrachloride, ethyl and methyl alcohols, as well as esters, ketone, acetone, lacquer thinner and stuff like that there have a harmful effect on plexiglass. So be careful what you expose it to.

Another of its less admirable characteristics is its brittleness at colder temperatures. If a little localized stressing happens to develop, the stuff is quite prone to crack or break suddenly. During cold weather you have to be especially careful when drilling holes with a hand-held drill.

If your timetable permits, plan to do your window and windshield fabricating operations in the warmer summer weather. The plexiglass then will be softer, less brittle, and more forgiving of your abuses.

HANDLING

We all know that plexiglass scratches easily. Therefore, you shouldn't remove the masking paper until all of your fabricating work is complete. Be especially careful in sliding the material across rough or dirty work areas during cutting operations.

Do not expose masked sheets to prolonged sunlight, as the adhesive on the paper will harden and the removal of the masking paper will turn into a major operation. People who work a lot with acrylics remove the masking paper by first getting an edge started with a fingernail and then rolling the paper tightly onto a piece of tubing.

CUTTING PLEXIGLASS

Over the years since plexiglass first made its appearance in aviation, some unusual cutting techniques have been tried on both hot and cold plexiglass sheets. For the amateur builder the band saw with a metal cutting blade (18 teeth per inch) seems to be the best and safest of all to use. With the band saw, irregular and curved shapes are easy to cut. About the only precaution to exercise here is to make sure that the plexiglass, at the point of cut at the saw blade, is being held solidly against the saw's table. Of course, you should not force the plexiglass into the blade but rather let it cut gently under deliberate control.

If you have to make long, straight cuts, you could use your bench saw. Do not, however, use the regular wood blades or combination blades. Where you will only be cutting plexiglass occasionally, the fine-tooth crosscut blade you use for plywood would work fine. Actually, with great care, you can even use a saber saw with metal-cutting blades. Do not use any regular large-tooth wood-cutting blades, as they will chip the plexiglass in spite of the precautions you take.

LAYOUT AND MARKING OF PLEXIGLASS

Quite naturally, if your layout is drawn directly on the masking paper covering the plexiglass, you can use either a pen or a pencil. To mark on unmasked plexiglass though, your best marking tool is a "china-marking" pencil. Always wipe off all marks before any heating work. As in metal work, do not scribe any lines on the plexiglass unless they are to be cut away.

FILING AND SMOOTHING THE EDGES

Plexiglass is easy to file. A 10- or 12-inch smooth-cut file makes it easy to smooth and trim up the edges. In filing plexiglass, as in filing aluminum, it may help to keep the teeth of the file from clogging if you work the file back and forth without removing filing pressure.

While edges of windshields need not be polished, they should at least be filed or sanded smooth to remove all saw marks. It is a good practice to also remove sharp corners and edges, if for no other reason than to protect your hands from cuts.

ADHESIVES AND ACRYLICS

Commonly used wood adhesives such as Plastic Resin, Recorcinol and Aerolite have little merit in working with acrylic sheets and should only be considered for minor nonvisible functions. If used for attaching cloth or wood to plexiglass, the surface of the plastic to be glued should be roughened or scuffed to provide a better gluing surface. Flexible epoxy adhesives do a good job of gluing plexiglass to other materials such as wood, metal and plastics.

When cementing acrylics to other materials such as wood or metal, there will be two long range problems to contend with:

1. The coefficient of expansion between the plexiglass and the material being cemented may vary so much that the adhesive bond will not hold unless it has flexible characteristics such as have Pliobond or Miracle Adhesive No. HT-4620.

2. Whatever the adhesive used, take care in its selection that it does not contain ingredients which will attack the plastic and ultimately cause crazing.

DRILLING HOLES

Even though good work can be done with a hand-held drill, whenever possible do your drilling in the drill press. Before you start, make sure the plexiglass is held down firmly near the point where the hole is being drilled. There may be a tendency for the drill to grab and for the plexiglass to be forced upward as the bit goes through. This can really crack the stuff.

Because plastics are soft, it is better for the drill to be ground so that it has a scraping rather than a cutting action. To convert your drill bit all you have to do is grind the sharp rake angle from the cutting edge. To get this scraping action you will need to grind small flat areas onto both cutting edges of the drill bit using a medium or fine-grit grinder.

MODIFYING DRILL BITS FOR PLASTICS

This is easily done by holding the drill parallel to the side of the grinding wheel so that the small

flat areas you are grinding onto the cutting edges will be parallel to the length of the drill. These flat areas need not be large . . . . 1/32-inch wide is plenty. (Figure 1)

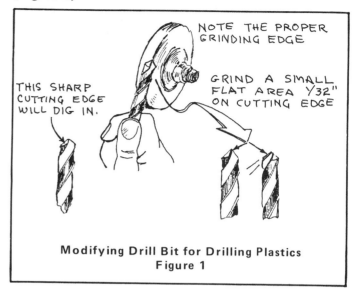

NOTE THE PROPER GRINDING EDGE

THIS SHARP CUTTING EDGE WILL DIG IN.

GRIND A SMALL FLAT AREA 1/32" ON CUTTING EDGE

**Modifying Drill Bit for Drilling Plastics
Figure 1**

If you don't have an electric grinder, you can still modify your bit with a small emery or pocket whetstone by hand.

It is very important that you always back up your work with a scrap piece of wood or plywood so that the drill, as it penetrates the plexiglass, can continue into the solid material beneath with the lessened likelihood of chipping the hole.

Any nicked, chipped or rough edges can make the acrylic sheet crack-sensitive under adverse conditions. This goes for badly drilled holes too.

When you are through using your specially ground drill bit, wrap a small piece of masking tape around its shank, label it "plastics", and reserve it strictly for that use.

FORMING PLEXIGLASS

Plexiglass can be bent cold. You can even force it into a curved frame, for example, but the minimum radius of the bend or curvature must be at least 180 times the thickness of the acrylic sheet. You can bend a 1/16-inch thick sheet into a 22-inch diameter circle. The minimum bending or curvature radius, then, for 1/16-inch sheet is 11 inches, and for 1/8-inch plexiglass, 22 inches.

If the curvature required for your windshield is not circular or is somewhat sharper than the minimum bend radius mentioned, you will have to resort to heat-forming your plexiglass.

As acrylic sheet is a thermoplastic material, it can (when heated to approximately 340 degrees F) be stretched, shaped or formed into almost any shape you want. As it cools, it will harden again, retaining its formed shape.

DRAPE—FORMING OF PLEXIGLASS

Homebuilders are a daring lot and some methods developed by them to form plexiglass are enough to grow hair on a bald aero-engineer. Plexiglass windshields have been bent using welding torches (with the flame played directly on the area to be bent), localized strip heater elements, electric irons, heat lamps, hot oil baths, Bunsen and gas burners, kitchen ovens, barbeque grills, and even workshop space heaters. The method you choose may reflect your need for adventure.

For small windshields and sharply curved landing light covers, etc., the kitchen oven may be used,

provided you can arrange for diplomatic immunity from your wife. Most standard kitchen ovens can accommodate plastic pieces up to 18 inches long.

A typical exercise in drape-forming a landing light cover with two dimensional curves is illustrated in Figure 2.

BASIC HEAT FORMING

Remove the masking paper before any heat forming operation. And another thing, when you put the plexiglass in the oven, never lay it on a bare metal tray, rack, or form, as that will result in "mark-off" areas. Your wood or plaster forms should be prepared by covering them with cotton flannel cloth.

Avoid excessive and prolonged heating of the plexiglass. For simple forming operations, preheat the oven to about 250 degrees F and slip your mold and all into the oven. Heat it for 5 minutes or until the plexiglass droops and limply embraces the form. Remove the form and plexiglass from the oven, and using cotton gloves, make sure that the plexiglass stays snugged down around the form as the acrylic piece cools. Do not remove the plexiglass from the form until it has cooled below 175 degrees F. All acrylic sheets will shrink approximately 2 per cent when heated, therefore, if there is a requirement for a dimensionally accurate piece, it might be better to make your piece oversize a bit, and later trim it to the exact dimension.

INSTALLING PLEXIGLASS

The acrylics manufacturers caution users of their products to avoid the creation of localized stresses, especially those caused by the use of bolts, rivets, screws or fasteners of any type. Although you may not immediately realize that you have imposed high localized stresses on initial installation, you may be sure that if such stresses do exist, they can, at a later date, blossom out in the form of crazing — an artistically fascinating sight but not entirely conducive to pride of ownership.

To avoid local stresses, design your installation so that the total load is spread over a large area. Logic leads to the conclusion that to be able to do so means the elimination of screws and all direct bolting of plexiglass. Unfortunately for the homebuilder, installing windshields or windows without using screws and bolts is difficult because he doesn't have the fancy custom-formed channels and strips that are used in the store-bought aircraft.

TYPICAL WINDOW INSTALLATIONS

The discerning builder will notice (Figure 3) that, especially in the case of a wood aircraft, he

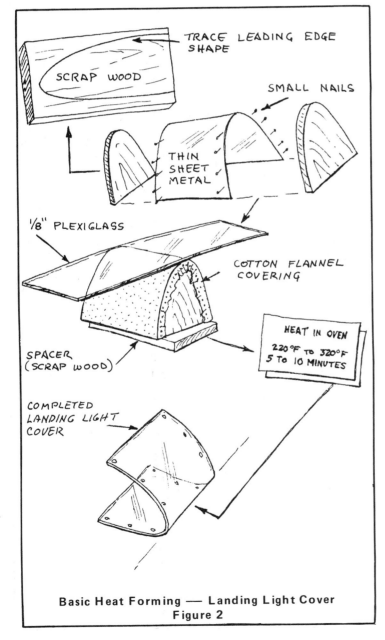

TRACE LEADING EDGE SHAPE

SCRAP WOOD

SMALL NAILS

THIN SHEET METAL

1/8" PLEXIGLASS

COTTON FLANNEL COVERING

SPACER (SCRAP WOOD)

HEAT IN OVEN
220°F TO 320°F
5 TO 10 MINUTES

COMPLETED LANDING LIGHT COVER

Basic Heat Forming — Landing Light Cover
Figure 2

could easily enough fabricate a window frame by gluing in a plywood strip and a wood spacer around the window opening. Even for a metal-skinned bird, it would still be easy to form a straight, simple "S" type channel. However, if you need to form one curved to fit around a large pear-shaped opening, you do have a job on your hands. In this case, fiberglass molded channels and frames could solve the problem. These illustrated installations utilize a rubber channel strip that acts as a snug retainer for the plexiglass and also serves as weather stripping.

WINDSHIELD INSTALLATION

In any windshield installation you should take into account the fact that the plexiglass very definitely will expand and contract with temperature changes, and it will be subjected to deflections under wind loads. A 24-inch square sheet of 1/8-inch plexiglass will expand and contract by about 1/8-inch through a 100 degree F temperature range. It is, therefore, important that any fastening system used for your windshield be capable of permitting some movement to take place. Figure 4 illustrates the proper use of round-headed self-tapping or machine

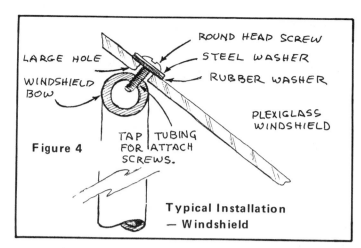

Typical Installation — Windshield

screws in the installation of plexiglass windshields. This is o.k., and it is really one of the preferred methods endorsed by acrylic manufacturers. Notice though, that the installation is neither aesthetically nor aerodynamically clean.

It is best not to use countersunk flat-head screws in the installation of large windshields unless the direct stresses of the screw heads can somehow be diffused.

FLUSH—MOUNTED INSTALLATION

A unique benefit of sandwich installation (Figure 5) is that a nice slot is automatically created for the insertion of a weatherstrip seal. You will notice that in the drawing the upper aluminum strip prevents the screw head from pressing into the plexiglass while the bottom aluminum strip helps diffuse localized pressures. The outer aluminum strip is countersunk as needed to accommodate the screw heads. Notice too, that the mounting holes in the plexiglass are oversize to permit the expansion and contraction of the acrylic sheet.

WEATHERSTRIPPING AND CAULKING

Be careful what you use if you plan to glue your weatherstrips directly to the plexiglass. The

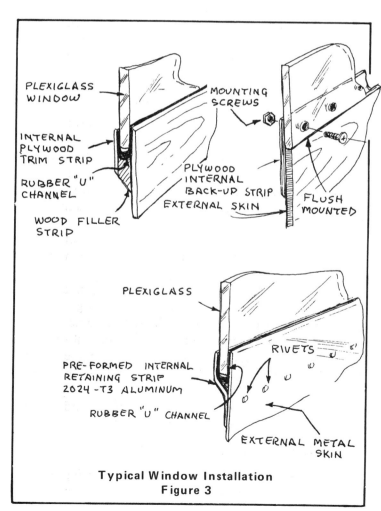

**Typical Window Installation
Figure 3**

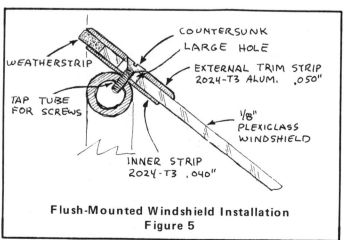

**Flush-Mounted Windshield Installation
Figure 5**

wrong material might attack the plexiglass and eventually cause it to become brittle and to craze. Polysulfide sealants are o.k. Butyl tape can sometimes also be adapted to serve the same purpose.

FLUSH—HEAD SCREWS IN PLEXIGLASS

If you intend to install your windows using flat-head screws, countersunk in place, I suppose you can expect to get pretty good results in most cases even though the method is not one approved by purists. If you are daring enough to risk it, here is a thing or two to consider. First, drill the holes in the plexiglass oversize for the size screws used. Normally, holes 5/16- to 3/8-inch in diameter will do. Countersink the holes in the plexiglass . . . . preferably on the drill press using a regular countersink bit and not a large high-speed drill bit. On installing the screws, tighten each very lightly but uniformly. Then go around again, and this time, after tightening each of them snugly, back each of the screws off about a quarter to a half turn. This will allow the window to expand and will help avoid any stress problems. Play it safe and do not tighten bolts and screws in plexiglass

any more than absolutely necessary. Believe me, the windows will not fall out.

PAINTING AROUND WINDOWS

Since plexiglas does expand and contract considerably, a guy is only fooling himself if he tries to install plexiglass with invisible seams. Sure, the seam may be invisible while the airplane is in your workshop, and for a while after it has been freshly painted, but within a few days or weeks, the difference in the coefficients of expansion of the plexiglass and the adjacent structural material will cause the development of a meandering, unsightly crack in the paint. Since you know this is bound to develop, why ignore it? Why not minimize the potential effect? Go ahead and make your "invisible joint" and paint it. After the paint has dried, take an art knife or some other sharp-edged tool, and carefully, using a straight edge, lightly scribe a knife cut along the joint line between the edge of the plexiglass and the structure surrounding it. It will look good, and when the expansion crack does come, it will not show as a crooked crack. You will have a nice straight joint.

Most homebuilts require a tailor-made canopy.

Fitting and Installing Canopies

Are you faced with the slightly overwhelming thought of fitting and installing that big, newly acquired plexiglass bubble on the airplane? Like many of us, the very first thing you probably did was to place it on the airplane and marvel how nice it looked. Now I'll bet you are equally eager to begin the installation work.

Take a good look at that canopy on the fuselage. Do you get the feeling that it seems a bit too high . . . . or is it too low? Are you beginning to wonder if you will have enough headroom above, and head space to either side? These doubts will be dispelled quickly once you get started, even if your plans happen to be somewhat vague regarding the canopy details.

Climb into the cockpit and have a 'volunteer' position the canopy where you want it. Then, have him block it up, if necessary, to provide you with the proper headroom. When you are satisfied with things inside the canopy, make note of any shims or blocking used and at what points.

This does not end the exercise as yet because you should see for yourself how the profile looks from the outside. Therefore, trade places with your helper and have him sit in the cockpit while you eyeball the overall effect.

Notice how much headroom there is and where it is. Try to visualize how the canopy will slide back. Will it have enough space, or will it hit something like a dorsal fin or antenna. (I'll bet at least one of you gents has already installed an antenna right smack dab in the middle of the turtleback . . . . just where the canopy is supposed to slide back to, tsk, tsk.) incidentally, is your live "cockpit man" at least your size? At this stage, it might be a good idea to reassure yourself that the seat is built-up to the exact height that you will have after the upholstery is installed.

It could be that your canopy did not need to be blocked up, but rather you may have to cut it down a bit. Don't get too preoccupied with trying for a low profile. There is such a thing as reducing the headroom too much. A 2-inch clearance around your head is not considered excessive. Too many homebuilt pilots surprise themselves when they first turn their head, at some time during that ever-so-exciting first flight, and bang their noggins smartly on the canopy. They find that they can't even lean slightly to look out the side to admire the scenery.

On the other hand, the importance of adequate headroom notwithstanding, I can't visualize anything that looks sillier than a canopy so tall that it looks like the shell on a snail's back. Still, you are your own judge and there is no way you can squirm out of that decision. If the general appearance is satisfactory to you, that's all that matters . . . . except for aerodynamic considerations, of course.

CANOPY FRAMES

Canopies, particularly the larger two-seater types, require a frame which will serve as an attachment base for the plexiglass and provide points of attachment for the guides or rollers.

This frame should be light, yet rigid, as the general outline of the frame also establishes the planform shape of the canopy. Usual practice is to make the frame of steel tubing although aluminum tubing, laminated wood, or reinforced fiberglass frames are also used.

A good fit of the canopy depends on the relationship of the windshield bow to that of the canopy bow. Both must have identical contours even though the canopy bow will undoubtedly have to be taller and perhaps a bit wider. Of course, the curvature of the windshield and canopy bow should be reasonably close to the shape of the plexiglass bubble.

The proper height measurement for the canopy bow is obtained directly from the propped up canopy. After this dimension is established, you must determine how you will affix the canopy. After that, it may be that you will have to subtract more from the overall height for one installation than for another. I am speaking now of the allowance for the space to be

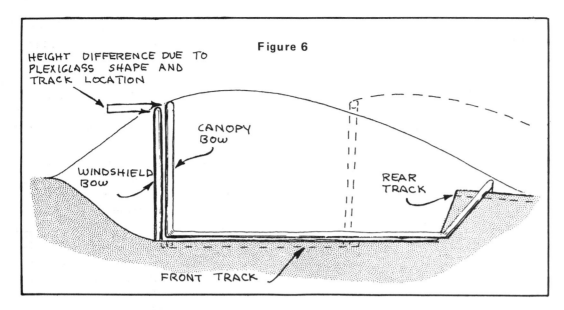

Figure 6

HEIGHT DIFFERENCE DUE TO PLEXIGLASS SHAPE AND TRACK LOCATION

CANOPY BOW

WINDSHIELD BOW

REAR TRACK

FRONT TRACK

taken up by the rollers or guide assembly. Here are three ways to install the tracks:

1. Attach them to the top of the longeron.
2. Attach them to the inside of the cockpit on the top longeron.
3. Attach them to the outside of the fuselage at the top longeron.

Once you have decided how your canopy tracks are to be mounted, you can arrive at the precise height for the canopy bow.

If wood laminations are used to construct the canopy bow, it will be necessary to develop the outer surface of the bow so that the slope of the frame matches the slant of the plexiglass.

Tubing, being round of course, does not present this problem in fitting as the surface of the plexiglass will always contact the tubing along a line of tangency perpendicular to its centerline. (Did I say that right?) This makes the fitting much easier.

When the canopy frames are made of steel or aluminum tubing they are welded into a single rigid unit with the bottom side members of the canopy frame bent, or curved, to conform with the fuselage and canopy shape. Whether the frames come to a point at rear, or to some other configuration depends completely upon the shape and treatment given the turtleback of the fuselage.

If the bottom side frame members are made of wood to match the canopy bow, they too are laminated to the desired curve and glued into a single unit using additional reinforcements at the juncture of the canopy bow.

CANOPY TRACKS

Canopies, like many other components in

aircraft, often depend on the principle of the "magic triangle" for their rigidity.

A three-point suspension for the canopy is light, rigid, and highly recommended. While there are a number of ways of installing sliding canopies, service experience seems to prove that the most practical one is the three-point suspension operating in slides or tracks. This kind of installation allows the canopy to be easily pushed back far enough to provide free access to the cockpit. When closed the tracks are invisible. This, of course, requires a separate fixed windshield installation.

A tricky innovation in sliding canopies utilizes three or four pivoted arms which cause the canopy to rise considerably as it is pushed back. This type of installation must be well designed and built or it will result in a rather flimsy arrangement. Good results are difficult to obtain

Up and over. This canopy clears the pilot's head, permitting the bubble to be installed in one piece without a separate windshield.

198

without excess weight. Its best feature rests in the fact that a separate windshield installation is avoided. Check the figures and drawings. They show essential details common to a variety of applications being used by most homebuilders today. (See Figures 6 and 7)

Ordinarily, tracks or rails are made of extruded "C" channel, "I" sections, or of square aluminum extrusions with a slot cut along its centerline. Either aluminum or stainless steel are the preferred materials, although some builders are using office desk drawer tracks and mild steel sections. The material easiest to obtain for stainless and aluminum tracks is approximately ¾-inch x ¾-inch x .050-inch. If square aluminum tubing is used, you can safely cut a slot in it using a bench saw equipped with a small-tooth blade. (You might stick some plugs in your ears and hope that the neighbors aren't home during the slotting process.) When using small bearings as rollers, the inside dimensions of your track channel must be just right for the bearings used.

If you elect to mount the canopy rails on top of the fuselage longerons, you should realize that when the canopy is opened, that area will be subjected to the wear and tear, and body weight of those who enter or leave the aircraft. Furthermore, a canopy track with the slot facing upward may become a handy receptacle for chewing gum, dirt, and other debris, which could certainly impair the canopy's smooth operation.

On the other hand, securing canopy rails to the outside of the fuselage sometimes results in the aft end of the track projecting away from the fuselage. This is most often manifest in small single-seaters whose top longerons are highly curved. Nevertheless, it is possible to make this type of installation look very nice, although not without a considerable amount of extra work.

An objective second only to properly securing the rails to the fuselage is to ensure that the tracks are parallel to each other. In other words, the dimensional space between the two tracks at the front on the windshield end should

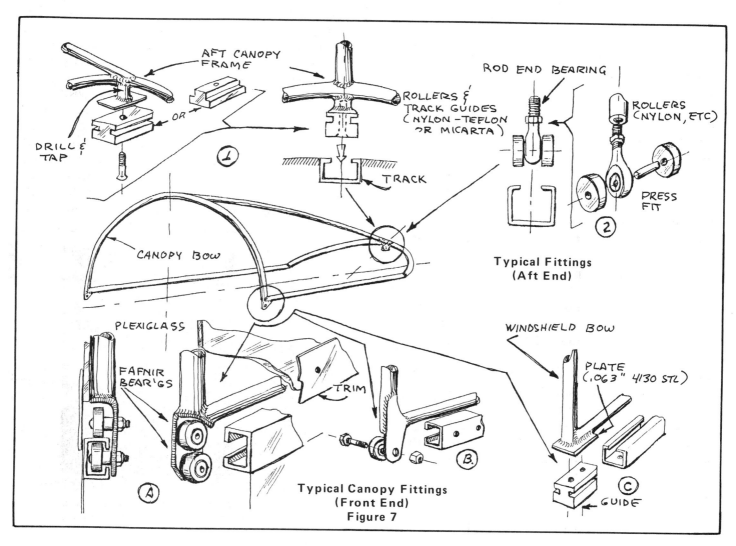

Typical Canopy Fittings
(Front End)
Figure 7

be the same as that at the rear end of the main track channels.

Still, you may have to compromise and install the rails so that they are a bit closer together at the rear. The canopy will still slide all right simply because it can flex to a degree since there are no cross braces up front.

Mounting the channel tracks on the inside of the top longerons seems to provide the best installation. The rails are not visible from the outside when the canopy is open or closed, and they are better protected. Unless the fuselage sides are flat in this area, it will be necessary to shim behind the track channel to eliminate any bending in the track.

Some builders of wood aircraft prefer to avoid drilling unnecessary holes in the longerons and this is a darn good attitude to have. Instead they first bolt their track to a strip of wood and then clamp and glue that assembly permanently to the longeron.

Tracks are secured to the metal fuselages by using flat-head or recessed machine screws so that there is no bolt head for the rollers or guides to catch on and jam. Some may elect to rivet the track channels with flush rivets. Future removal, if necessary, becomes more difficult.

The forward ends of the tracks should be secured to the windshield bow in some manner so as to tie the two units together. A considerable amount of stress occurs in this area, and the track is always subjected to the additional wear

A well-fitted, smoothly operating bubble canopy adds much to the appearance and value of a homebuilt.

Note how fiberglass trim is used to conceal the externally mounted canopy track.

A sliding canopy, military style. Reminiscent of the very effective canopy installation of the old USAF T-6 (SNJ, you Navy lads).

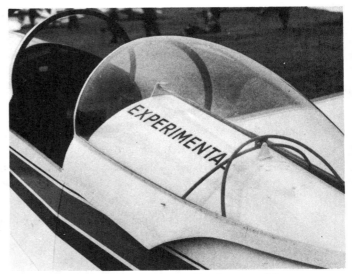

Canopy too high? Note how effective use of large fiberglass side panels provides a perfect fit for a difficult situation.

and tear that results from the entry and exit of the pilot and passengers. A solid attachment in this area is therefore necessary.

"T" shaped guides, rollers and bearings all seem to share equal popularity with the homebuilder, although I prefer the use of standard, easily obtained K3L Fafnir bearings over the micarta, nylon or teflon sliding guides. Of course, the matter of material availability is always a preference breaker. Whether you use the rollers, slides, or bearings, they should slip into the track channels easily but without an excessive amount of play. Loosely fitted track assemblies would permit the canopy to rattle and to work sloppily. Teflon, micarta and nylon guides, especially, must be fitted so that they slide easily within their slotted tracks. Use of a double ball bearing mounting produces the smoothest working canopy of the lot.

So far I have been talking only of the side rails and of the two front mounting points for the canopy. Once they are installed you should be able to raise the aft end of the canopy by hand by as much as one foot and still have a canopy that slides easily. The point to be made here is that the rear rail securing the aft end of the canopy not only holds the end of the canopy down, but it also directly controls the vertical movement of the canopy's aft portion.

When a canopy is slid back on a flat-decked fuselage it may cause rub marks and ruin the paint job. Avoid this problem by raising or tilting the rear track so that, as the canopy is pushed back, it will rise away from the fuselage slightly. The rear track adjustment is very important for this reason.

An additional precaution . . . . a fuselage with a rounded turtledeck often has a track that is tilted downward to coincide with the fuselage lines. The track, so installed, causes the canopy to also tilt downward as it is pushed back. This is a common arrangement that results from the rear track being flush-mounted on top of the fuselage. Because the track does not show, you may forget that it creates a natural path for

water. Ensure that water cannot drain into the fuselage at this location.

Positive stops should be placed in the track channels to limit the full aft movement of the canopy. It would be very useful to be able to remove the canopy from its tracks without a great deal of work. Don't overlook this simple need.

Very few of the larger sliding canopies with a single center track at the aft end are rigid enough to prevent the canopy from lifting a bit during higher cruise speeds. Many builders solve this problem by making a wedge type of fixture that engages when the canopy is closed.

SEALS AND WEATHERSTRIPPING

There is an art to installing canopy seals and weatherstripping around doors and hatches. It takes a little thinking about the slipstream and the actions imposed on the canopy. You have to figure just what happens as the canopy is slid back. Is it better to attach the seal strip to the canopy, or to the fuselage and frame? Remember also that sliding canopies, on two-seaters especially, tend to bulge outward amidships in high cruise. How are you going to seal against that? These are just a few things that you will have to work out for yourself and your own particular aircraft. The effort you make will be well worth it if you can reduce much of the kind of wind noise you hear in many other aircraft.

Even weatherstripping will not help, however, if the canopy is permitted to lift at any point because of excess looseness of the rollers or slides in the tracks, or because of the tendency of the aft end of the canopy to rise away from the fuselage. Some clever means have been devised and used by builders to tightly secure the aft end of the canopy when it is in the closed position. The installation method used must result in a tight fitting installation. The alternative might be the sudden and embarrassing departure of the canopy in flight. This sort of thing has happened in our circles, and it continues to happen from time to time . . . . even in the best of circles.

Canopy Access Details

Not everyone likes the naked sameness of a bubble canopy perched atop the fuselage. For that matter, not everyone likes the conventional cabin, or canopy, or open cockpit arrangement either. It really is surprising to learn how many builders are building just to have something a little different. This desire to be different is exhibited in many ways by the variety of canopy installations seen at any fly-in.

The appearance of some individual canopy designs, however, could be enhanced with just a bit more work on the part of the builder. Very often the builder will construct his windshield frame and install a nice slanted windshield. He will then build up an arch behind him and cover that with plywood, metal, or even fiberglass, fairing the whole thing nicely into the fuselage. Now he has to decide what to do about the cockpit area. Should he make separate doors hinged at the windshield frame or should he make hatch-like windows hinged along the roof line?

Many builders take the easiest alternative and avoid compound curves in the cabin area. After all, obtaining compound curves that are aerodynamically superior to the straight slab doors and windows would require the build up of an expen-

sive and time-consuming foam and plaster form over which to stretch the plexiglass. Of course, this would then lead to the requirement for a huge oven, etc., etc.

The straight roof line treatment of the cabin is characteristic of the Globe Swift's canopy . . . . and it looks good. Many low-wing two-seaters appear to use the straight roof as a simple means of enclosing the canopy. The simplicity of the straight roof is partially realized because it permits the effective use of ordinary piano hinge stock. These are probably adequate although the use of an extruded type of hinge would make a stronger installation.

A hinged canopy will not work smoothly unless the hinge line is straight. You can get by with some curvature when you install piano hinges as cowl fasteners, but when using them as hinges no curvatures should be allowed.

The hinge wires, when installed, should be inserted from the front end or from the top so that the slipstream or gravity (as the case may be) helps to keep them in place.

Overhead-hinged hatches (found on some of the earlier Jodel aircraft) seem to be simple and practical, however, with but a single hinge along

Large door affords easy entry to the cabin. Slab-sided windows and windshield require no complex forming and are low drag too.

Side-hinged canopy on a PL-4. This type of canopy should be easy to fit and to secure.

Note the light tubular door frame, simple latch (as detailed in Figure 13), and easy access to cockpit.

Unique hinging permits accommodation of a highly contoured roof profile. Distance beyond hinge points should be kept to a minimum.

the centerline, it may not be possible to open both doors at the same time. Most likely it will turn out that each door will have to have separate hinges.

If each door is to be provided with its own hinge, you should leave a space of about 2 or 3 inches between the doors. This will provide enough space to permit the doors to be opened simultaneously. This is particularly important if the plexiglass doors have compound curvatures in them.

The plain straight roof profile could be made a bit more aesthetically appealing with a bit of cosmetic treatment. A slight curve could be built into the roof line by using polyurethane foam glued in place and shaped to whatever streamline form space permits. If the cabin roof has (at least) a 6-inch space between the doors, the effect can be very pleasing. This shaped foam should then be overlaid with dynel or fiberglass cloth using epoxy resin. When finished and painted, the cabin profile will create the appearance of a nicely contoured installation.

If you just happen to have a plexiglass bubble on hand that is cracked in the wrong place or otherwise won't be used in your project, toy with the idea of cutting it off and using the front part as a windshield. How about the aft portion? To carry this brainstorm a bit further, would it be possible to cut a couple of doors out of that "salvage" bubble and fit them into separate doors? Could it be attached permanently to the fuselage and faired in with fiberglass trim? If it is cracked at the edge somewhere, the crack might be covered by an overlapping trim. Fiber-

glass cloth layed on plexiglass works miracles.

To provide the cabin occupants with some degree of protection from the sun, portions of the plexiglass overhead could be coated with epoxy and fiberglass cloth and then painted to match the aircraft.

The real problem in providing doors for a cabin canopy is in providing for easy access. The size of the canopy, as well as the size and positioning of the door opening, affects the ease of entry into the cockpit.

If the door is too small, and particularly if it is poorly located, it would almost certainly require the pilot to be something of a gymnast. Assuming that you are indeed athletic in ability and svelte of figure, what about your friends? Could they manage to get in?

If you had any doubts about the ease of entry, it would be wise to build and try out a cardboard and wood mockup.

A tilt-away, side-hinged canopy may be perfect for many high-performance single-seaters, but only a few canopies on larger homebuilts are hinged on the side. Very few aircraft have canopies hinged at the front end (Minicab), and rarely at the aft end, military style.

All in all, large heavy canopies hinged at the side, or front, or back, are uncommon, perhaps because they seem to present an awesome sight when opened in all their splendor.

Ordinarily, the side-hinged canopy is less desirable for the two-seater (side-by-side) because of the canopy's bulging sides and considerable weight.

If you wish to swing the whole canopy, you

will need to use strong hinges and a frame of fairly rugged construction. This will ensure adequate distribution of canopy loads.

DOOR AND CANOPY RESTRAINTS

Hinged canopies require some sort of restraint to limit their open position. Many canopies that are hinged along one side of the bottom edge are restrained with a simple flexible cable. One end is attached to the canopy and the other to the fuselage. The difficulty here is that the stupid cable (yes, amigo, some inanimate objects, like coat hangers, cables and ropes can be obstinate and stupid) will somehow manage to get trapped in the door edges as you close the canopy unless you figure out a simple device to keep the cable out of the way while the canopy is being shut. Either that or maybe you can develop some kind of two-handed technique.

Plexiglass areas should not be permitted to bang or hit on any part of the aircraft's structure when the doors are open.

Unfortunately, hinged canopies that are restrained in their open position by only a piece of flexible cable are sometimes subject to abuse from itinerant gusts of wind. These gusts cause the canopy to rise, and then suddenly drop, twanging the single restraining cable sharply. Too much of this sort of thing will have you headed back to the workshop for unscheduled maintenance.

There are problems with doors too. Whenever the wind catches an open door .... Wham, it slams shut. Lightweight aircraft doors can't tolerate much treatment of this nature without suffering damage. For this reason alone, a means of securing the door in its open position would be useful. Besides, it is difficult to get into or out of an airplane on a windy day while fighting to keep the door from slamming in your face.

The problems with door and hatches are quite similar. Some sort of stay-strut or brace mechanism must also be devised to hold the hatches in their open position (in spite of breezes that blow). These restraints must be designed so that they will not take up a lot of the cockpit space and be in your way after the hatches are closed.

Examine a stereo (or Hi-Fi set) and note how the stereo lids prop in an open position. Maybe you could adapt something like that to your own use. Upward-opening hatches are very flimsy in their open positions because both ends of the raised lightweight hatch cannot be effectively braced.

FITTING DOOR FRAMES

Don't be afraid to make the door frames a bit smaller than the door opening. A uniform gap or space all around the frame makes it easier to install the weather seals or strips. It also eliminates the rubbing of the door frame against the structure as often happens when the fit is too snug. An equalized gap ensures that your doors can be closed without jamming.

The use of external metal or fiberglass trim strips over the plexiglass will cover even the widest of door gaps without detracting from appearances. As a matter of fact, a wide trim strip makes it possible to achieve a very nice fit all around.

As you may have already discovered, the door frame must match the contour of the door opening. When made of tubing, the individual pieces for the door frames, like canopy frames, are first bent to shape and then welded into a single rigid unit.

Frames of laminated wood are built up by laminating wide strips of wood in place in the door opening. Remember to insert spacers at least 1/8-inch thick all around the opening to make sure that the laminated frame will not fit too tightly when completed. The laminated wood frame is then hand-shaped to match the cabin opening while it is still in position. After this is

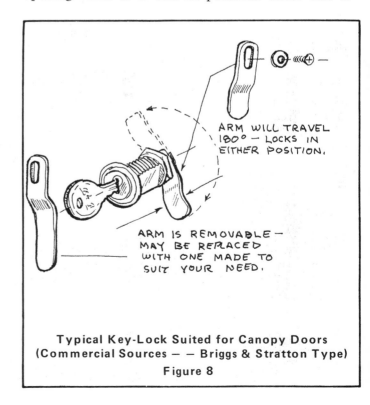

Typical Key-Lock Suited for Canopy Doors (Commercial Sources − − Briggs & Stratton Type)
Figure 8

done, it may be removed and the inside portion of the frame trimmed to a uniform thickness. In making a wooden frame that will be fitted to a bulged piece of plexiglass (one with compound curvature), remember to bevel the frame to match the slope of the plexiglass surface.

LOCK IT UP

It is really essential to install canopy and door locks for your airplane. Almost any airplane with a door can be locked by installing a simple, lightweight, key-operated lock. (Figure 8)

There is usually some place where this installation will fit. Since a lock does not have to be in any particular location, it could even be located at the aft end of a canopy.

Install the key-operated lock so that it is necessary to apply a little forward pressure to the canopy as you turn the key. This ensures that the seal between the windshield and canopy will be compressed, and if it should rain on your bird, it will not also rain in your bird.

Now that we two-seater jockeys are required to have ELTs, we have all the more reason to lock our birds, even if the pencil, earphones and mike have already been stolen.

A side-hinged canopy on larger aircraft can be heavy to operate, although it does provide total access to the cabin area.

Canopy Latches

Did you know a bubble canopy (essentially an airfoil in character) has a tendency to slide shut of its own accord in flight? That's right. So, if on occasion you like to fly with a sliding canopy slightly open, it will be necessary to fashion some kind of a position latch to make the canopy stay where you set it. You might assume that no latch is needed to lock the canopy in its closed position. Maybe not, in some cases. However, if your homebuilt has a good rate of acceleration during fast applications of full power for takeoff, you may have already experience an unexpected and spooky Yo-Yo like opening of the canopy, just when you don't **need** any distractions. But even if the canopy does not slide open during takeoff, the effect of the airflow over the canopy is not strong enough to cause it to be held shut tightly enough to keep out the wind noise. This means a good latch must be installed to remedy the annoyance.

One type of latch merits an unqualified recommendation for use with sliding canopies. That is the kind that exerts a clamping action. This clamping action is essential if a cockpit is to be relatively free from wind noise. Designing a suitable latch for your installation can be a satisfying experience.

Every now and then some builder brings up the issue of access to the cockpit from the outside in the event of an accident. Some say a canopy or door must be constructed so that it can be opened from the outside . . . . others aren't so sure.

A simple lightweight latch that can be operated from both the inside and the outside of the aircraft is difficult to devise and consequently good examples are rather **rare** in homebuilts. It could be that one of the best examples of such a latch is the type used on the old Navions. Of course, such an installation utilizes a rather large handle that sticks out into the slipstream, a condition not totally acceptable to the builder, who is determined to eliminate all external

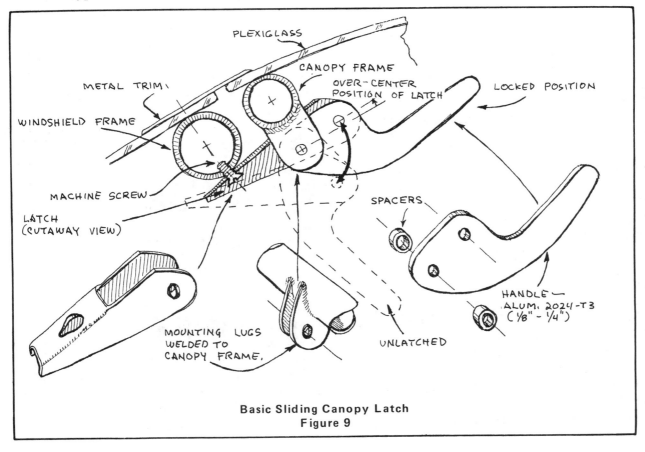

Basic Sliding Canopy Latch
Figure 9

protuberances contributing to drag.

If it is not practical to construct your door or canopy so that it can be opened from both the inside and outside of the cockpit, other safety precautions could be incorporated. Often it is possible to install individual door hinges so that they have removable pins or some other emergency release feature. On the other hand, it might be practical to make the entire canopy jettisonable.

Some builders don't appear to be particularly concerned with such precautions, and believe that their plexiglass windows can easily be broken out if the need should arise. At any rate, this is a matter worth considering and resolving to your own personal satisfaction.

For single-seaters, one must be careful to select a latch design that will not endanger the pilot's head. Unfortunately, the best location for most any latch happens to be above, and on a direct line with the pilot's head. Some latches, you may have noticed, could turn out to be real skull cleavers. (Figure 9)

This potential danger isn't nearly the problem in a side-by-side aircraft because the latch can be located between the pilot and passenger, safely out of alignment of either head.

An alternative to the overhead latch is the practice of installing separate latches on either side of the canopy frame adjacent to the slide or track. Two such latches are very effective in clamping the canopy tightly shut. Designs for these latches range from simple pegs that drop into holes drilled in the canopy rails and longerons, to a complex of levers. However, the problem of locking and unlocking two canopy latches does make the opening and closing routine more complex. (Figure 10)

It should also be easy to locate without groping for it, and simple to operate with either hand, and from either side of the cockpit.

Illustrated in Figure 9 is the basic type of latch used extensively on T-18s. It is simple to make and quite effective. It clamps the canopy tightly when secured. Its greatest deficiency is that it cannot be adjusted. When initially installed, the builder will fit it to obtain the necessary clamping effect. However, with the passage of time, the weatherstripping will become compressed and an increase in wind noise will ultimately follow.

Two alternative designs are shown (Figures 10 and 11) which can be adjusted to effect whatever clamping pressure is desired. A number of other methods of accomplishing this kind of adjustment can probably be devised by the builder if he applies a little bit of thinking to the problem. These latches can be made of aluminum sheet, extrusions, bolts and

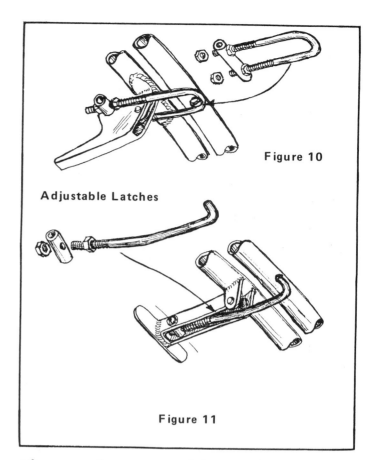

Adjustable Latches

Figure 10

Figure 11

other scraps from your workshop goody box. Decorative wood handles could be fitted to the thin aluminum handle, if desired, to give it greater bulk. These latches need not be large, and the overall length can be limited to 5 inches, possibly less.

You will notice that there are two hinge axes. The main axis pivots in the mounting lugs and the latch-catch on the other axis, obtaining its locking action by rotating beyond the centerline of the main axis. (Gad!) Why bother to figure out that description when you can simply refer to the drawings. (Figures 9, 10 and 11)

LATCHES FOR DOORS

Some variation of the sliding bolt latch is usually used for cabins and canopies equipped with doors. These are easy to make, durable, and free from problems. All that is needed is a small spring, a short piece of rod (about ¼-inch to 5/16-inch in diameter), a washer or two, a cotter pin, and a section of tubing to serve as a guide for the rod. Most of these latches work identically in that the spring forces the rod into a small hole in the door frame behind it, wedging the door shut. (Figures 12 and 13) Some sort of a handle or knob is used to pull the bolt back to permit the door to open. These handles can be as simple or as fancy as your whims dictate. Use your imagination to adapt the principle to the variation best for your instal-

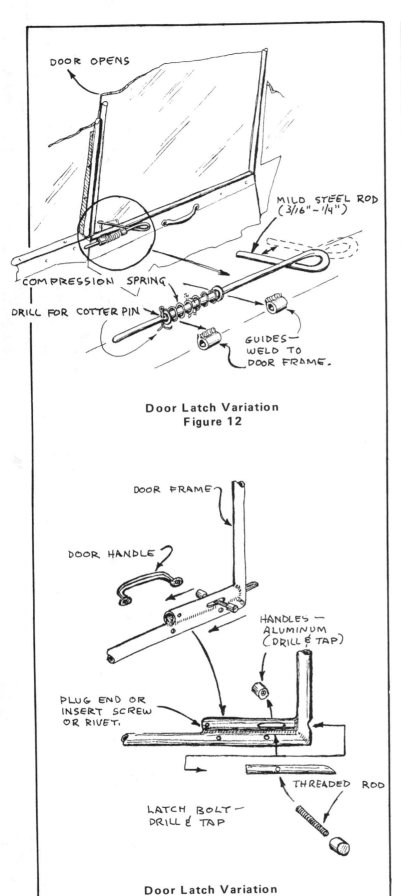

DOOR OPENS

MILD STEEL ROD
(3/16" - 1/4")

COMPRESSION SPRING

DRILL FOR COTTER PIN

GUIDES —
WELD TO
DOOR FRAME.

**Door Latch Variation
Figure 12**

DOOR FRAME

DOOR HANDLE

HANDLES —
ALUMINUM
(DRILL & TAP)

PLUG END OR
INSERT SCREW
OR RIVET.

THREADED ROD

LATCH BOLT —
DRILL & TAP

**Door Latch Variation
Figure 13**

Some door handles, complete with a key lock, can be adapted by an innovative builder.

This is the door latching mechanism inside a Stits Skycoupe.

An overhead latch such as the one in the center of this 2-seater can be operated from outside as well as from inside the aircraft. A good safety feature.

208

lation.

A fixed handle attached to the inside of the door is a very useful aid in closing and latching the door since it will help you apply the necessary pressure to compress the door seals.

When your door is closed, it should fit snugly enough so that daylight is not visible around the edges. In addition to a snug fit, you'll need a good seal strip to keep the air and wind noise out, especially at the forward end of the canopy or door. Incidentally, air must not be allowed to get under the front edges of windshields, doors or hatches as it might contribute to the loss of a canopy or door with a sudden POW! That would be a definite safety hazard.

Fancy door frames with compound curves are difficult to match fit to canopy door openings. They also suffer, in flight, from the same invisible lift forces that are generated by the flow of air over bubble-like canopies. Designs like the Emeraude, some Jodels, and other aircraft with similarly contoured canopy doors, require the addition of an extra latch overhead to keep the aft portion of the doors from being sucked outward by the slipstream. If not so secured, the resultant air gap becomes a source of much noise and some added drag.

LATCHES FOR HATCHES

Any latch suitable for a door would also probably work on a hatch that is hinged along its topside. Most builders utilizing a swing-over canopy or a hatch, install some variation of the double-action latch illustrated in Figure 14. It secures both the forward and aft ends of the hatch effectively, and it permits the locking and unlocking of the hatch in a single action. This type of installation also requires an inside handle to assist the pilot in the closing and

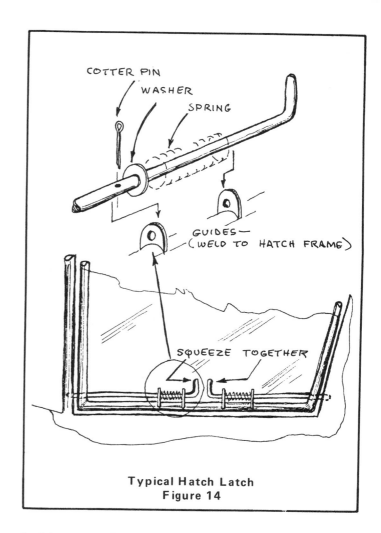

Typical Hatch Latch
Figure 14

locking operation.

These few examples of latches merely scratch the surface of a design feature usually left to the builder to work out. If you have always felt that you could do a good job of designing your own airplane, I suggest you first begin with a good, simple latch design that works from both sides . . . . if you can.

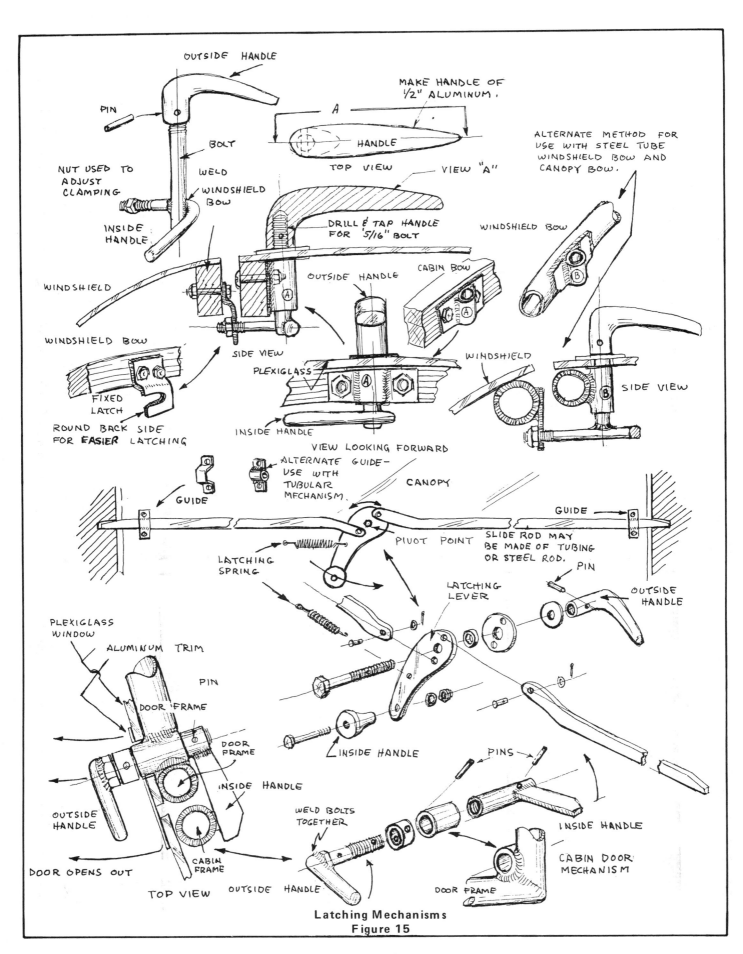

Latching Mechanisms
Figure 15

210

Aircraft camping at the EAA Oshkosh Convention.

ELECTRICAL SYSTEMS

Aircraft Electrical Circuitry

What image is conjured in your mind when someone tells you he has a full electric system in his airplane? Have you ever seen a half-full electric system? What of the builder who says he has a complete electrical system in his bird? Pray tell, how does an incomplete one work? This is silly, I know but it does offer an excuse to point out that electrical systems can vary greatly in complexity from the bare minimum to those chock full of all sorts of lights, buzzers, switches and dials.

What do you want in your electric system? A good basic system will provide you with an electric start capability, power for a radio and a variety of lights. Such an installation can be deluxed by the addition of all sorts of other devices depending upon the complexity of the airplane.

Homebuilders usually aren't lucky enough to get plans that include a master wiring diagram or a wire table and equipment list. Most builders therefore, although familiar with basic electricity and common circuits, naturally feel a bit unsure about undertaking an aircraft wiring job on their own. Let's remove this uncertainty.

The circuitry of most electrical systems is similar. Only the details vary from aircraft to aircraft. Because of this uniformity, it is practical to present a basic electrical system which should be adequate for most aircraft. A discussion of the installation and functions of each of its components follows.

THE BATTERY

The battery is the basic power source for the electrical system. Although an engine-driven generator (or alternator) provides all electrical power (other than ignition) during flight, as well as maintains a battery charge, don't lose sight of the fact that the battery supplies power for initial starting and serves as an ever-ready auxiliary source of power in the event the generator fails.

With a new or untried voltage regulator installation, it is quite possible for the battery to suffer from excessive overcharging in flight. If this should happen, a dangerously explosive condition may develop. Therefore, always install a vent tube from the battery box vent opening to a point of negative pressure outside the aircraft. Don't underestimate the importance of this provision. Incidentally, a battery installed in a light aircraft without a generator (VW installations, for example) does not require a venting and drainage system because no gassing will occur.

Your battery should be located as near as possible to that heavy current user .... the starter. Working counter to that requirement, however, is the need to protect the battery against high temperatures when it is installed in the engine compartment. Battery separators deteriorate when subjected to temperatures much over 110 degrees F.

Make your two battery cables of different lengths to help prevent an inadvertent reversal of the connections at the battery terminals. Always attach the negative terminal last and remove it first as a guard against objects dropping across the terminals (mostly screw drivers and pliers).

And a final note, remember that poor accessibility to the battery leads to infrequent servicing and inspection.

MASTER SWITCH

The master switch is used to control the operation of the battery and generator system. Actually, its function is to disconnect the battery from all electrical equipment.

As you know, the engine will continue to function whether the master switch is ON or OFF.

The master switch controls two circuits so it must be a double-pole, single-throw (dpst) switch. It can be a toggle, rocker or push-pull type of switch. The rocker-type scores high in popularity today.

A look at the schematic illustration (Figure 1) shows that half of the master switch completes the battery-to-starter circuit through a battery solenoid. The other half of the master switch completes the circuit between the F (field) terminal of the generator and the F terminal of the voltage regulator. Fear not, both the connector on the generator and the one on the voltage regulator are marked or embossed with the letter F for identification. In reality then, when the master switch is turned on, you activate the aircraft's electrical power system (battery and generator).

SOLENOIDS, CONTACTORS, RELAY SWITCHES

Cessna calls them contactors (battery contactor and starter contactor). Others call them solenoids (battery solenoids and starter solenoids). Still others refer to them as relays (battery relay and starter relay). While there are technical differences, they may all be talking about the same gadgets.

Relays and solenoids (or contactors) are electromagnetic switches which can be remotely operated from the cockpit to activate heavy current circuits such as the one from the battery to the starter.

These units should be located directly between the power source and the unit to be controlled in order to keep the cables carrying the heavy current as short as possible.

Since relays, solenoids, or contactors require only a small wire and a slight amount of current

to activate, they eliminate the need for running the heavy battery-to-starter cable all the way to the cockpit master switch. This saves weight and removes a potential fire risk which would be created if a long, heavy power cable had to be connected to the cockpit's master switch.

These electromagnetic switches must be selected for the function to be performed. Some are designed for continuous operation, others are not. The starter relay (or starter solenoid) is made for intermittent operation and would overheat if used continuously. The battery solenoid (or battery relay switch), on the other hand, can be operated continuously because its coil has a high-resistance which keeps it from overheating.

To keep cables short, the battery contactor (battery relay or battery solenoid also referred to as the master solenoid) is usually bolted directly to the battery case or on the firewall nearby. Adjacent to one larger terminal of the battery contactor will be the word "BAT" stamped into its case. This terminal should be connected to the cable from the battery's positive post. The other contactor terminal must be connected to the cable running to the starter. The third, and smaller terminal, is for the master switch wire.

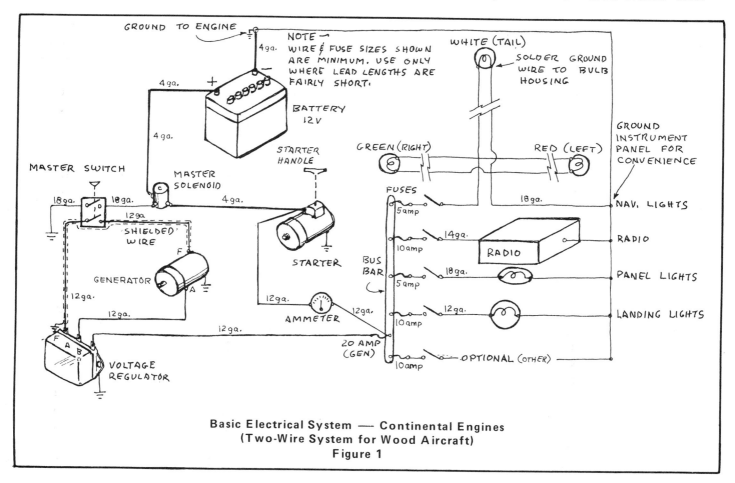

Basic Electrical System — Continental Engines
(Two-Wire System for Wood Aircraft)
Figure 1

If the engine is a small Continental with a manual pull-to-start switch, no starter solenoid is necessary. As the starter is engaged manually, the electric circuit is activated simultaneously (Figure 1).

With a key-start switch or a pushbutton-start operation, you will also have to obtain and install a starter solenoid. It can be wired into the system as shown in Figure 2.

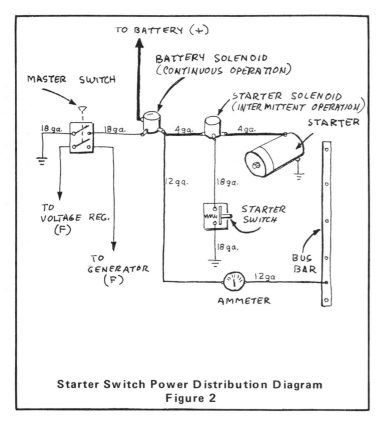

Starter Switch Power Distribution Diagram
Figure 2

GENERATORS AND VOLTAGE REGULATORS

Energy for the in-flight operations of the electrically operated equipment in the aircraft depends upon the electrical output supplied by the generator (or alternator). Adding the generator to the electrical system is a simple matter. Its case automatically provides the ground for the unit on installation to the engine. All that remains for you to do is to connect the voltage regulator to the generator using the two terminals provided on the generator. One terminal is marked with an embossed letter "A" and the other, a letter "F". The A connector is to the armature and the F connector is to the generator's field. The voltage regulator, likewise, has terminals identified as "A" and "F". A third is marked "B".

The typical voltage regulator consists of three electrical units mounted on a common base

and enclosed in a single case. This explains the three terminals. One of the elements is the reverse current cutout (generator cutout). It opens and closes the circuit magnetically between the battery and generator when the engine starts or stops, preventing a wasteful discharge of the battery through the generator. Another unit is the current regulator. Its function is to prevent the generator from exceeding its maximum rated output. The third is the voltage regulator portion which protects the circuit from high voltage and prevents battery overcharging by tapering off the generator output as the battery nears its full charged condition.

Connecting the voltage regulator to the generator is also simply a matter of matching the cables from the terminals on the generator to like connectors on the voltage regulator. The A terminals are cable-connected directly to each other. The cable connecting the F terminals of the voltage regulator and the generator runs through the master switch.

The B voltage regulator's terminal connects a cable, through a fuse or circuit breaker (to protect the generator), to the bus bar providing a power source for all electrical equipment.

Select your voltage regulator to match the output characteristics of the generator used. Automotive regulators, if used, will require adjustment in some instances. Since the initial voltage regulator adjustments are often made on the ground with the engine running, a degree of bodily risk is involved. This is particularly true if access to the voltage regulator is difficult. So be careful!

In general, the voltage regulator should be as close to the main bus as practicable to provide uniform voltage for all loading conditions, and to keep the heavier cable lengths as short as possible. Incidentally, if not otherwise grounded, the voltage regulator must be grounded to the engine.

Some antique and classic aircraft rebuilders might be faced with the prospect of utilizing a wind-driven generator. Failure of the propeller of a wind-driven generator has been known to cause serious structural damage. The prop disc, when extended, should not intersect cockpit locations in the aircraft, unless protection is afforded.

A protective barrier of .032-inch aluminum or a piece of ¼-inch plywood probably will furnish adequate protection.

AMMETER

An ammeter is a valuable instrument for an

216

electrical system, as it indicates the amount of current flowing to or from the battery. A low battery, with the engine operating at cruise speed, will cause the ammeter to show full generator/alternator output when all electrical equipment is off. When the battery is fully charged and cruise rpm is maintained and all electrical equipment off, the ammeter should show a minimum charging rate.

Normally a generator starts charging at 1,000 to 1,200 rpm. Alternators, however, produce charging current at much lower rpms. Note that the ammeter is hooked up between the power cable to the starter and the bus bar. (Figure 1)

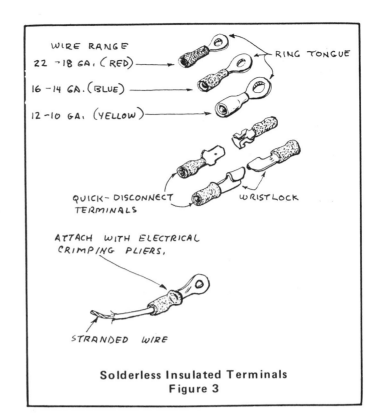

WIRE RANGE
22 –18 GA. (RED)
16 –14 GA. (BLUE)
12 –10 GA. (YELLOW)
RING TONGUE

QUICK- DISCONNECT TERMINALS
WRISTLOCK

ATTACH WITH ELECTRICAL CRIMPING PLIERS.

STRANDED WIRE

**Solderless Insulated Terminals
Figure 3**

Electrical System Details

THE BUS BAR

It is impractical to connect all of the wires from each of the electrical units directly to the battery. Therefore, the power to operate the radio, navigation lights and other electrical equipment is obtained from a central pickup point called the bus bar. The bus bar receives its power from the battery when the master switch is turned on.

Inasmuch as the bus bar must be an excellent electrical conductor, it is made of a piece of heavy copper wire or, preferably, a 1/8-inch copper bar about 3/8-inch wide and about 5 to 6 inches long to accommodate all of the circuit protectors you require.

Normally, one terminal of each circuit protector (fuse or circuit breaker) is attached to the bus bar to simplify wiring. If you choose to install fuses, attach them by soldering one terminal of each fuse directly to the copper bus bar. Circuit protectors are secured to the bus bar, their opposite terminals can then be individually connected to the different switches and to the electrical units to be operated.

CIRCUIT BREAKERS VS. FUSES

Circuit breakers or fuses are installed to protect individual circuits from electrical overloads.

You will probably find fuses to be lighter in weight and somewhat more economical to buy than circuit breakers. However, in service they could be a bit inconvenient since they have to be replaced when blown, whereas circuit breakers can often be safely reset after they pop.

Technically, fuses and circuit breakers are not intended to protect the equipment. They are installed to protect the cables and not the units activated. In other words, when a cable is matched with the recommended capacity circuit breaker or fuse, that protective device will open the circuit before the cable gets hot enough to start smoking. The fuse capacity of any cable is the maximum current it can safely carry.

In general, all essential circuits should have separate protective devices. Otherwise a fault in the landing light circuit, for example, could result in the loss of the position lights if a common protective device were shared. This does not mean though, that a single protective device cannot be used for all the position lights, nor does it mean that you can't use a single circuit breaker to protect a couple of unrelated circuits of lesser importance.

Put your circuit breakers or fuses where they can be serviced in flight. Label, or otherwise identify the function (and rating, if not already embossed) of each protective device adjacent to its mounted location.

Provide a place to stow spare fuses for easy replacement in flight. At least one spare fuse, or 50 per cent of the number installed, should be provided for each fuse rating.

WIRING CONSIDERATIONS

The only special tool required for wiring your aircraft is a pair of electrical crimping pliers for securing terminals to the cables. You will also need an assortment of insulated terminals to fit the cable sizes selected and a few short machine screws with nuts, for making connections to switches, circuit breakers and/or fuses. (The proper aircraft term for wire is cable, but . . . .)

Stranded electrical cable (not the solid, single-core wire) is used in aircraft because it resists breaking better under the abuses of installation and prolonged in-flight vibration.

By all means, use standard aircraft cable, as it ordinarily is more abrasion resistant than automotive wire, and it will not support combustion or emit toxic fumes. Before considering the use of nonaircraft cable, put a match to it to see how it reacts to open flame.

If no wiring diagram and equipment list came with your plans, you should draw your own detailed layout, for even after your aircraft has been wired, such a schematic will always be useful. Retain it with the aircraft records for future reference. It is surprising how quickly the details of installation are forgotten.

You might find it expedient to adapt one of the electrical systems shown. Simply eliminate any equipment circuit not needed. Figure 4 illustrates a typical alternator system. Although it may appear complex when viewed in its entirety, tracing each circuit, cable by cable, will reduce the jumble to simple operational segments.

Mentally relate to your aircraft, the location for each of the items of equipment to be installed. This process should provide you with a rough estimate of the amount and type of cable that will be needed.

Some electrical units, the generator, starter, and navigation lights, for example, have fixed locations and cannot be relocated. Nevertheless, exercise restraint and give plenty of thought to the routing of all cables, because in most complex aircraft, it is ever so easy to assemble a wiring maze rivaling, in appearance, a bombed-out spaghetti factory.

The cable gages noted in the schematic electrical systems previously illustrated are suggested only as a general-use compromise. Some builders may want to substitute other sizes for those shown, not for technical reasons but because they happen to have something else. There is really no problem with substitution if a larger cable is to be used. None, that is, except for extra weight. The use of smaller gages than those shown, however, can be troublesome so be careful. Remember that the cable gage selected must be capable of carrying the current required of it without getting so hot (even during sultry summer days) that it starts to smoke.

Cable determination is based on the current consumption of each particular unit, taking into consideration the voltage drop over the length of the cable required. After a calculation of the maximum voltage drop, at rated equipment current, the smallest cable size to meet that requirement is selected. However, once in a while, although a cable size may be adequate as far as the heating effect is concerned, a larger cable must be used because the voltage drop becomes excessive due to its length. Long battery cables are a problem in this regard and the longer they are, the heavier they must be. For motors, and other rotating equipment applications, the cable size is selected on the basis of the equipment's normal operating current rather than on the starting load. Ordinarily, a starting load is imposed for a short time only.

WHY SHIELDED WIRES?

It is necessary to use shielded cable for some portions of the electrical system to keep the cable from emitting radio frequency noise. As I understand it, the cable's metallic shielding causes the high frequency voltage or interference to be induced in the shield mesh of the wire rather than in other nearby units. For example, we all know that two types of ignition harness (and spark plugs) are in use. Shielded ones are used when there is a radio, and unshielded ones are used where no radio is installed. Many builders, however, may be unaware that it is as important to use shielded cable, for similar reasons, for the generator/alternator circuits. (Figure 4) Also, not commonly known is the need for grounding at least one end of the cable's shielding. A short portion of the shielding mesh can be unraveled (use a needle or ice pick for this purpose) and a terminal crimped on (or soldered) to provide an attachment point to a nearby ground connection. (Figure 5) Shielded wire is easily recognized by the metal mesh encompassing the insulation. Frequently, however, the shield will have a fabric cover over it making it difficult to identify as a shielded wire until the cut end of the cable is examined.

ELECTRICAL BONDING, GROUND RETURNS

Bonding is the process of connecting the various nonconnected metal parts of the aircraft to form a continuous, low resistance, electrical ground path.

The bonding strips used in aircraft are made of a tinned-copper braid containing 120 strands of No. 36 tinned-copper wire. A larger braid capable of carrying 40 amperes is required for bonding the engine mount. Two separate bonding straps are recommended for this purpose.

The bonding jumpers and strips can be used as a convenient grounding source in wood aircraft. An electrical unit's ground wire is simply connected to the bonding strap wherever the need arises. Otherwise, a separate ground cable must be strung along with the power cable to complete each electrical circuit. This is one complication common to wood aircraft since there is no natural common ground as in metal aircraft.

Not having a common ground is a bit of a handicap for the wood aircraft builder because equipment such as navigation and landing lights do not have a negative terminal connector built in. As a result, the builder has to solder the ground wire to the unit's case or housing.

The claim is frequently made that electrical bonding is important in minimizing the danger of

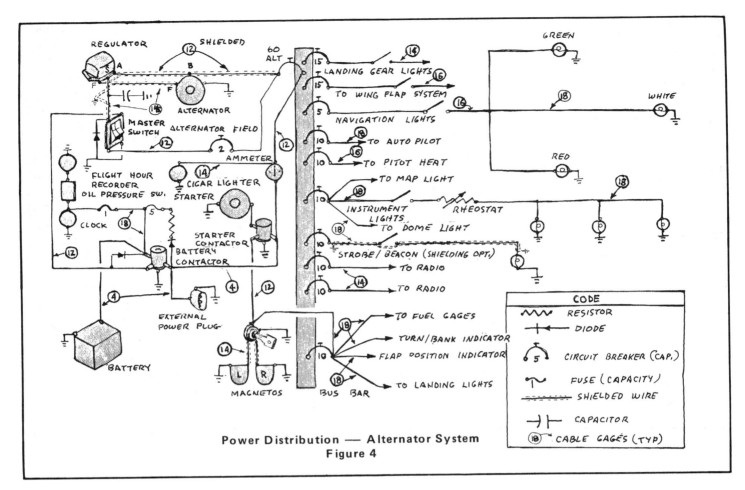

Power Distribution — Alternator System
Figure 4

lightning discharges (what are you doing out in that thunderstorm man?) and in preventing the build up of static charges between parts of the aircraft. This, in turn, eliminates a potential fire hazard.

Bonding also allows the structure to serve as a counterpoise ground for the radio circuit and reduces radio interference from electrical disturbances . . . . especially important in wood and composite structures.

All-wood and composite aircraft require a convenient ground connection in the cabin area. The instrument panel, if made of aluminum, can serve in this capacity. An effective and handy ground terminal may be made as follows. Drill a 3/16-inch hole in the instrument panel in some inconspicious area for the installation of an AN-3 bolt about 1 inch long. Cut extra threads on the bolt and secure it to the panel with a self-locking nut. The extra threaded portion of the bolt protruding behind the panel serves as a convenient attachment point for ground wires terminating in the cockpit area.

Be sure to obtain a good electrical connection to bare metal. It might be worthwhile to install two such ground connectors, one on each side of the panel. Don't forget to run a ground wire from the instrument panel to the engine.

SOME MISCELLANEOUS NOTES

Although we are occasionally confronted with a dead battery, small sportplane engines are so easy to hand start that I see little merit in providing for an external power receptical . . . . just so much more weight going along for a free ride. In view of some of the past severe winters, however, some of our ice country homebuilder/

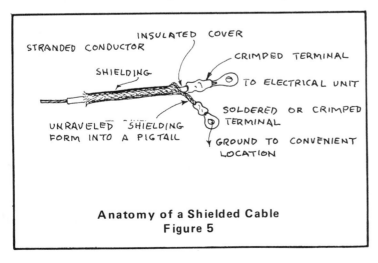

Anatomy of a Shielded Cable
Figure 5

fliers may disagree. If much cold weather flying is done, of course, an external power source could be used to save wear and tear on the battery.

Identify and label each wire at both ends of the circuit using indelible ink and a small tab made of adhesive tape. Even a tab of masking tape is better than nothing. This is particularly advisable for wood aircraft which, of necessity, utilize a two-wire system. Using a black wire for all grounding purposes helps with the identity bit.

When an electric clock is installed, it should be wired so that it will continue to run after all the power has been shut off. You can accomplish this by running the plus cable from the clock to the battery side of the master solenoid. Include a 1 or 2 amp fuse in the circuit.

You will find that most electrical systems include a radio interference capacitor at the alternator. Note also which of the wires are shielded.

In some installations, a silicon diode is used to protect the transisterized radio equipment. When used, the cathode or plus terminal of the diode connects to the battery terminal side of the battery connector. The anode or the negative terminal of the diode connects to the same contactor terminal as the master switch wire. This places the diode directly across the contactor solenoid so that, as one radio whiz phrases it, "inductive spikes originating in the coil are clipped when the master switch is opened."

People sometimes do forget to turn off the master switch after a flight. When this happens, the next time they arrive at the hangar, they find the battery dead. So, the inspiration might come to combine the ignition switch with the master switch function in a single control. Not a good idea because a fault in one system could affect the other.

My own experience leads me to believe that the electrical system can be one of the most trouble-free installations in the homebuilt. Install the proper-size wiring, adequately support it to keep the cables from chaffing, make good connections, and you will be rewarded with a reliable system subject only to the frailities of the store-bought motors and like equipment.

The Battery....What to Do About It

You don't have to try to justify something if you really want it.

Still, many builders find it difficult to decide whether an electrical system is justified for their particular project.

Sometimes this decision is easy to make. For instance, engines like the Continental A-65, the C-85-8, and the VW do not, ordinarily, have provisions for the installation of an electrical system, as there is no place to hang a generator or starter. If your airplane is to have one of these engines, you will have undoubtedly, already concluded that you will not install a battery, and will rely instead on the hand-prop system. However, the fact that a particular engine is manufactured without pads for the mounting of accessories, does not always deter homebuilders. There are homebuilts with VW engines, for example, modified to accommodate a starter and generator. Nevertheless, if the installed engine is one of the smaller basic powerplants, you would normally have to be content without an electric start capability.

It should be acknowledged though, that many homebuilts are flying which could have been equipped with an electric start capability but their builders had decided against such an installation.

An electric start system ordinarily includes a battery, battery case, a relay and/or battery cables and some additional wiring. All of these items cost the builder extra cash, usually in excess of a few hundred preinflation U.S. dollars. In addition, the complexity of the installation for the added electrical capability means construction time will probably be dragged out another month, perhaps more, as shopping and searching for the required parts and materials will take time. Certainly not the least important consequence is the effect of the added weight of the electric system on a homebuilt's performance. A full electrical system, built around a standard aircraft storage battery weighing about 21 pounds (that's right, 21 pounds), will undoubtedly add at least 50 pounds to an engine installation such as for the Continental C-85. (Battery, 21 pounds; starter,

16 pounds; generator, 9.75 pounds; regulator, battery box, solenoid, switch, wiring, etc., easily add another 4 plus pounds).

This being the case, how does one decide whether an electrical system can be justified for a homebuilt?

More arguments, it seems, can be made against the installation of an electrical system than for it. Nevertheless, one big argument for it does carry tremendous clout . . . . SAFETY. Obviously, the principle purpose of the electrical system in a homebuilt will be to supply the electrical energy necessary to start the engine. The danger of hand propping is eliminated.

In the more sophisticated homebuilt, the battery must also be relied upon to operate all of the electrical equipment, like radios, fuel gages, flaps, navigation lights, and whatever other goodies strike the builder's fancy during low engine speeds. And, in the event the generator (alternator) fails, the battery will be important in bringing you down safely.

Of course, during normal engine operations, the generator furnishes the electrical energy for operating all electrical units and the battery just goes along for a free ride.

You will probably be quick to point out that when consideration is given to installing a battery for the sole purpose of providing an electric start capability, the attractiveness of that feature diminishes after the added weight of the storage battery and of its support systems is like-wise considered. It is no wonder, you say, that the builders of small aircraft like the Cassutt and the Pitts forego the "luxury" of a battery installation.

True, but don't be too quick to jump to conclusions. The electric start capability a battery provides to the safety of your aircraft operation cannot be measured in costs or weight alone. Or for that matter, as an undesirable trade-off for a little better rate of climb in some cases.

Not only is the electric starter one very nice luxury, and something of a status symbol, it is, literally, a life saver! There is no doubt about this. Statistics show that your aircraft would be much safer with the electric start capability the battery provides.

BATTERY LOCATION

The battery is heavy, bulky, and the biggest problem it creates is in finding a suitable location for it. After all, a 21-pound object cannot be placed just anywhere in a small aircraft without having a considerable effect on the weight and balance. This could be desirable since the battery can be used as a weight in controlling or correcting the c.g. location.

Three locations are frequently used for battery installations in homebuilts.

1. A firewall location: Whenever the c.g. adjustment is not a factor, the battery should, by all means, be located with consideration for its electrical load and operational requirements. That is to say, because of the high ampere load imposed when starting the engine, a location fairly close to the starter permits the system to get by on a lower ampere capacity. The firewall location allows easy access to the battery for inspection and servicing. The battery cables are short and effective. One difficulty this location presents in single-seaters is the lack of space on the firewall for a battery. This is particularly true where a short engine mount is used. Another drawback is the detrimental effect of heat on the battery when poorly positioned.

2. A cockpit location: The least desirable location for a battery is in the cockpit area, usually between the pilot's feet or behind something builders call a console. A cockpit location is not the best but it is often the only choice in a small single-seater because of space limitations and c.g. considerations. Effective venting of a battery at this location is essential. The routine inspections of the battery may be difficult to accomplish in this location. But there is one advantage worth noting. The battery will, ordinarily have little or no effect on the c.g.

3. The aft fuselage location: A location someplace behind the seat aft of the cabin is quite common for both factory-built and homebuilt aircraft. This location is frequently a compromise to weight and balance as well as space requirements. A battery buried someplace in the dark depths of the fuselage is often not very accessible. The battery in such an installation is likely to receive less attention than it would at other locations. The act of inspecting the battery becomes difficult under the circumstances, and servicing it is likewise awkward. Battery leads being much longer have to be of a heavier size to effectively carry the electrical load. Putting the battery in this location could create a dangerously tail-heavy condition. On the other hand, with bigger engines being installed these days, an aft battery location might provide just the right corrective moment needed.

Aft location of battery is a weight and balance consideration. Unusual mounting is apparently needed to clear control cables.

THE BATTERY BOX

Unlike the auto installation where the storage battery is held in place on a rack by means of a couple of long bolts, aircraft installation utilizes a battery box which is secured to the aircraft structure. The battery, therefore, obtains its security by being fully enclosed in this container. So, before you can even install a battery, you must obtain or fabricate a battery case for it.

These are some of the few extra complications stemming from your decision to have a battery on board.

A durable battery case, bent up from a single sheet of aluminum and riveted together is easy to make. As a matter of fact, making a battery box is a good exercise in sheet metal work and might convince some builders that the next project should be an all-metal one.

A bicycle valve stem salvaged from some kid's bike makes an excellent fitting for the attachment of the vent hoses. Ideally, a battery case is equipped with two such vent nipples. One connection near the top is used to vent the battery through a small plastic or rubber hose to some point in the slipstream where it is exposed to ram air pressure. The other vent nipple is in the bottom area of the box and simply serves as a drain sump outlet which, likewise, is connected by tubing routed to some overboard location. Remember, fumes or spillage draining out of this hose is corrosive and must be conducted away from fabric and metal parts of the aircraft. This dual venting arrangement of the battery box is especially recommended if the battery must be located inside the fuselage.

THE NEW BATTERY

You can, if you like, use almost any battery in your homebuilt provided it has enough capacity to crank the engine. The primary difference between the auto 12 volt storage battery and an aircraft battery is that the aircraft battery has nonspill filler caps. These large plastic caps are hollow with a bell-shaped lead weight inside them that drops down within the cap, closing the vent anytime the aircraft is inverted. It also seals the vent under negative G forces. (Figure 6) Of course, if you can scrounge a set of vented caps you could put them in any other battery you obtain. The vented caps for the battery are essential if the aircraft is semi-aerobatic and may be flown through unusual maneuvers.

A new, dry-charged battery may be kept indefinitely if it is not put into service immediately after purchase by adding the electrolyte. Follow the directions received with the electrolyte, and be careful. Once a battery is activated, no additional electrolyte should be added to it while the battery remains in service. If the electrolyte level falls below the normal while in use, add only distilled water to bring it back up to the proper level. The dry-charged battery will be ready for operation within minutes after the electrolyte has been added. If the battery will remain idle while you work some more on the airplane, you had better charge the battery in accordance with the manufacturer's recommendation.

The electrolyte (sulfuric acid) will burn you if it comes in contact with any part of your body, so be sure you have a plentiful supply of clean water around for immediate washing of the affected area. Acid splashed on clothes makes nice free-form holes in them.

Keep the battery cables as short as practical without imposing undue stress on the battery terminals. Such a strain on the terminals, coupled with engine vibration, can cause the posts to part company with the battery. Anchor cables wherever they come in contact with the aircraft structure. This will prevent chaffing of the cables.

Never connect or disconnect the battery while the circuit is loaded. Arcing at the connections is apt to occur. If at the same time, the filler caps happen to be removed, sparks may ignite the gasses from the cells. So make sure the master switch is OFF before messing with the battery.

It is advisable to always remove the ground cable first when disconnecting a battery. This precaution prevents an accidental shorting of the

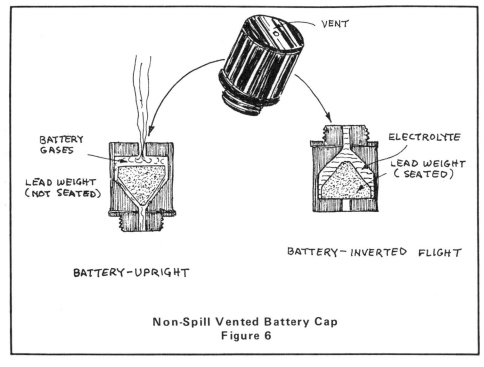

BATTERY GASES

LEAD WEIGHT (NOT SEATED)

VENT

ELECTROLYTE

LEAD WEIGHT (SEATED)

BATTERY — UPRIGHT

BATTERY — INVERTED FLIGHT

Non-Spill Vented Battery Cap
Figure 6

battery to the airframe by tools, wrist watch or whatever metal objects might get in the way. Disconnect the positive terminal last. On reinstalling a battery, reverse the procedure and secure the positive cable first.

To ensure maximum electrical efficiency, the cable ends and the battery posts must be brightened up with emery cloth before hook-up (the lock washer goes on first and then the plain washer, next to the wing nut). After the cables are tightened, coat the cable ends and battery terminals with a lubricating grease.

Should you spill any electrolyte on the external parts of the battery or any place nearby, neutralize its corrosive effects by applying common baking soda (sodium bicarbonate) mixed with water .... about 3 tablespoons to a glass of water. Formula is not critical. (Sodapop is all right but it leaves things a bit sticky unless rinsed). Continue to add the soda solution to the area being cleaned with a brush until all bubbling has ceased. Complete the process by rinsing the area with clean water and wiping it dry.

MAINTENANCE AND INSPECTION

Prevent corrosion from taking place in hard to reach places like the metal seams of the battery box and at the bracket attachments. One of the corrosion-inhibiting sprays such as WD-40 has an excellent penetrating characteristic that is effective as an anti-corrosion treatment if applied periodically.

If you fly the airplane weekly for an average flight time of at least 30 minutes, your aircraft battery should remain in a good state of charge and should serve you well for at least five years. About once a month you should check the level of the electrolyte in each of the cells. The level should not be too high in the cell, but it should at least cover the plates. The water level, if maintained about 3/8-inch above the internal baffle plates, would be just about right. There is a need to check the water level in the battery more often in hot weather than on the cold winter days. If water needs to be added, you need not use distilled water unless your tap water is too hard and would be unsuitable for use in the battery. It is usually a simple matter to collect rain water in some plastic containers and save it for future use in your batteries. It does take a deliberate effort to achieve that goal, however.

Some batteries fail because of electrical problems or neglect, but it is quite probable that yours will serve you well until it gives up from old age.

Battery Box Construction

A few years ago, investigation of a serious accident revealed that one of the elevator control cables had broken at a point adjacent to where the battery was installed in the aircraft. Failure of the cable was attributed to severe deterioration in a localized acid environment . . . . the culprit, the battery. Who would ever think that the battery (used primarily for starting the engine) could develop into the causative factor leading to an accident?

The purpose of relating the incident, of course, is to point up the importance of a good battery case, one that is securely attached to the structure and adequately drained and vented.

A battery box may be purchased, of course. Check your current catalogs of EAA suppliers. A new ready-made box would be a welcome acquisition but if you think the price is a bit expensive for a simple "tin can" that doesn't do anything but sit there, maybe you are right.

Since most of us can spare more time than money, the construction of a battery box seems like an attractive alternative. Before resigning yourself to the task of making a battery box, do not overlook the last ditch hope of locating a second-hand box from some local aircraft salvage. If you could pick one up for a few bucks, it would really be worth it. Don't be too hasty in turning down a box that is bent or slightly damaged. Most such boxes could probably be straightened and refurbished much more easily than a new one could be built. If your potential acquisition exhibits signs of corrosion, you might prefer exercising your option to build one yourself.

As with any component made for your aircraft, try to keep the battery box simple and light. Adequate strength for the function at hand must not be sacrificed, however. Generally, battery boxes are designed and installed so that they are capable of withstanding the G loads to which they might be subjected during the life of the aircraft. These so-called "G loads" are arbitrarily accepted as being 6.6 Gs downward, 3.0 Gs upward, 9.0 Gs forward and 1.5 Gs sideways. Aerobatic aircraft are expected to withstand somewhat

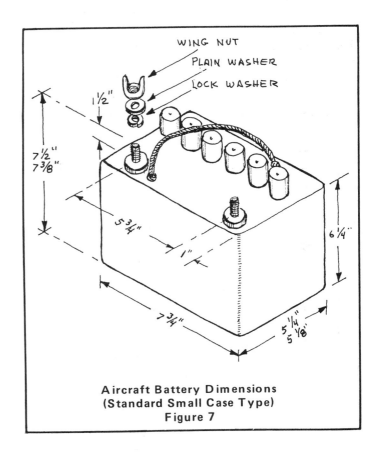

WING NUT
PLAIN WASHER
LOCK WASHER
1½"
7½"
7⅜"
5¾"
1"
6¼"
7¾"
5¼"
5⅛"

**Aircraft Battery Dimensions
(Standard Small Case Type)
Figure 7**

higher G loads, 9.0 Gs downward and 4.5 Gs upward, the other two values remain the same.

To better visualize what kind of a load 6.6 Gs represents, multiply the typical 21-pound weight of a small standard aircraft battery by 6.6. This yields a figure of 138.6 pounds. Similarly, an aerobatic aircraft would be expected to absorb a maximum G load of 189 pounds (21 x 9) downward without failure of the box or its attachments.

These limits can easily be met by either of the two battery box designs illustrated, provided their mounting brackets or racks are properly designed and adequately secured to the aircraft. It is possible to design a battery box that is made from a single sheet, but it would require some very precise measuring and bending.(Figures 8 and 9)

An innovative builder can rig a way to test his battery box installation if he is so inclined.

He could, for example, use shot bags to build up the necessary test loads. Perhaps a hand-held spring scale may be attached to measure the results with you hanging on one end. But then, you might have to call somebody else to read the scale for you. However you measure the potential strength of the installation, be sure that you distribute the load adequately throughout the box and brackets, otherwise it might crack or tear.

A leak-proof battery box illustrated in Figure 9 is much easier to make than you might first believe.

The bottom metal piece is formed around a block with the same dimensions as the battery to be used plus 1/16-inch (5 ¼ inches or 5 1/8

inches x 7 ¾ inches). Cut the block out of ¾-inch plywood or fiberboard. Round the edges to a radius of about 1/8-inch and the corners to an approximate 3/8-inch radius. Cut another rectangular block from ¾-inch stock but make it about ¼-inch smaller in overall dimensions. Except for the corners, the edges need not be rounded as their only use is as a back up for the metal being formed.

The general procedure and forming technique is adequately illustrated and need not be detailed here. A few pointers might be helpful, however. When hammering down the sides of the bottom piece being formed, it is very helpful to press an iron weight or hammer against one side while

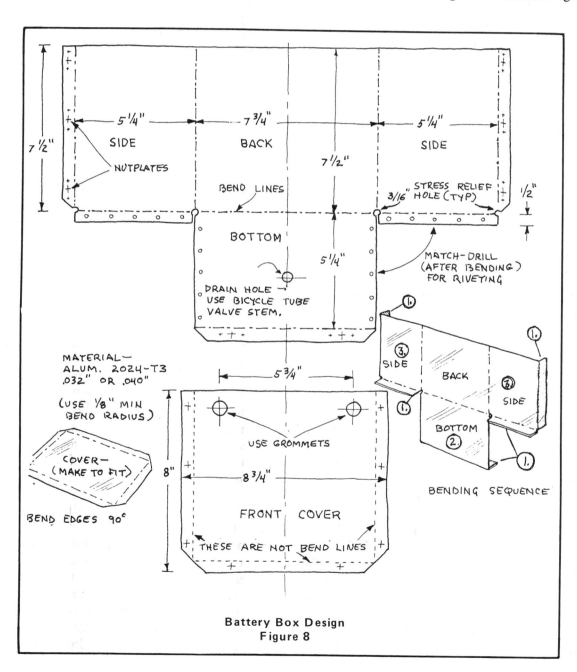

Battery Box Design
Figure 8

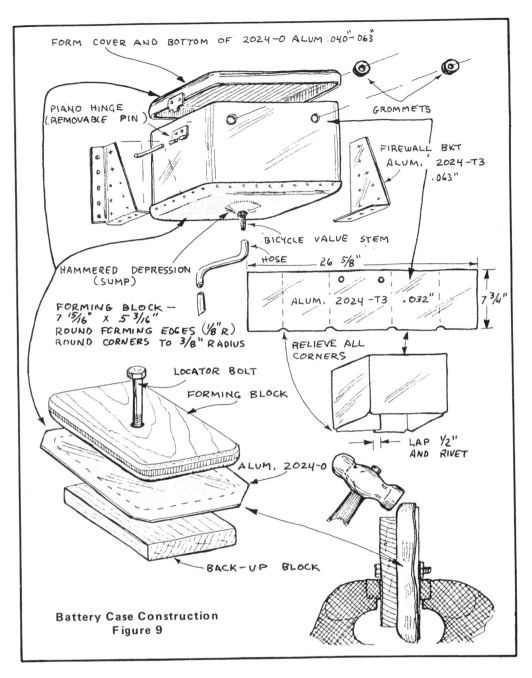

FORM COVER AND BOTTOM OF 2024-O ALUM .040"-.063"

PIANO HINGE
(REMOVABLE PIN)

GROMMETS

FIREWALL BKT
ALUM. 2024-T3
.063"

BICYCLE VALVE STEM

HOSE

HAMMERED DEPRESSION
(SUMP)

26 5/8"

ALUM. 2024-T3 .032"

7 3/4"

FORMING BLOCK —
7 15/16" x 5 3/16"
ROUND FORMING EDGES (1/8"R)
ROUND CORNERS TO 3/8" RADIUS

RELIEVE ALL
CORNERS

LOCATOR BOLT

FORMING BLOCK

ALUM. 2024-O

LAP 1/2"
AND RIVET

BACK-UP BLOCK

**Battery Case Construction
Figure 9**

hammering and stretching the metal on the opposite side. This is particularly true when bending and forming the metal around each corner. You will be able to stretch and shrink the metal around the corners easily enough after a bit of practice so don't worry about it now. The soft 2024-0 or the 6061-0 aluminum sheet is very ductile and formable. The bent up edges for the formed bottom piece and cover for the battery box need only be ½-inch high. This will be sufficient to provide the proper riveting edge distance for the rivets.

After the forming operations are completed for the cover piece and the bottom, trim and file the edges to a uniform ½-inch height. The only other major parts for the battery box are the sides. They are bent up from a single sheet of aluminum to fit inside the formed bottom piece. Note that a radius must be filed into each corner to permit the battery box body to slip into the bottom piece deeper.

It is suggested that the rivet heads be on the inside of the box and that the formed heads be on the outside. Pop rivets may be used to simplify assembly considerably. Regular 1/8-inch aircraft rivets if used may be upset with a hammer. If you have a heavy duty vise, it can be adapted to serve as an anvil for the job. Clamp a section of heavy steel channel, 3 or 4 feet in length (or any other hunk of iron), in the vise

228

so that one end extends about 8 inches from the jaws. Do your rivet setting over this convenient anvil. The reason for using a long piece of metal as an anvil is to make it easier to keep it immobilized while hammering rivets on the short end.

Use a bit of epoxy on the joints in the final assembly and you will be assured of leak-proof and corrosion-proof seams. Before assembling either type of battery box, a small depression should be stretch-hammered into the bottom where the drain hole is to be. This drain location need not be at the center of the bottom but should be in the low spot of the box when installed in the aircraft.

An old bicycle tube valve stem serves as a good drain fitting. Remember to remove and discard the valve core, though. Since the valve stem is threaded, it is a simple matter to secure it to the box with a nut. To complete the drain installation, slip a short section of plastic hose over the installed drain fitting to provide a path for any corrosive battery drippings that might develop. It is important to route this drain hose so that it drains overboard and away from any of the aircraft's structure. Otherwise, the consequences could include a ruined paint job.

Aluminum angles or brackets are used to attach the battery box to the firewall or elsewhere. These brackets are riveted to the battery box and, in some instances, also to the firewall. A few builders, with ease of removal in mind, prefer to attach the battery box to the structure with AN-3 bolts. But this is a personal preference.

It is essential that the battery box lid be easily removable so that the battery can be serviced easily. To secure the cover, use the simplest device possible. For example, how about riveted straps fastened by means of a metal clip or safety pin? Another good fastener is a short section of a piano hinge riveted to the battery case cover, with a removable hinge wire.

At the points where the positive and ground cables enter the box, install rubber grommets or otherwise ensure that the sharp edges of the box will not chafe battery cables.

One final requirement is to paint the box with an acid-proof paint. This paint usually is black and is obtainable from some aircraft service centers. However, the purpose would probably be served equally well if you painted the battery box in some delicate pastel shade using good grade epoxy paint. Wouldn't that make a charming addition to an otherwise drab engine compartment?

To Fly at Night

A majority of the two-seater homebuilts appear to be equipped with an assortment of position (navigation) lights and landing lights. But, anti-collision lights, which are mandatory for night flying, are noticeably absent on many of them. Does that mean none of these airplanes are used for night flying? I wonder.

I wonder also how many of the builders of these same aircraft were jolted at some recent recertification period when they first learned from their FAA inspectors that they could not operate their homebuilts at night because they were not properly equipped.

You know, it seems like only a few years ago all that was necessary on an airplane for night flying in the U.S. was a red navigation light out on the left wing tip, a green one on the right wing, and a white tail light. Alas, this is no longer true. Now, should you want to fly at night, your homebuilt must be equipped to comply with the current FAR Part 91.33c, Visual Flight Rules (night), otherwise the FAA EMDO inspector will not, cannot, amend the aircraft's operating limitations to include that privilege.

NIGHT VFR REQUIREMENTS

What are the requirements for flying night VFR? In addition to your instruments and equipment specified for VFR flight (FAR Part 91.33c) you must install:

1. Approved position lights (many of the current crop of homebuilts already have these)

2. An approved anti-collision light system

3. Spare fuses (unless you have circuit breakers)

4. Finally, and believe it or not this is a requirement, an adequate source of electrical energy

As you know homebuilts cannot be operated for hire, therefore the mandatory requirement for one electric landing light can be ignored.

POSITION LIGHT INSTALLATION

These are the lights most of us think of when we think of installing lights. The entire night flying system is designed around position lights. All other lights must be installed so as not to detract from these.

The forward position lights must consist of a red and a green light, spaced laterally as far apart as practicable. These are installed forward on the airplane so that with the airplane in normal flying attitude, the red light is on your left wing tip and the green light is on the right tip. A rear position white light must be mounted as far aft as practicable. All three lights must form a single circuit so that they will light up simultaneously.

FAR Part 91.33 states that each light must be an approved type. However, I've seen home-made installations where a common automotive bulb (without any cover) was screwed into a socket affixed to the aircraft where it served as a white tail light. A similar arrangement was effected for the wing tip lights except that over each of them was a red or green plastic cover. Be careful though, an installation like that might strike your local FAA inspector as being unsuitable, even under the flexible "amateur-built" classification.

Each of the three position lights must project an unobstructed light pattern of 180 degrees plus or minus 90 degrees vertically. Laterally, the wing tip lights should be visible through a range of 110 degrees left and right from straight forward. The white tail light should cover a range from straight back to plus or minus 70 degrees either side of the tail. Refer to Figure 10 for instant clarification.

Those of you with existing position light installations should check to see if you are getting sufficient light pattern coverage.

The standard E series wing tip navigation light (Figure 11) is highly recommended for any installation as it is small, neat and easy to install. The white tail light often requires some modification of the trailing edge before it can be accommodated. This is one good reason to decide during the construction phase whether lights will be installed.

The navigation lights each have only one wire which runs to the cockpit NAV light switch, circuit breaker (or fuse) and bus bar. The base of the light serves as the ground connection when installed in all-metal aircraft. Installing these lights in wood wings, fiberglass wing tips or composite structures requires the addition of a ground wire. You can do this by soldering a wire to the base of the light and running its other end to the closest grounding point.

ANTI–COLLISION LIGHT INSTALLATION

The requirement for an approved anti-collision light system became mandatory for all powered civil aircraft with Standard Category U.S. Airworthiness Certificates on August 11, 1972.

"Aha," you say, "mine is a homebuilt and not a Standard Category airplane, therefore . . . ." Good thinking amigo, but be advised that the rule has been interpreted as also being applicable to homebuilts. As a matter of fact ALL airplanes flying at night now must have anti-collision lights. Navigation lights alone are insufficient. Homebuilts with operating limitations issued prior to August 11, 1971 can get by with only a token compliance as only 100 ECP (effective candle power) is required to fulfill their anti-collision lighting requirements. On the other hand, any homebuilt whose original operation limitations

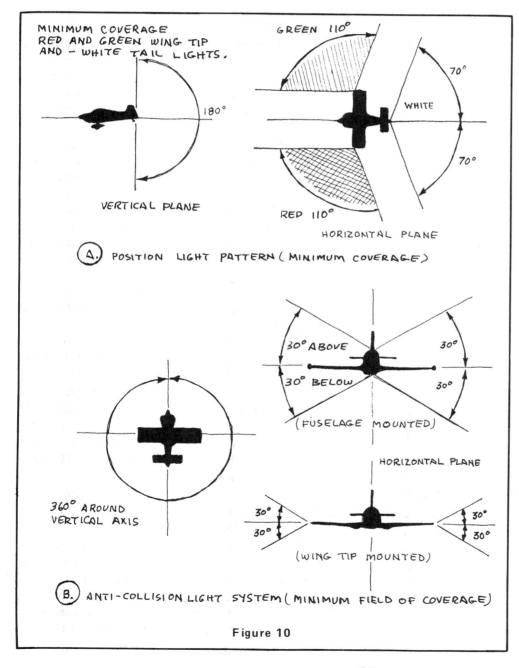

Figure 10

231

A variation of the piggy-back combination of regular
wing tip navigation light and strobe light (top photo).
In bottom photo is home-made wing tip strobe.

Landing lights are not required for homebuilts, but
they are useful if you fly much at night.

was issued after August 11, 1971 must have an anti-collision (strobe) light system that complies with the revised 400 ECP requirement.

Most suppliers of aircraft lighting systems (such as Grimes, Whelen, Aeroflash, etc.) put out a piggyback strobe light modification for the conventional wing tip lights. Installation is simple. All you need to do is drill a ¼-inch diameter hole in the base of each wing tip light for the strobe wires.

Some strobe lights utilize a single power supply unit which can be mounted to any convenient location in the fuselage.

The Aeroflash units employ two small strobe power supply units. One such unit is fastened internally to each wing tip rib. The strobe light tube is connected and assembled to the navigation light housing. A small wire is then run from the strobe switch in the cockpit to each of the power supply units. Of course this type of installation makes it necessary to have access to the wing tip rib. No problem if the tip is a typically removable fiberglass cover. Otherwise, an access hole in the wing will be necessary.

Units commonly sold by Whelen and Grimes use, for the most part, a single power supply designed to flash two wing tip strobe light head assemblies simultaneously or in an unsynchronized manner depending upon the type of power supply unit used. These, however, require the use of

more wires in the installation. Radio interference could also be a factor with the fuselage-mounted power supply. Electrical power requirements of course will increase with the installation of anti-collision lights. A two-strobe light installation, for instance, will draw from 2 amps to 5 amps depending upon the power supply units used.

FLASHING CHARACTERISTICS

Store-bought strobes will flash with a frequency of between 40 and 100 cycles per minute. If you are building your own unit from one of the designs available, be sure that your unit flashes within this flash frequency.

But before you start dreaming of saving yourself a bunch of bucks by using homemade strobe lights, check with your FAA inspector to see whether such equipment is acceptable within his office's guidelines. No use proceeding with an installation that cannot later be approved.

FIELD OF COVERAGE

The anti-collision system must consist of enough lights to illuminate the vital areas around the plane. Specifically, when viewed from a distance as close as 1,200 feet, the strobe lights should be visible from any direction and provide a field of coverage extending at least 30 degrees above and 30 degrees below the horizontal plane of the aircraft. (Figure 10) It is usually unavoidable that small areas of the aircraft will block out the strobes from some angles. This is generally acceptable.

There are different types of installations which will meet the light pattern requirements for an anti-collision strobe light system.

1. The minimum would be the installation of a single anti-collision strobe light on the vertical fin of the aircraft. This may be acceptable for only a few aircraft configurations however.

2. The most practical means of assuring adequate coverage is to add a piggyback type of strobe light to each of the two standard (type E) wing tip position lights. (Figure 11)

3. In most cases when the position lights are enclosed in the wing tips, a third strobe light must be added to obtain the required light pattern. This third light may be added to the tail or to the vertical fin. If mounting space is a problem, some companies sell a combination tail position and strobe light assembly which can be used to replace the original white light.

4. Another common method of obtaining the required coverage is to mount one strobe light to the belly of the fuselage and one to some location on top of the fuselage. Two strobes would be necessary to achieve the required vertical coverage in such an installation.

Great care must be taken when selecting the mounting position for the fuselage top strobe. It must be located on the centerline in order to reduce reflection (on low-wing aircraft). Furthermore, its direct light must not impair the pilot's night vision or otherwise create a disturbing environment in the cockpit. For that matter this caution is also applicable to all other lights.

LANDING LIGHTS

As previously stated, it is not necessary to install a landing light on a homebuilt as it will not be flown for hire. However, is there a night flying homebuilder amongst us who would install a lighting system for his homebuilt and not include a landing light? Maybe, but not likely.

Be sure that it provides enough light to be useful in making night landings. (A sealed beam should put out at least 100 watts.) Also, if landing lights are installed they must not create a dangerous glare for the pilot or reflect annoying flashes off the propeller.

Store-bought aircraft emit a landing light beam spread of approximately 13 degrees horizontally and about 11 degrees vertically. Obviously if this light is to be used primarily for taxiing, a wider horizontal spread is desired to improve peripheral vision. Always place the landing light on a separate circuit, adequately fused to take the rather high amperage flow.

Another consideration. Mounting the landing

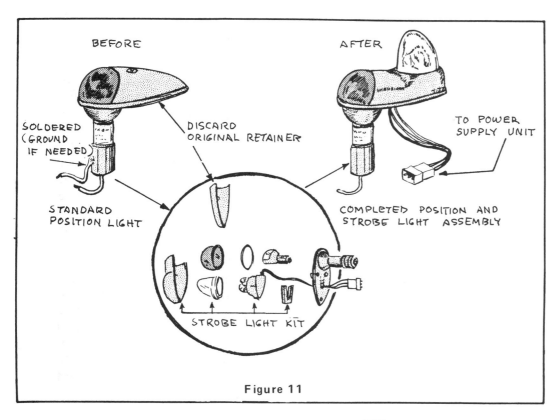

BEFORE
AFTER
SOLDERED (GROUND IF NEEDED)
DISCARD ORIGINAL RETAINER
TO POWER SUPPLY UNIT
STANDARD POSITION LIGHT
COMPLETED POSITION AND STROBE LIGHT ASSEMBLY
STROBE LIGHT KIT

Figure 11

light in the leading edge of a cantilever wing could be risky structurally if the designer has not approved such an installation.

INSTRUMENT LIGHTS

Don't overlook the need for each instrument and control to be easily discernable at night. Potential problems with cockpit lights are direct rays and rays reflected from the windshield or other surfaces which can shine in the pilot's eyes and play havoc with his night vision. Individually lighted instruments are nice, but expensive. Incidentally, don't think for one minute that a cabin dome light can serve as an economical instrument light. Again, night vision would suffer. Regaining night vision after an inadvertent exposure to white light can take just long enough to let you fly into trouble.

OPERATING LIMITATIONS

All your preparations and installations notwithstanding, there must be authorization in the aircraft's operating limitations to fly the homebuilt at night. This authorization or amendment of the operating limitations is worded something like this in my area of the state of Texas.

[X] "... Day/Night flight VFR only when properly equipped."

You will notice from that phrase that the burden of proof that the airplane is properly equipped for night flying will be with the owner and not with the FAA inspector.

If you have an installation problem with the aircraft lighting due to peculiarity of design, I suggest that you refer to FAR Part 23 (23.1381 through 23.1397) for detailed installation requirements and engineering data.

INSTRUMENTATION

9

VFR Instrumentation

Instrument panels in homebuilts are frequently quite different from the usual run-of-the-mill installations. A few are so different that only builder knows where to look to find his readings. This unique display of individuality can be traced to the typical nature of the builder. Building an airplane takes a long time, in whatever relative terms you want to measure it. During this period the builder is continuously on the hunt for materials and equipment for his project. He acquires all sorts of wonderful gadgets and goodies that he could use, will use.

The time arrives for developing the instrument panel layout and suddenly he realizes that he has more instruments than he really needs. He hates to discard anything and often installs several extra instruments merely because he has them. For one thing, an instrument panel that is "loaded" does look impressive, doesn't it? So why not? If the extra weight is not critical and you have the space, you might find it quite pleasurable to give in to your own special need to be just a bit different. It is a lot better to relieve this impulse to be different and experiment with different panel instrumentations than it is to change any of the structure that the designer has carefully worked out and proof-tested to ensure the airplane is a safe one.

If you are not particularly interested in cluttering an instrument panel with goodies, you can simply install the minimum of instruments necessary to get your little sport plane airborne... legally. You are aware I'm sure, that some instrumentation is required by the FAA.

When an aircraft is first granted its airworthiness certificate, the FAA inspector issues a document known as the Operating Limitations. This document details exactly what that airplane will be permitted to do, where, when, and how. This paper also states whether the airplane is to be operated in other than VFR, Day Only flight conditions. That is to say, it is also possible to obtain certification of an aircraft for VFR Day or Night, or IFR.

Regardless of your preference for the type of operating limitations you want approved, the type of flight conditions your aircraft will be permitted to operate under will, essentially, be determined by the type of instrumentation and equipment installed. Of course, the inspector also has to be convinced that the aircraft is capable of performing under the conditions designated.

In other words, the FAA stipulates what instrumentation and equipment is necessary for your aircraft under different flight conditions. Just installing a bunch of instruments will not automatically qualify your aircraft for IFR, or VFR Night Operations, or even plain old VFR, Day Only, if you don't have the right instruments and equipment. (Figure 1)

FAR Part 91 speaks only of the instrumentation required of standard category aircraft, and is silent on the subject of amateur-built aircraft. Nevertheless, Advisory Circular AC 20-27A suggests that your amateur-built aircraft be equipped to conform with the applicable paragraphs of FAR Part 91, Section 91.33 as follows:

VFR DAY ONLY (This is the minimum instrumentation for any aircraft.)

    AIRSPEED INDICATOR
    ALTIMETER
    MAGNETIC DIRECTION INDICATOR (Compass)
    TACHOMETER (For each engine)
    OIL PRESSURE GAGE (For each engine using an oil pressure system)

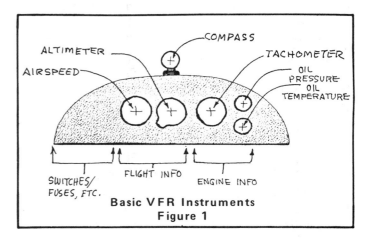

Basic VFR Instruments
Figure 1

The panel at left still has a couple of instruments to be installed. Compass in the panel may be affected by magnetic influences. Panel in center is a little more than minimum. The turn/bank indicator will require an external venturi tube or engine-driven pump. At right is a neat arrangement for a simple, VFR panel.

OIL TEMPERATURE GAGE (For each air-cooled engine)
TEMPERATURE GAGE (For each liquid-cooled engine)
FUEL GAGE FOR EACH TANK
LANDING GEAR POSITION INDICATOR (For retractables)

Incidentally, the FAA inspector usually lists the above instruments as necessary for VFR operations, so in effect, FAR Part 91.33 does apply to the homebuilt too.

THE AIRSPEED INDICATOR

This ordinarily is a store-bought instrument weighing somewhat less than one pound and fits a 3 1/8-inch hole in the instrument panel. It can be obtained to read in kilometers per hour, miles per hour, knots, or a combination of mph and kts. For that matter, you can even make your own airspeed device and calibrate it in yards per hour if you want. The rule requirement is for an airspeed indicator. Most builders are quite content with the usual store-bought gages.

Certainly an airspeed indicator should be capable of indicating the maximum diving speed that the aircraft is capable of reaching safely. However, I think it should also be obvious that an airspeed indicator that reads 0 to 140 mph is more appropriate for a slow sport plane than one that reads 0 to 700 mph. Sensitivity in the lower speed range of the scale is more important than a conversation piece.

THE ALTIMETER

The regular altimeter also fits into a 3 1/8-inch hole. It is usually calibrated to read in feet. For our purpose, altimeters are divided into two basic kinds, the sensitive altimeter and the nonsensitive altimeter. Take the sensitive type if you can

get it. Not because it is more expensive, but because it is far better suited to the light plane. A sensitive altimeter will register even a modest change in altitude while the nonsensitive altimeter will not even move its stubborn hands until you have gained or lost many feet of altitude.

THE MAGNETIC DIRECTION INDICATOR

The only instrument smart enough to tell you where to go . . . .

A regular aircraft magnetic compass will take care of the requirement for a magnetic direction indicator. Homebuilders seem to prefer the small Airpath Compass (C 2300 series) rather than the larger variety, including the WW II surplus stuff.

Although I have seen automotive and boat compasses installed in aircraft, I personally think it is poor economy, if indeed, they are cheaper than serviceable aircraft units. Most FAA inspectors will not permit their use as the primary magnetic direction indicator.

A compass cannot be installed just any place there happens to be space. Finding a good location can present a problem, especially since it must be located where it can be seen and still be least affected by the magnetic influences of the aircraft's steel structure.

If you have a galvanized fuel tank behind your panel, it will affect the compass. If you happen to have a biplane, all of that tubing, cabane struts and wires could generate enough magnetic activity to cause the compass to whirl and gyrate about like a tired belly dancer. Because of this, some builders are locating their compass in the top wing cut-out directly overhead. In other designs, it seems best to locate the compass on top of the instrument panel just behind the windshield. Perhaps the all-wood aircraft builder enjoys the easiest time of it when it comes to installing the compass in a magnetic-free location.

SWING IT

Once you have decided on the best location possible and installed it, it may still not provide satisfactory directional indications until you adjust it by "ground swinging." Here's how it's done:

1. First make sure the fluid in the compass is clean and the level adequate, and that the indicator swings freely.

2. Move the aircraft out to an open area away from the other aircraft, the influence of steel structures, autos, underground pipes, reinforced concrete, etc.

3. Raise the tail to a level flying position.

4. Depending upon the type of compass you have, and before swinging:
   A. Remove the compensating magnets from their chambers, or;
   B. Reset the fixed compensating magnets to neutral positions.

5. Align the aircraft on a magnetic NORTH heading. If necessary, compensate with compensating magnets. NOTE:
   Some airports have a compass rose that is painted on the pavement. Otherwise, use runway number for reference.

6. Repeat for the EAST magnetic heading.

7. Then, turn the aircraft to SOUTH and WEST magnetic headings, and remove half of the INDICATED error by adjusting the compensators.

8. Finally, check readings on successive 30-degree headings through 360 degrees. Prepare a compass-correction card showing correction to be applied at each of those headings.

NOTE: The FAA Advisory Circular (AC 43.13-1) tells you all this should be done with the engine running and in a level flight attitude. That can create a serious safety problem. Don't take any chances if you can't do the thing safely. It might be better to adjust the compass on its cardinal headings with all wheels on the ground and then proof-fly it in the air by aligning yourself with known runway headings at the airport of your choice. It might take longer, but it is practical and safe if you keep your head out of the cockpit and keep your eyeballs on a swivel.

THE TACHOURMETER

Consider installing a tachourmeter, or a "recording tach" as it is often called, rather than a plain tachometer. In addition to showing the engine revolutions per minute that you need to know, it also logs engine hours.

The FAA approves of this method of logging engine hours, as without a doubt it does much for the accuracy of maintenance and flight records. People do forget to log their flight time regularly and accurately and, as a result, many an engine or aircraft is older than the log book record indicates. That advertised, "only 1,245 hours since new" engine might really be closer to 2,000 hours since new . . . . how can you tell? Incidentally, be sure you obtain the right kind of a tachourmeter for your engine. Some are

Quite a bit different than the basic VFR instrument panel, Eh?

right-hand rotation and others are counterclockwise. So always give the engine type and dash number when ordering the instrument. For example, a C-85-12F will take a different tach than will a C-85-8.

THE FUEL GAGE

Any type of fuel gage will be sufficient to satisfy the requirement if it indicates the quantity of fuel in each tank. This means, of course, that the time-honored wire and cork float gage is acceptable. Fuel gages vary more in style, design and installation than any other instrument found on aircraft. Whatever type you use, be sure it has a reasonable degree of reliability and accuracy. If you plan to use a clear plastic or glass tube in the cockpit which shows the level of remaining fuel, I suggest you first check with your FAA inspector, as he may not approve of such an arrangement in the cockpit area because of the possibility of fuel leakage.

THE LANDING GEAR INDICATOR

Although it is hard to visualize an airplane sophisticated enough to have a retractable gear being matched up to minimum instrumentation, it is possible. So, in keeping with that concept, all that would be necessary is just a simple wire or indicator which would show the gear's position.

OPTIONAL INSTRUMENTS

If you want a panel with a bit more utility than the bare minimum VFR instrument requirements, consider adding a turn-slip (turn-bank) indicator. Of course, if you add a turn-slip indicator you will have to install a venturi or a vacuum pump.

High on my priority list of optional instruments are a cylinder head temperature gage, a 0 to 2,000-foot vertical velocity indicator (rate of climb), and a "G" meter. During the early testing stages the cylinder head temperature gage helps reassure you that your cowling, baffles and cooling system are doing their jobs effectively. The rate of climb is a nice, deluxe item, and the "G" meter is very important during the testing period.

NIGHT FLYING REQUIREMENTS

For VFR flight at night, the following equipment must be added to the minimum VFR Day Only instruments and equipment previously listed.

Approved position lights
Anti-collision light system
An adequate source of electrical energy for
   all installed electrical and radio equipment
One spare set of fuses, if fuses are installed
   instead of circuit breakers

NOTE: A landing light is not required except for aircraft used for hire.

FAA says nothing about cockpit lighting of the instruments yet obviously, some provision must be made for that sort of thing. It should also be apparent that approval for night flight operations virtually requires the installation of a complete electrical system including a battery, generator and voltage regulator. Since you are going that far, why not include a starter too? The whole package will mean an additional 40-60 pounds to the aircraft's weight. Would you fly at night often enough to make it worth carrying all that weight around permanently?

From Pitot to Panel

You can develop a well balanced instrument panel by first working out different instrument arrangements on a full-size cardboard pattern. Use cut-out cardboard circles (3 1/8-inch and 2¼-inch diameter) to simulate different instruments. These mock instruments can be labeled, taped in place, and the various combinations studied until you get the arrangement that pleases you. After checking to see that each instrument, as located, does not interfere with any framework or structure behind the panel, you will be ready to cut metal (or plywood). Even large instrument panels, if properly supported, could be constructed of .060-inch 2024 T-3 aluminum or 1/8-inch plywood. Although a single instrument is fairly light in weight, several of them together make a pretty heavy load. So make sure that the panel material does have enough rigidity to do the job. If the aluminum is thinner than .060-inch, or the plywood less than ¼-inch, avoid cutting the instrument holes too close to each other. In addition, the instruments should not be located so close to the top of the panel that they will be partially obscured by the coaming and panel padding.

A panel constructed of .125-inch 2024 T-3 aluminum would be stout all right, but it would also be heavy in spite of all those large holes cut in it for the instruments.

The holes for the instruments may be cut out with a circle cutter, also known as a "fly" cutter (available from most hardware stores). ALWAYS clamp the panel to the drill press. Not doing so is very dangerous. NEVER use a hand-held drill with a circle cutter. Use a slow speed if the hole is being cut in metal and a relatively high speed for plywood.

In the absence of a drill press and a fly cutter, you could drill a series of small holes (3/16-inch diameter) closely spaced around the circumference of each scribed instrument hole. A small cold chisel could then be used to cut between perforation-like holes to remove the metal circle cut-out.

A half-round file will remove the remaining excess metal down to the exact scribed outline. Needless to say, this is doing it the hard way. Of course, if you can obtain the use of an instrument shop's hydraulically operated instrument panel hole cutter, that would be the easy way to do it. Those dies come in two regular sizes. One is for the 3 1/8-inch size and the other for the 2¼-inch instruments.

If you are using automotive oil pressure, oil temperature and ammeter gages, take care. These are only 2 inches in diameter, and you may have to resort to one of the manual cutting processes to accommodate them. Hole cutters may be successfully used for the 2- inch and 2¼-inch holes.

INSTRUMENT GROUPING

It is common practice to group the flight instruments apart from the engine instruments. In the simple VFR panel, you would consider the airspeed, altimeter, and the magnetic compass as flight instruments. They are, therefore, located together except in the case where it would be preferable to mount the compass over the panel. Some pilots like to include, along with the minimum instrumentation, a vertical velocity indicator as a desirable addition to the VFR flight group.

WHEN ARE SHOCK MOUNTS NEEDED?

There is really no need to shock mount most instruments. About the only instruments that are sensitive to shock and vibration are the gyro instruments. Since the airspeed indicator and the altimeter are not gyro instruments, it is not necessary to concern yourself with building the more complex shock mounted panel for a "VFR ONLY aircraft".

Small aircraft, single-seaters in particular, have very little space for instruments and are therefore ideally suited to a simple VFR panel. The lack of space is more of a problem with the builder who is not content with just the minimum instrumentation, even though he has no intention of qualifying the airplane for IFR flight.

THE INSTRUMENT PANEL

If you put your instrument panel too far out into the cockpit, it will add to the difficulty of getting into and out of the airplane. Likewise, if the panel is improperly positioned, getting your legs under the panel may become a problem.

Sufficient hook-up space behind aircraft instruments is often lacking because a fuel tank has been situated immediately behind the panel. Some instruments require a lot of space. Two of these, the vertical velocity indicator and the rate of turn indicator, for example, are each 5½ to 6 inches in depth. An additional two or more inches is needed behind these instruments to allow space for the installation of the fittings and the attachment of hoses or tubes. This means that a total open area of 7 to 8 inches is required behind at least a portion of any well equipped panel.

Sometimes space behind the instrument panel can be gained by mounting the instruments on the front side. If you do install the instruments this way, don't forget to allow an extra length of connecting hose behind each instrument to allow easy removal. Another way to gain that needed bit of extra space, especially for that extra long instrument, is to construct a small false panel that projects from the face of the regular panel.

The magnetic compass and the other instruments are normally fastened directly to the instrument panel using No. 6-32 or No. 8-32 black oxide finish brass (instrument) machine screws. They are about 1 inch in length. If the instrument screws cannot be obtained, use regular brass machine screws and paint the heads black. Somehow these slotted screws just don't look as nice as the cross points. Some instruments have built in nuts while others require the use of a separate nut for each screw. Naturally, you must have access to the back side of the instruments for removable nuts. It is a wise builder who installs nutplates wherever access is difficult.

Don't embarrass yourself by overtightening the screws as the mounting ears on the instruments can be broken if overstressed.

EASY ACCESS FOR MAINTENANCE

There is no such thing as easy access to an instrument panel from beneath. An encounter with any automobile instrument panel should convince you of this. Yet, you will need to assure access for future maintenance. So, why not consider making a completely removable coaming over the instrument and gas tank areas?

Perhaps a fold-down center panel section that is hinged on the bottom by a piano hinge would be the easiest solution.

Or maybe you should make the entire panel easy to remove by installing it with nut plates. This type of installation must include longer wiring and plumbing behind the panel so that you can pull the whole thing out far enough to obtain access behind it for working.

INSTRUMENT CONNECTORS

The problem of determining what fittings are needed for the hook up of the different aircraft instruments becomes even bigger when you have to order them from an aircraft supply house sight unseen. You simply must have the correct "numbers" to get the items you need . . . . the first time you order. (Figure 2)

There really are only a few types of fittings worth familiarizing yourself with when selecting connectors for the static and pitot lines, hydraulic lines, and fuel lines. AN fittings, common to these systems, are standard and are obtainable in easy to recognize aluminum (blue in color) and steel (black). Corrosion-resisting steel fittings are natural in appearance as are brass and nylon fittings. Let's disregard as undesirable all but the aluminum and the nylon (or plastic) fittings in the interest of weight saving and ready availability. Plastic or nylon fittings are desirable for static and pitot connections as very little pressure is involved.

Cessna uses stock nylon connector fittings and polyethylene tubing for their instrument hook ups. Builders will find these fittings readily available in most parts of the country. More so, perhaps than the standard AN and MS types.

The ¼–inch aluminum tubing or the ¼–inch plastic hose is standard for most instrument lines, while the 3/8-inch tubing is the size commonly installed for gyro instrument lines.

If you are not already familiar with them, learn to recognize the two types of threads used on the various connectors. The pipe thread (PT) end of the fitting is the one that looks slightly tapered with a flat or squared off end. This end usually screws into the instrument or other component which will have a 1/8-inch female pipe thread. The other end of the fitting may have a variety of forms. It could have a hose (slip-on) connection, or an external threaded end. Those with the threaded ends are intended for use with a sleeve (AN 819) and a coupling nut (AN 818) which are slipped over the end of the tubing. The tubing must then be flared with a flaring tool.

No matter whether you use the flared aluminum tube or the slip-on hose for the installation, you must still obtain the proper fitting to screw into the instrument to establish a starting point for the pitot and static system hook up.

When ordering fittings always use the specification number for the type of fitting wanted plus the dash number that corresponds to the desired size and material. (Figure 2)

YOU CALL THIS LOGIC?

I don't know who originally dreamed up pipe thread sizes, but they always seemed wrong for what I wanted .... it was always an eighth

of an inch smaller than what I thought I needed. If I wanted a fitting to use with a ¼-inch line, I had to remember that it took a 1/8-inch pipe thread. If I wanted a fitting for a 3/8-inch line, I would have to think twice to convince myself that I really needed a ¼-inch pipe thread!

All standard aircraft airspeed, altimeter and vertical velocity instruments accept a 1/8-inch pipe thread connector fitting, the other end of which is then mated in some manner to a ¼-inch line.

Most of us have no idea how to go about finding a point on the fuselage where a reliable static pressure may be obtained that would be accurate throughout all normal flight conditions. So, unless the designer shows a particular location for such static ports, you may as well run a static line to the same location as the pitot tube and parallel with the ram-air pressure line. The airspeed indicator is the only instrument that

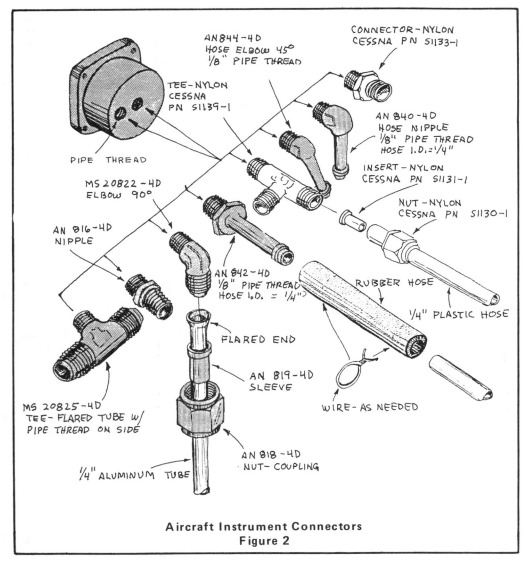

Aircraft Instrument Connectors
Figure 2

requires both ram and static pressures.

Do not locate the pitot tube within the propeller blast area as it will result in inaccurate airspeed indications.

Mounting the pitot tube in the nose of my Flaglor Scooter just under the prop, gave me an astonishing cruising speed indication of 85 mph. Of course, I suspected the validity of that terrific cruise when I became aware that the rotation speed for takeoff was a sizzling 55 mph.

You may find it difficult to decide just where to locate the pitot/static pick-up point. After all, haven't you seen these pick ups located in the leading edge of the wing, under the wing, on the strut, on top of the fin, and who knows where else? Almost anywhere that the flow of air is undisturbed is acceptable.

A pitot head projecting from the leading edge of the wing is vulnerable as it is subject to much abuse on the ground by people (including the owner). It is always being bumped into, bent or broken. A safer location for low-wing aircraft and mid-wing types is under the wing. There, the pitot tube assembly can be mounted about 8 to 12 inches below the wing surface and positioned so as not to protrude beyond the leading edge. Adjust the assembly so that the tubes are aligned parallel to flight.

One tube of the pitot assembly has an open end and admits and conveys ram-air pressure to the airspeed indicator. The other tube is sealed off at its forward end. This closing is accomplished by pinching, welding, inserting a sheet metal screw, or by gluing a plug in with epoxy glue. The closed tube has 6 to 8 staggered No. 60 holes drilled around it. Thus the tube is open to the ambient (static) air pressure. It too is connected to the airspeed indicator by a ¼-inch polyethylene or aluminum tubing. (Figure 3)

A "T" fitting is normally inserted into the static line behind the instrument panel and the static pressure for the airspeed indicator is shared with the other static pressure instruments — the altimeter and the vertical velocity.

Some builders (ugh) install the altimeter and the vertical velocity indicator with absolutely no static line connections. They are merely attached to the instrument panel. The instrument's static opening in the rear is left open to the cabin or cockpit atmosphere. This is sloppy practice even for a strictly VFR Putt-Putt, and provides, at best, very nervous and inaccurate gage readings. For example, in such an installation, when a cabin ventilator is opened or closed, the vertical velocity indicator will immediately indicate an unwarranted descent or climb.

HOOKING UP THE SYSTEMS

Before permanently connecting the pitot and static lines, blow them out to be sure that there are no obstructions or workshop varmints hiding in them.

Never blow into any instrument, as it may be damaged. So, before blowing out the lines, be absolutely sure they are disconnected from the instruments.

Leaks, obstructions, or even moisture in the pitot system will generate false airspeed indications while similar problems in the static system will likewise affect the altimeter and the vertical velocity readings.

Static pressure ports (holes), where built into the fuselage sides, should be flush with the fuselage skin, as an airflow disturbance in that area at cruise can cause false airspeed readings. After connecting the static lines to the static ports, route the first 2 inches of the static line upwards (vertically) from the static ports to make it difficult for water to enter the lines.

The plastic hose or aluminum tubing used in connecting your system, should be installed in a single continuous length. Any required connections (i.e. wing, fuselage juncture) should be

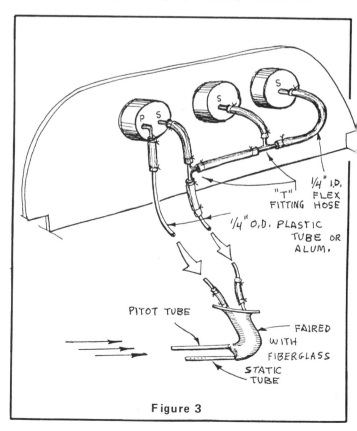

Figure 3

highly accessible.

Secure each line at sufficiently close intervals to prevent the possible development of future air leaks from the abrasive effects of vibration on unsupported lines.

Ordinarily, in assembling pitot-static connectors there is no need to use a thread lubricant or sealer, as the pressures involved are very low. If necessary, use it sparingly and apply it only to the male threads of the assembly.

While all of this cut-and-try installation work is going on, do not overlook the need to protect your instruments. Treat them gently. Cap all open lines and cover each instrument opening with a plug, or tape over the holes with a bit of tape until permanent installation is made.

VENTURI REQUIREMENT

Install just one gyro instrument and you will have to provide a drive system to operate it, either electrical or vacuum. In most cases, that single gyro instrument would be a vacuum-driven rate-of-turn indicator, and the vacuum system would turn out to be a short tube connecting the instrument to an externally mounted venturi tube. A standard small venturi will operate the rate-of-turn indicator satisfactorily for the VFR airplane as this instrument requires less vacuum to operate than any of the other gyro instruments.

The venturi, if used, is mounted on the fuselage in the path of the propeller slipstream. It is obvious that an externally mounted venturi causes drag, but how much? Well, it has been estimated that the drag from the larger venturis could cost you at least 5 mph in the cruise speed of faster aircraft. If that penalty is too stiff to pay, you will have to do without the rate-of-turn indicator or consider converting to an engine-driven vacuum system and pay the alternative price of higher cost and complexity in the aircraft. However, it seems hardly justifiable to install an engine-driven vacuum system just for a single gyro instrument in a VFR Day Only category sport plane.

INSTRUMENT PANEL FINISHES

Clear-grained birch or mahogany plywood makes a nice looking panel. However, mounting instruments in a wood panel requires some special attention in the finishing of the hole cut-outs, as the instruments will appear to be recessed. The recessed look might be just what you want, but if the holes are roughly cut, the entire effect will appear crude.

Wood grain in a plywood panel takes on a very attractive hue when finished with several coats of satin sheen polyurethane varnish. Glossy varnish can also be used and the gloss removed (if objectionable) by rubbing the panel with pumice stone or rottenstone. There is no reason, however, why plywood panel cannot be painted if that is your preference.

Some builders like the effect created by a panel overlay, as it hides the cluttered appearance of the mounting screws. A simple overlay may be made from imitation wood grain formica sheet or from one of the many special decorating materials now available. Check with the parts departments of the Big 3 automakers, they may stock instrument panel overlay material.

Traditionally, instruments have a dull black finish and luminous dials. However, the builders are gradually getting away from the dull basic black panel and are beginning to use more pastel shades of gray, green, blue, buff, etc. An attractive panel can be created by using crinkle paint finishes. Take care though, as some of these spray can finishes are very difficult to apply uniformly. Often the resulting finished rough surface makes it difficult to attach those nonaesthetic, but necessary identification labels. Such handmade labels, you should realize, will not stick very well to a rough textured finish.

A beautiful smooth panel texture can be obtained by using regular spray enamel over a properly primed surface. After a couple of good spray coats of enamel have been applied and properly cured, the finish should be rubbed down with a damp rag or sponge sprinkled with pumice stone or rottenstone powder. This fine abrasive rubbing removes the gloss finish and leaves a smooth satin sheen finish free from glare.

LETTERING AND PLACARDS

For really sharp lettering for your aircraft and instrument panel, try transfer sheets like INSTANTYPE or DECA-DRY.

These sheets of letters may be purchased at most art or office supply houses. The lettering comes in a multitude of sizes and styles. Each sheet contains the alphabet and numbers 1 through 0. The sheet has about three sets of each number and letter, depending on its frequency of use in the language of our country.

Using these letters is simple. All you have to know is how to spell. The letters from the sheet can be transferred to any smooth surface. To placard the instrument panel, for example, place the sheet on the panel and slide it around until the letter you want is where you want it on the panel. Then rub the letter, using a smooth hard object such as the back end of a ballpoint pen, knife handle, or rounded dowel. The letter will then be transferred to the panel. Move the sheet until the next letter is in place and rub it off the sheet. There is a small line under the letter which will help in alignment of the lettering. Caution! — if you don't want that line transferred to your panel, don't rub over it.

There is another form of lettering called ARTYPE. It too comes in a myriad of styles and sizes. However, it is a bit more difficult to use as each letter must be cut out of the sheet. The cut-out scrap containing the letter is then placed in position and rubbed to stick it down. Lettering can be further protected by spraying with clear varnish. Perhaps you had better test clear sprays on a sample first to make sure it doesn't curdle the letters.

You might call this a VFR deluxe panel. Flight instruments are grouped in the top portion; engine instruments are below.

LANDING GEAR

Controlling Alignment

Misalignment of the gear may not be very noticeable, but it can result in some mighty exciting runway performances during the high-speed taxi tests and particularly before and after that important first flight. Some builders proclaim the wisdom of adding a tiny bit of toe-in, while some others say a dab of toe-out is best. Some like camber, others don't. Regardless of which school of thought you subscribe to, the least you can do is to assure yourself that both wheels have the same amount of whatever it is you want.

Some landing gears and wheels cannot be adjusted. The axles, being welded to the struts, likewise cannot be adjusted. This type of gear needs to be properly aligned and jigged before welding. To accomplish this the airplane has to be raised to a level attitude and a reference or centerline established on the floor to provide guidance in jigging the gear for the alignment and welding.

Other landing gears using the vertical strut and scissors arrangement can often be adjusted to a degree by adding or removing washers from between the scissor elbow hinge (scissor elbow hinge!?)

The tapered steel whip rod gear is another that has to be jigged very accurately before the welding is attempted, as it too lacks a means of adjustment after installation.

The spring steel gear is a popular installation, and it has the additional attraction of being ground adjustable.

Of course, no matter what type of gear installation you use, every attempt should be made to ensure accurate alignment at the very outset. At any rate, you can easily adjust the toe-in and camber on a spring steel gear in accordance with design recommendations. In the absence of any such guidance, it is suggested that the best alignment is one that gives you a zero toe-in and a zero wheel camber at normal gross weight. The proper amount of camber is especially important with spring steel gears.

If your aircraft is larger than a single-place job, but you normally fly alone and at less than gross weight, you might want to adjust your wheel camber **to give** a zero angle reading at this lesser operating weight to reduce wear along the outer edge of the

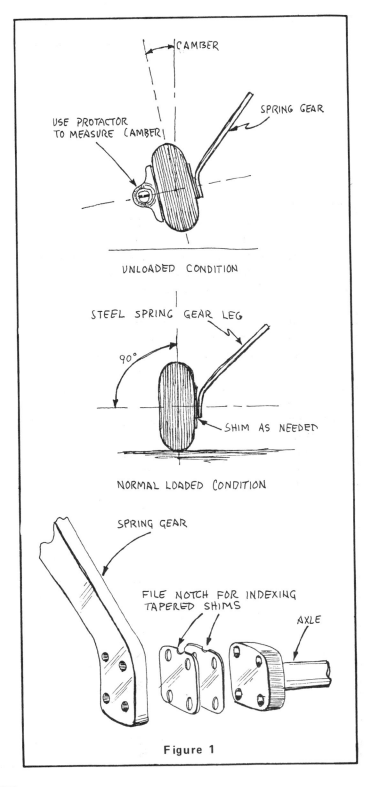

USE PROTRACTOR TO MEASURE CAMBER

CAMBER

SPRING GEAR

UNLOADED CONDITION

STEEL SPRING GEAR LEG

90°

SHIM AS NEEDED

NORMAL LOADED CONDITION

SPRING GEAR

FILE NOTCH FOR INDEXING TAPERED SHIMS

AXLE

Figure 1

tires. (Figure 5)

To make these adjustments, tapered metal shims are used to obtain the exact alignment and camber desired. After you have driven yourself batty trying different combinations of shims to get the wheels aligned the way you want them, you may be receptive to a suggestion. Index or mark the shims. Installation in exactly the same position will then be guaranteed. Make your index marks by using a small rat–tail file to cut a small groove across the top of all the shims. File the notch off-center so that the shims cannot be inadvertently reversed in assembly. Use one notch for the shims in the left gear, and two notches across the shims for the right gear.

Any time in the future that it may be necessary to remove the axle from the gear leg, the shims will already be marked, assuring rapid and positive reassembly. This, of course, will guarantee that your wheel alignment is not disturbed any time you have to remove a wheel and axle.

Level the aircraft, and establish a centerline (use a taut string or draw a line on the floor).

Hang a plumb bob from the centerline of the firewall and from the tail end of the aircraft to ensure that the airplane is aligned with the line on the ground.

Obtain a couple of straight-edge strips of wood, and clamp one straight-edge against the outside rim of each wheel. If the tires hold the straight-edge away from the wheel rims, use short wood blocks as spacers. Your straight-edge must contact the wheel rim in two places. (Figure 2) I guess a fairly accurate job can be done by clamping the strips directly to the tires also.

Using a steel tape, measure the distance A and A'. If both of the distances are the same, the wheels are parallel with each other and aligned — although they are not necessarily in alignment with the aircraft centerline.

To make sure that the wheels are aligned with the centerline of the aircraft, measure the distances B and B'. When both measurements are identical, your alignment is correct. Both checks must be made.

You will notice that I have avoided saying anything about toe -in or toe-out. For my part, I shoot for a perfect alignment of both wheels to the aircraft's longitudinal axis.

These measurements must be made with the gear clamped in position and prior to drilling the landing gear attachment holes to ensure proper accuracy. If, in spite of all the care you exercise, the gear alignment is slightly off, it may sometimes be possible to make fine adjustments through the use of shims, spacers, or washers, depending upon the gear design being used. Just take your time. Double check everything, and always measure twice before drilling once.

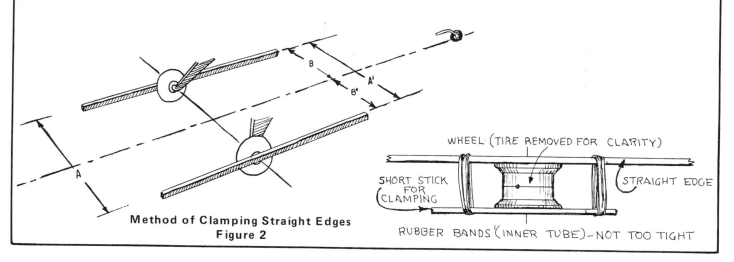

Method of Clamping Straight Edges
Figure 2

WHEEL (TIRE REMOVED FOR CLARITY)

SHORT STICK FOR CLAMPING

STRAIGHT EDGE

RUBBER BANDS (INNER TUBE)—NOT TOO TIGHT

Bungee and Spring Shock Absorber

Not long ago, I received a phone call from one of the FAA inspectors who asked if I had anything on how Bungee cord was supposed to be secured. It seems that a builder of a Starduster Too intended to use Bungee cord for the landing gear of his bird.

Well, the subject was as common as old hat years ago, but like everything else that is simple, the exact details kind of slip the mind. After a persistent search, however, I did finally find a couple of brief references to Bungee cords in my own library and was able to pass on the information. Incidentally, the proper name is Shock Absorber Cord. I wonder where the old timers got the word Bungee?

Anyhow, now that this common knowledge has become too uncommon, it might be a good idea to rediscover this simple art and duly record it for the benefit of future builders.

SHOCK ABSORBER CORD AND RINGS

Shock cord is nothing more than a rope of rubber strands tightly encased in a woven fabric cover or stocking to protect the rubber strands from the detrimental effects of oil, fuel, sunlight, and other hostile environmental conditions.

The weave of the fabric covering material is such that when the shock cord is subjected to tension, the weave spreads open, permitting all of the load to be carried by the rubber core and not by the fabric casing.

Shock cords may still be purchased, even in this aerospace age, from a number of parts suppliers. One reason it is still available is that it is a standard item for a lot of the older store-bought aircraft. Shock cords for these old birds are available in preformed standard size rings. Naturally, it is quite an advantage to be able to adapt for your use a standard shock ring as used on the Piper J-3 or any of the other older aircraft, as it is already formed to the exact size, and you have no terminal eyes to make. This permits a quick, easy installation. If you are designing your own installation, don't overlook such an opportunity to simplify your work.

WHAT SIZE SHOCK CORD?

Well, later model J-3 Cubs and the Aeronca 15-AC use a preformed 8-inch shock ring that is made of ¾-inch cord, which supposedly will test as high as 950 pounds. The older pre-war Taylorcraft uses a skinnier 9/16-inch x 9-inch shock ring, and it tests to 400 pounds. So, unless your airplane is much heavier than either of these, the shock cord you need for your aircraft could probably be met by any size from ½-inch to ¾-inch in diameter.

Those builders who cannot use any of the standard shock rings because of the design of their gear can make their own shock cords to whatever length is needed. There may be an installation where standard ring shock cord would not work anyway, so be pre-

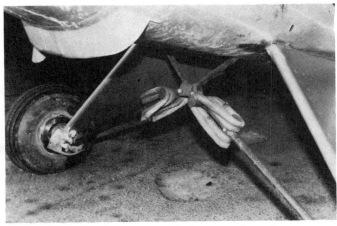

The original J-3 Cub gear with Bungee adapted to homebuilt use.

A J-3 type gear with compression springs substituted for Bungee shocks. Advantage is less drag.

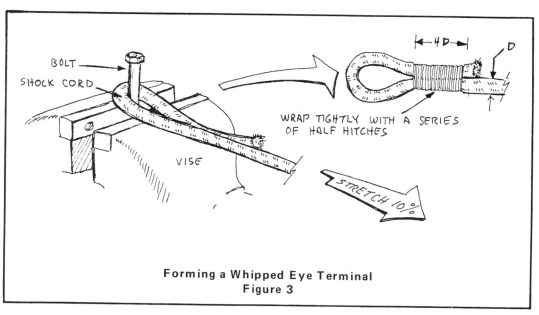

Forming a Whipped Eye Terminal
Figure 3

pared to form your own with an eye terminal or loop on each end of the cord. When installed, the shock cord should be looped tightly around its anchor points on the gear, since it must support the static weight of the aircraft while on the ground without sagging. So measure the length accordingly.

FORMING A TERMINAL LOOP

After you have determined the length required, the eye terminal is formed on each end by stretching the cord around a bolt or a short piece of tubing clamped in the vise, and whipped as shown in the drawing. (Figure 3)

The cord should be stretched about 10 per cent of its original condition while you or your helper whips (serves) the shock cord with rib stitching cord or some equivalent substitute.

It is important to ensure that the shock cord is stretched somewhat during the whipping operation, otherwise the free end of the eye (loop) will, under working conditions, pull out from the served terminal. You say you don't know what whip and serve mean? Well sir, that is old time talk for tightly wrapping an object, a rope or a fishing pole, for example, with a cord or string for strength and protection. Oh yes, make sure the terminal loop formed will be large enough to slip over its anchor points on the airplane.

Do the whipping with regular rib stitching cord using a half-hitch with each turn of the cord. What's a half-hitch you say? Aw, come on, fellas.

The completed serving should be about 2 inches long on ½-inch diameter Bungee cord. Years ago, to protect the completed serving, the served ends of the shock cord were given a couple of coats of clear dope. I think a better treatment would be a good coating of polyurethane varnish.

The excess end of the shock cord remaining after the serving is completed, can be trimmed with a stiff-backed single-edge razor blade, using a sawing action. Slip a piece of cardboard between the two cords to guard against slicing into the cord you intend to use.

SHOCK CORD FASTENERS

There is another way to form a terminal eye. A neater, less bulky installation is possible if you use those store-bought cone spring hooks and locking rings for your terminal fasteners instead of fashioning the whipped loops. (Figure 4)

The fasteners come in different sizes, as the cones must fit the cord. No special tools are needed to form the terminal on the shock cord with these shock cord terminal fasteners.

The buyer has the option of purchasing shock cord from surplus sources. But be careful that you don't buy stock left over from the Civil War. Buy old cord, and you will have to replace it sooner than you'd like.

The manufacturer weaves colored strands into the fabric cover of the shock cord to serve as a code identifier for the date of manufacture. The code is simple and quite clever, as the color of the identifier strands are changed for each year of manufacture. The color code covers a 5-year period before it repeats itself.

It works like this: Three colored threads are woven into the shock cord's fabric cover. Two of these threads are of the same color and they identify the year of production. The third thread is a contrasting color and represents the particular quarter of the year in which the shock cord was manufactured. Of course, the system has a built in trap for

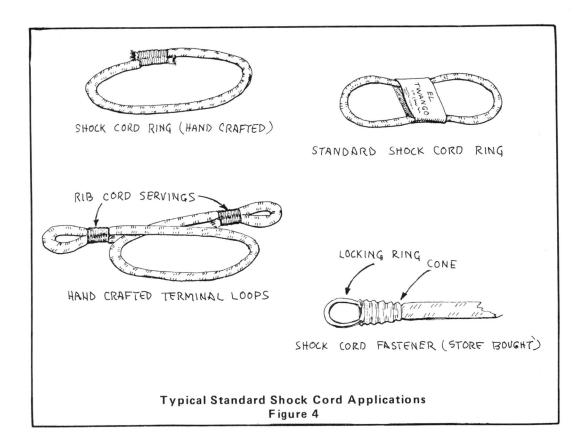

Typical Standard Shock Cord Applications
Figure 4

the surplus buyer, as he can't tell whether his cord is 5, 10, 15, 20, or 30 years old. (Remember, the code repeats itself each 5 years.) Obviously, a close inspection of the rubber strands making up the core is in order. A sample pulling and breaking of one or two of the strands protruding from the end of the Bungee cord may give you a rough idea of the life left in the shock cord, but maybe not. See chart below.

While shock absorber cord is listed as Specification MIL-C-5651A, Elastic Exerciser Cord (Specification MIL-C-5650) may be mistaken for it, as it is similar to the standard shock absorber cord. You can easily identify this type of cord since its 4-color threads differentiate it from the 3-color thread of the standard shock cord. Otherwise, the same color coding applies.

In addition to being able to see the difference between the two cords, you should know that the exerciser cord is used primarily as an opening elastic on parachutes and for other applications where a shock absorbing cord of low initial tension is required. I am told that exerciser cord will test to only 50 per cent of the load that the regular shock absorber cord is capable of taking. So if you use exer-

SHOCK ABSORBER COLOR CODE

	Year Marking *		Quarter Marking		
YEAR	THREADS	COLOR OF THREADS	QUARTER	THREADS	COLOR
1979	2	yellow	Jan., Feb., March	1	red
1980	2	black	April, May, June	1	blue
1981	2	green	July, Aug., Sept.	1	green
1982	2	red	Oct., Nov., Dec.	1	yellow
1983	2	blue			
1984	2	yellow			

*NOTE: Code Repeats Itself Each Five Years

ciser cord, you must consider this and evaluate your own requirements. For example, this type of shock cord might be suitable for securing the nose ends of the skis for winter flying.

Although unused shock cord might look as good as new, most mechanics would not purchase stock that has been in storage more than 18 months. I suppose that automatically rules out a lot of surplus stuff.

COMPRESSION SPRING SHOCKS

Another neat little shock absorber installation is the compression spring type found on a good many of the Miniplanes. It is quite effective and, unlike the Bungee installation, presents a much smaller frontal area (less drag). Best of all, it is not difficult to make. However, how the thing works seems to be a puzzle to many, so it is not surprising that a number of builders have expressed an interest in its details.

The basis of the device is the heavy compression spring 2 inches in diameter and about 8 inches long. (Sorry, but I don't know of a current source of supply for these springs.) This type of shock is suitable for most any light, single-place job which utilizes a "Cub" type welded tube gear.

It seems to work quite well, and outside of a dab of lubricant now and then, doesn't require much attention in service.

An opportunity recently presented itself for me to examine the discarded upper and lower tubes of

such a gear. Except for a slight elongation of the pin or bolt hole in the upper end of the smaller tube, there was no other sign of excess wear. This particular unit, in service for about 3 years, had to be replaced because it had been subjected to a rather uncoordinated and unplanned ground loop.

The drawing illustrates and identifies the various parts. The most important thing to remember in its assembly is that the spring and sliding collar must be slipped onto the upper tube before both the lower spring retainer washer and upper attach bushing is welded in place. (Figure 5)

The tubing size to use would, of course, be influenced by the gross weight of the aircraft. The sizes used on the strut inspected appeared to be (4130 normalized steel tubing) ¾-inch x .065-inch for the lower tube, and 7/8-inch x .052-inch for the upper tube. The sliding collar can be machined from a single piece or welded up from a short length of 1-inch x .058-inch tube and a heavy steel washer. Steel washers may be cut out of 1/8-inch 4130 stock if commercial 2-inch washers cannot be located. The width of the 1¾-inch long slot should be only sufficient to permit the easy sliding action of the 5/16-inch AN bolt. Naturally, the two tubes comprising the shock strut should also have an easy slip fit with each other. Study the drawing. The idea is simple in spite of the confusing fact that the struts are usually subject to tension loads, and yet, the shock works through a compression loading of the spring.

Bungee shock absorber as installed on a retractable gear amphibian.

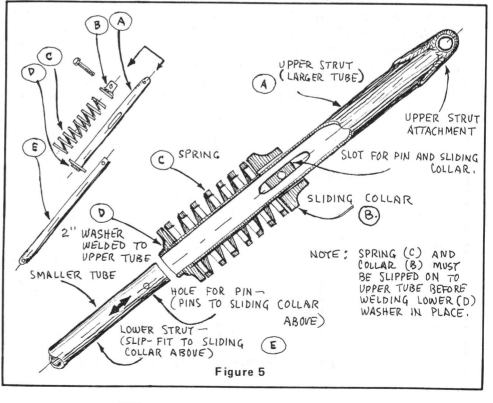

Figure 5

255

A Bit About Brakes

Every airplane should be equipped with brakes. There never seems to be any doubt about this in the builder's mind when he is building a fast or a sophisticated aircraft, but just let him start on an antique, a minimum-type of bird, or an ultra-light, and he begins questioning the worth of a brake installation. Why? There should be no doubt at all! All aircraft should have operating brakes. The days of yesteryear with their unimproved sod fields, sparsity of people and planes, provided a different environment and operating situation. Those were times when airplanes landed in a three-point attitude at 30 or 40 miles per hour under calm conditions with the tail skid acting like a dragging brake. It even took plenty of rpms to taxi under such conditions with the skid digging into the turf. Now, with tail wheels, or any other arrangement of ball bearing-equipped wheels, the airplanes roll nice and easy. They are much harder to slow down and stop on pavement. Not only that, but with many other expensive airplanes parked all around the area, you have a liability problem to think about too. It could ruin your whole day to roll helplessly into a parked Cessna 310 with your brakeless Splinter Sport Special (even leaning back hard won't get you stopped).

THE BRAKING PRINCIPLE

The essential ingredient in any brake system is controlled friction, that is, if you can cause some object (brakeshoe) to rub against some part of the rotating wheel assembly with some degree of control, you have the makings of a brake system. The principle of operation of all brakes is essentially the same. The only real difference is in how the force is applied to the brakeshoe or puck.

TYPES OF BRAKE SYSTEMS

For our purposes, all brake systems can be divided into two groups, mechanically operated systems and hydraulically operated systems. Either type does a commendable job for you if properly installed and adjusted. Although some people think mechanical brakes are cheaper, there is usually no denial that they can be more complex to install and to adjust.

MECHANICAL BRAKES

Sometimes I wonder if installing mechanical brakes is less expensive when you add to the initial cost of the brake unit, the linkage and the welded brackets, cables, levers, and all the pulleys required to complete the installation. There are always some exceptions, naturally.

One of the simplest installations is the type employed on some gyrocopters and on some of the early Jeannie Teenies. A single pivoted shoe was installed over the nosewheel tire. By means of a lever and a control cable to the cockpit this pivoted shoe could be forced against the rotating tire, causing considerable friction and a braking action. The amount of braking action naturally is limited, as only one wheel is usually involved in such a rig. It is reasonably effective for the gyrocopters but its worth on a fixed-wing aircraft is debatable. Still, even this type of installation is better than nothing. Aircraft equipped with single ignition engines (VWs and other automotive types) do not require run ups at higher rpms for the purpose of checking the mags. If the engine is running, you are already checking the one and only magneto, so who needs heavy braking action?

A better system of mechanical brakes is the individually operated brakes with units attached to each main wheel. Go-Cart wheels and brakes are being used in increasing numbers on low-powered single-seaters now being built. These are quite effective for such light airplanes. These brakes are of the expanding

A mechanical brake installation. Lever is operated through a sheathed motorcycle brake cable.

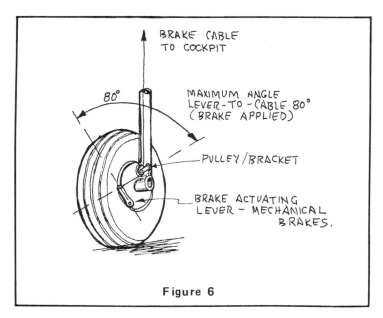

Figure 6

shoe type, with a simple brake drum bolted directly to the wheel.

The brake actuating lever on mechanical brakes usually operates equally well when moved in either direction, therefore, you do have some choice as to how it is positioned in the wheel. After the brake cable is attached to the lever, you will notice that no matter how it is positioned, an immediate and major change in direction in the cable must be made to route it up the gear leg. This means that the builder must install a pulley at this point. It also means that a bracket to mount the pulley must be welded or bolted to the lower landing gear leg at just the right angle to route the cable from the control lever around the pulley and up the landing gear leg. (Figure 6) If the change in direction of the lower gear leg is not severe, it may be possible to use a copper tube brazed to the gear leg to accomplish the minor deflection. Motorcycle shops have plenty of brake cables and throttle cables, enclosed in good housings, that can be adapted. A 1/16-inch or 3/32-inch aircraft extra-flexible control cable may also be used. At the point where the brake cable enters the fuselage another pulley will be required. It too should be aligned and installed to take a considerable amount of the load. If you plan beforehand, you might be able to install the brake cable with as few as 3 pulleys per brake unit. The pulleys should be the ball bearing, heavy duty kind with a diameter of about 1 inch, certainly less than 1½-inches.

Mechanical brakes can be operated individually by pedals, or collectively by means of a single brake handle. In my opinion, the individually activated installation is more effective and desirable. Though it's not as important with tricycle gear installations as with tail draggers, individually operated brakes al-

ways provide better control.

The cockpit end of the mechanical brake system usually terminates at individually heel-operated pedals. I don't believe I have ever seen an installation of mechanical brakes hooked up for toe pedal operation. The complication is that the movement of the rudder pedal makes it difficult to avoid exerting an unwanted pulling force on the actuating cable. This could be minimized if the brake cables were routed around a pulley mounted close to the brake pivot point and then to a lever attached to the hinged toe pedal. I don't know how effective it would be, but it should work. (Figure 7)

The main problem with any mechanical brake system is in routing the brake control cable as directly as possible from the wheel to the brake pedal, using the minimum number of pulleys and changes in direction. To obtain the most effective force at the brake lever mounted at the wheel, the cable should be attached so as to pull at a 90-degree angle to the brake actuating lever. Actually, to apply an efficient force, the angle between the actuating cable and the brake control lever should not be over 80 degrees when the brake is fully applied.

The brake cables must be as friction-free as possible, and the brakes should release with a snap (figuratively speaking) to the off position. Mechanical brake systems may seem simple, but unless they are properly installed, the builder could be bothered with such things as cable stretch, play, and slack in the system. Any such deficiency would make the braking action pretty poor.

To show you that there is practically nothing

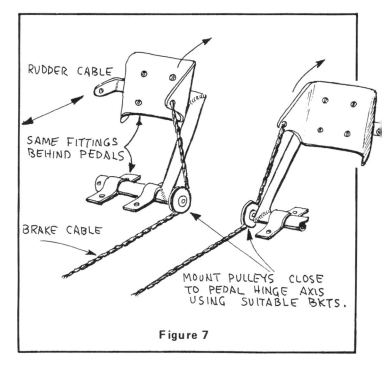

Figure 7

Aviation progress was set back 50 years when builder discovered the hand lever-operated mechanical brake (left photo). At right, same builder progresses 10 years with discovery of a parking brake potential for the hand lever brake system. Progress is where you find it!

new under the sun, take a look at the highly improved version of the Stagecoach or Conestoga wagon brake installation on my Scooter. (See photos)   The system is absolutely foolproof and reduced to stark simplicity. It has to be the simplest aircraft brake system ever devised . . . . with an integral parking brake installation yet! Just reach out and grab hold of the brake handle you want to use and pull back on it. For parking, reach out and pull both aft. Wedge them into the parking notches at the fuselage and there you have it. Unfortunately, the design is not worth patenting as it can only work on one aircraft design that I know of . . . . the Scooter.

HYDRAULIC BRAKE SYSTEMS

The usual hydraulic brake system makes use of one master cylinder mounted at each of the rudder pedals, the necessary connecting lines, a brake assembly in each of the main gear wheels, and a hydraulic fluid reservoir, if necessary. Depending upon the type of master cylinder used, a separate hydraulic reservoir may be installed. (Figure 8)

MASTER CYLINDERS

The master cylinder is a manually operated, single action, reciprocating pump which serves to build up fluid pressure in the system. Each main gear wheel is served by a separate master cylinder if the brakes are to be individually operated. If the brakes are to be operated by a single hand brake, only one master cylinder is used. (Figure 9)

A lot of builders use the "Cessna-style" master cylinders because of the availability of these units. These units incorporate a small integral reservoir that supplies the brake system with the hydraulic fluid

essential to the system.

The other commonly used master cylinder, let's call it the "Beechcraft-type" (Goodyear) is a slender tube-like unit which requires the use of a separate hydraulic reservoir. This separate external source is in the form of a container mounted on the firewall with a hose running down to a "T" fitting, which in turn has a line going to each of the two Beechcraft-type master cylinders. This reservoir can be a simple metal container with a fitting soldered or brazed in the bottom. A filler plug fitting is soldered in the top for servicing with fluid. I don't know how many of you remember the old Prince Albert tobacco can, but I do remember once seeing one of them attached to the firewall of an old rag wing airplane for use as a hydraulic reservoir.

A typical master cylinder consists of a piston-like affair with a coil spring providing the previously mentioned brake release or recoil action. The heart of the device is the "O" ring which insures a leakproof fit between the piston and the cylinder walls while the brake pressure is being applied. Some of the older Cessna-type cylinders with the built in reservoir had, as part of their mechanism, a short stiff piece of wire about .032-inch x 2 inches long which served to upset the seal when the brake pressure was relieved. Sometimes on disassembly, this wire can fall out and, if a builder is unfamiliar with the installation, he may never notice its absence. The brakes would still work without the wire, but would be difficult to bleed and to keep free of trapped air. When disassembling anything, work in a clean area of the bench or table and make sure you account for all the parts.

The base of the master cylinder should be mounted as close to the rudder pedal hinge axis as is

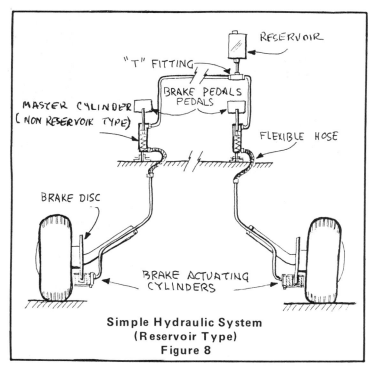

Simple Hydraulic System
(Reservoir Type)
Figure 8

practical.(Figure 10)Otherwise, when the rudder pedal is pushed forward, the brake pedal will be deflected and may cause the pilot to inadvertently apply a braking force when he least wants it.

HYDRAULIC LINES

Both the 3/16-inch and the ¼-inch rigid aluminum lines are being used for brake tubing. At the

wheels and at the rudder pedals, builders are using automotive-type flexible hoses to provide the flexing needed. The rest of the lines are all rigid tubing. Some builders use steel or copper tubing for their lines, perhaps because they are locally available. Still, the added weight, however little, contributes nothing worthwhile and certainly strength isn't a factor in these simple systems.

SERVICING HYDRAULIC BRAKES

As most of us know, the effectiveness of the brakes depends upon transmitting the applied brake pressure from the cockpit to the wheel brake through the fluid, which, for all practical purposes, acts like a solid pushrod . . . . unless air is trapped in the system. Air trapped in the system is indicated by a spongy ineffective action of the foot pedals. If by pumping the brake pedals quickly a few times the braking action improves, it is a sure sign that there is air in the system and the brakes must be bled.

Brake systems equipped with the Beechcraft-type master cylinders must be bled in the usual manner, from the top down, as it is impossible to remove the air behind the piston seal otherwise. However, any mechanic worth his salt knows that the easiest way to service a brake system equipped with the Cessna-type master cylinder is by filling the system from the bottom up.

Service the brake system from the bottom up

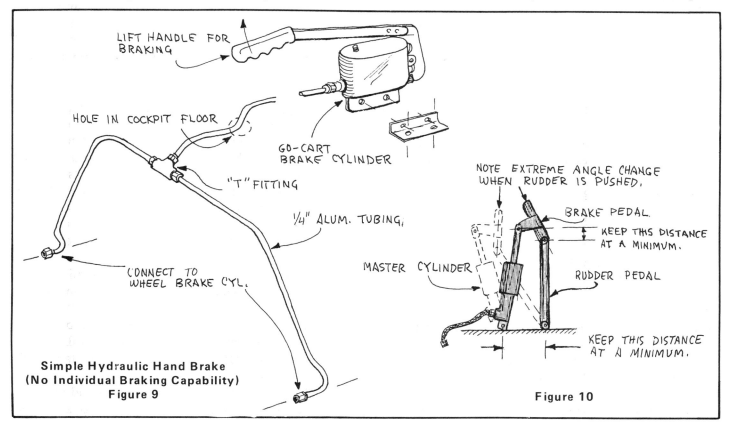

Simple Hydraulic Hand Brake
(No Individual Braking Capability)
Figure 9

Figure 10

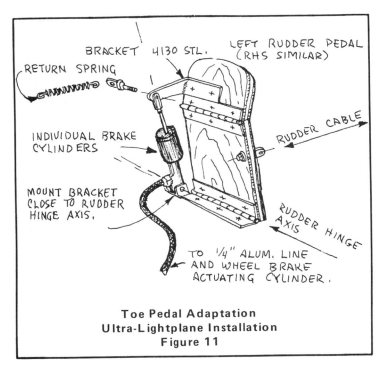

Toe Pedal Adaptation
Ultra-Lightplane Installation
Figure 11

by attaching, to the bleeder valve at the brake cylinder, a short flexible hose that is hooked up to a small hand pump (converted from a pressure pump oil can) filled with hydraulic fluid. First make sure the brakes are released and then start pumping the fluid in, causing it to flow back through the system carrying all the air with it. As soon as the fluid begins to run out of the filler plug opening in the master cylinder, the bleeder valve at the brake actuating cylinder is closed and the filling equipment removed. Reinstall the bleeder valve cap.

It would help to have someone in the cockpit to tell you when to stop pumping since you could easily overfill and cause a mess in the cockpit. You can also minimize the prospect of soaking down the cockpit by inserting into the filler plug opening of the master cylinder, a nipple with a hose attached. The free end of this overflow hose should be inserted into a can or jar. The excess fluid will then flow into the jar and not all over the cockpit.

Maintaining a proper fluid level in the master cylinder will prevent brake failure or the introduction of air into the system. Incidentally, the reservoir-type master cylinders should be at least half full at all times.

HYDRAULIC FLUID

I suppose even milk would work in a hydraulic system, but I would still prefer to use the right juice. Aircraft hydraulic fluid is red. It is formulated for aircraft use under varying conditions of temperature and altitude. Automotive hydraulic fluid is a clear yellowish color. Do not use automotive brake fluid

in the aircraft brake system as you may have a problem with the "O" rings. To check for the "O" ring compatibility with the fluid you intend to use, soak the "O" rings in some of the fluid for about a week to see if they swell up.

USED COMPONENTS

Many builders are prone, for economic reasons, to secure second-hand or salvage aircraft components. These include the wheels, brakes, master cylinders, and even the tubing and hoses. Nevertheless, these components, when inspected, overhauled and properly maintained, can provide the builder with hundreds of hours of good trouble free service.

The first thing to do with used wheels, brakes, and brake cylinders, is to clean, inspect and overhaul them, in that order. You can never do a decent job of inspecting unless the components are clean.

Not much can go wrong with hydraulic system components. However, check very carefully for any cracks around the attachment bolt holes and brackets especially, as brakes are subjected to tremendous temperature changes in addition to torque forces. If you find no cracks, about the only other business to concern yourself with is the replacement of the "O" rings.

All of the "O" rings should be replaced in both the wheel brake actuating cylinder units and in the master cylinders located at the brake pedals. Yes, replace them even if they do look good. If you don't do this, prepare yourself for the consequences.

One fine winter morn you will go out to the airport to fly your pretty bird and there, on the ground, you will find a red pool beneath the tires where the hydraulic fluid leaked out. The cold weather causes the aluminum pistons in the brake cylinders to contract considerably. The old "O" rings, having lost their resiliency, just can't fill the bill any more, so to speak. The fluid simply leaks out. If you are luckier than the usual builder, both wheel brake cylinders will leak out at the same time. You can then jack up the plane, remove both wheels and brakes, clean up the mess, and replace both sets of "O" rings as you should have done in the first place. If you are unlucky, only one brake will leak and you will probably replace it and ignore the other wheel. It may not even be a week later when . . . . Blah! There goes the other one.

Take it from one who has learned his lesson well. It is more convenient to replace the old "O" rings during the original installation of used wheels and brakes. You can then be assured that they will be good for several years. Those of you who run a tight ship may, of course, have a regular program for replacing the "O" rings.

How to Install Wheel Pants

If you add wheel pants (speed fairings) for good looks, you will undoubtedly come closer to being satisfied than if you add them to increase the speed of the airplane. On the other hand, properly done, you might just be pleasantly surprised and find that you have accomplished both objectives.

Some builders test and fly a new homebuilt without wheel pants, and this is a good practice. No use introducing more unknown elements than necessary in the early test stages. A poor wheel pants installation can unexpectedly begin to shake in a most distracting manner, or worse . . . . blow off. Fortunately, such cases are the exception. However, to play it safe, you might review the following helpful details.

One avowed purpose of speed fairings is to reduce drag. Wheel pants are, therefore, designed to be as small as possible in cross section in order to minimize drag. It is a great help that commercially available wheel pants are ordinarily of excellent quality and design.

You may, nevertheless, find that the wheel opening in some of these designs is much larger than necessary. A large opening causes drag and reduces the effectiveness of the speed fairing. If you are interested in speed as well as in looks, reduce the wheel openings to the minimum practical. And what might that be? I don't really know, but certainly, the usual 1-inch to fist-size gap between the tire and wheel pants is too much. Even some of the factory-built beauties now have reduced the clearance to approximately a half-inch. Such close clearances may be functional for aircraft operating from good paved runways, but what about those using unpaved surfaces and primitive strips?

MUD SCRAPERS

Sooner or later, the aircraft will have to roll through muddy areas. Under such conditions, wheels pick up mud rapidly, and before an airplane rolls very many feet, the wheel-to-pants clearance disappears and the pants become packed solid . . . . the airplane can't move any farther. If you will ordinarily be operating where poor runway conditions are common, you might be better off without the fancy pants. One good bit of insurance for the "turf strip set" is to make and install mud scrapers directly behind the tires. Mud scrapers are a useful precaution for any wheel pants installation. You should, however, make sure that there is adequate clearance (about 3/8-inch) between the scraper and the tire. If you make a set of mud scrapers, file the attachment holes in the scrapers into elongated slots to provide the adjustment range needed.

You may have heard that some builders install a bulkhead (partition) immediately behind the tire, sealing off the entire aft area of the wheel pants. The theory is that this will prevent the rear portion of the wheel pants from becoming loaded with mud and dirt. The value of this practice is debatable when weighted against the work and extra cost involved. Besides, as I see it, it would, in effect, only take less mud to pack and jam the wheel pants sooner.

Whether you buy a pair of speed fairings or make them yourself, all you will have before you, to begin with, are the two empty shells with not a single visible clue as to a means of support. Like many other things involved in the building of an airplane, the process of fitting the wheel pants can be difficult for anyone who has not had the opportunity to see how it is done. Perhaps the drawings in Figures 12, 13 and 14 serve the same visual purpose.

POSITIONING THE WHEEL PANTS

If the ready made wheel pants do not have some sort of an index mark or a small hole to identify the recommended location for the centerline of the axle, you will have to determine this for yourself.

Examine the wheel pants and you will see that the size of the wheel opening in the pants definitely limits the fore and aft placement of the pants over the tires. To a similar degree, the size of the tire limits how far the wheel will penetrate the pants before it rubs someplace. With these limitations, you will zero in on the approximate location for the axle's centerline. Except for racing aircraft, most wheel pants are installed so that a small amount of the wheel rim is visible beneath the pants. More often than not, as much much as ½-inch of the wheel's rim shows. All in all, wheel pants should not cover so much of the wheels and tires that, when the aircraft is at rest on the ground, it would be impossible to slide any sort of wheel chocks under the wheel pants, especially behind the wheels. I guess most pilots know that tires have a mysterious inclination to get a bit low once in awhile. If this happens, you may find that the airplane has settled and the pants are jammed against wheel chocks which can't be removed. This phenomenon usually portends damaged wheel pants.

Even after establishing the desired position for the centerline of the axle, one question remains. Should the wheel pants be centered over the tire (as viewed from the front) or should they be moved inboard so that they will also cover the brake instal-

lation? Pilot builders who are habitually heavy brake users should perhaps cut away some of the inboard portion of the pants to leave the brake housing exposed for better cooling. Positioning the inboard edge of the pants so that they are flush with the brake housing will still afford some drag reduction, and a reasonable amount of cooling air for the brakes.

Positioning some styles of wheel pants inboard of the centerline of the tires might permit enclosing the entire brake assembly and its drag-producing clutter. The easiest way to do this, however, is to center the pants over the tires and fabricate a separate bowl-like fairing or fillet to cover the clutter around

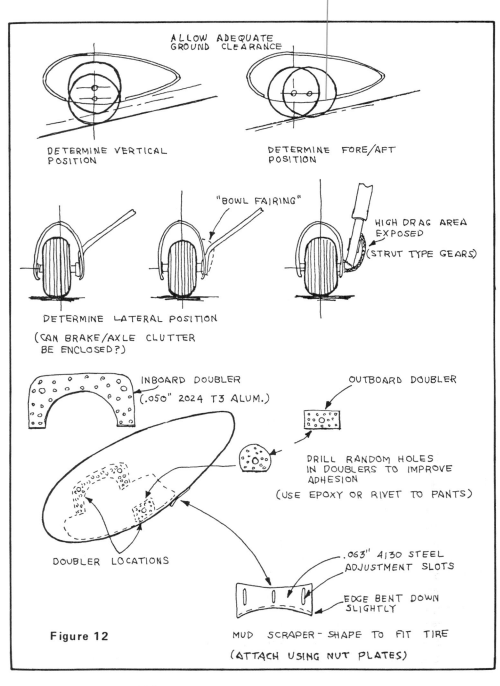

Figure 12

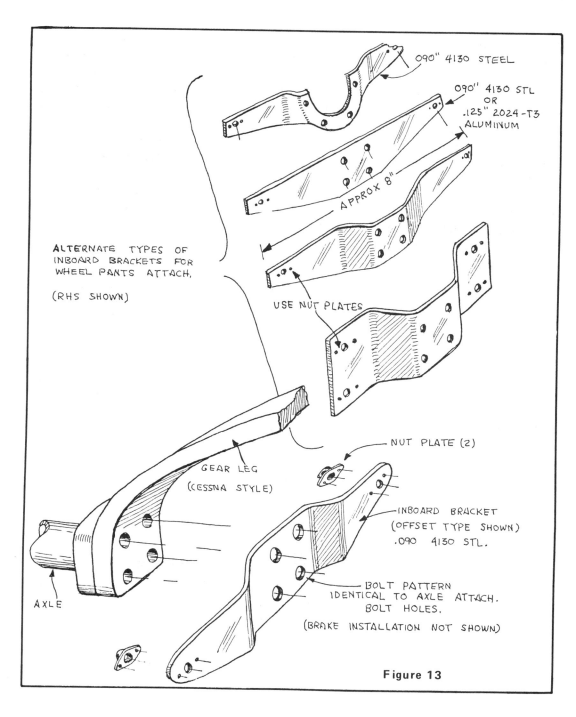

090" 4130 STEEL

090" 4130 STL
OR
.125" 2024-T3
ALUMINUM

APPROX 8"

USE NUT PLATES

ALTERNATE TYPES OF
INBOARD BRACKETS FOR
WHEEL PANTS ATTACH.

(RHS SHOWN)

NUT PLATE (2)

GEAR LEG
(CESSNA STYLE)

INBOARD BRACKET
(OFFSET TYPE SHOWN)
.090 4130 STL.

BOLT PATTERN
IDENTICAL TO AXLE ATTACH.
BOLT HOLES.

(BRAKE INSTALLATION NOT SHOWN)

AXLE

Figure 13

the brake area.

INSTALLATION OF DOUBLERS

Fiberglass wheel pants will require doubler reinforcements at each of the attachment points to help distribute the loads around the bolt holes. Reinforcement plates are made of aluminum sheet and are riveted or epoxied to the inside surfaces of the pants. If you use rivets in place of, or in addition to epoxy adhesive, the rivet heads will show on the outside of the pants unless you go to a lot more work to cover the rivet heads and refinish the pants. If you intend to forego the rivets, prepare the doubler to assure

better bonding by drilling a number of random holes through the metal plate. These holes will permit the epoxy to seep through for added reliability of the bonded joint.

A small 2-inch x 3-inch rectangular plate, or a similar size aluminum disc doubler is adequate reinforcement for the outboard attachment point at the axle.

On the inboard side, a larger plate must be bonded to the inner surface of the pants. A half moon sort of a doubler is effective as it permits the cutting away of a section of the wheel pants from around the brake housing, if desired. This type of doubler provides greater leeway in adjusting the ground angle for the pants without first having to know the exact attachment bolt locations.

Attaching wheel pants to spring-type landing gears (Cessna, Bede 4, Scooter, Sonerai, etc.) is much easier than to some of the whip-type gears (Tailwind Sidewinder, T-18, etc.). Somewhere in between in difficulty, are the scissors-type and the welded-tube tripod styles. A lot of the difficulty depends on the type of wheel and brake installation you have. Most landing gears are not difficult to equip with wheel pants if there is a plate, or disc, or bracket welded to the axle for the attachment of the brake torque plates. In most instances, the wheel pants are attached to a bracket that is held in place by the same bolts that secure the brake torque plates to the axle or gear leg.

A three-point attachment for the pants usually provides the most rigid and effective means. This arrangement requires one attachment point to be located at the outboard end of the axle. With the other two attachment points extending from the inboard side of the gear leg. The inboard attachment points are located on a bracket tailored to fit the gear and style of pants used. An offset type of bracket may be necessary to obtain the desired positioning of the speed fairings over the tires. (Figure 13)

Special sleeve-like axle nuts are in use for attaching the outboard sides of the pants. These are standard units for some production aircraft installations. Their cost is high and, as a consequence, they are not commonly available to most of us. A machinist could easily make his own. But for the rest of us, alternate or modified versions of the attachment are easier to make. For installation of the pants, you first drill the hole for the axle attachment through the pants. Then slip the pants over the wheel and insert and tighten that axle attachment bolt. This will permit you to set the wheel pants to the proper ground angle.

Before you drill the attachment holes in the inboard sides of the speed fairings, be sure that both

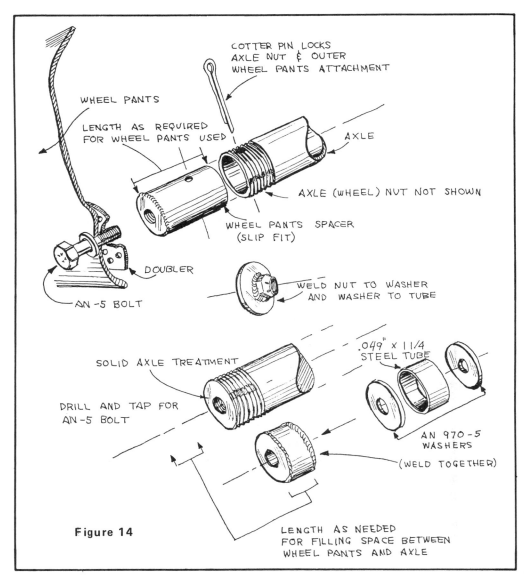

Figure 14

wheel pants are rotated the same amount. Back away and eyeball both wheel pants from either wing tip to be absolutely certain your measurements were accurate. When both are in alignment with each other, mark and drill each of the inboard attachment holes.

One final consideration is how to provide for the airing of the tires without removing the wheel pants. Some designs in which speed obviously is not the greatest consideration afford access to the valve stems by means of the rather cavernous opening around the wheels.

Often the wheel protrudes from the pants so far that access to the tire valve is possible. Tight fitting speed fairings, however, require some special accommodation for the chore of airing the tires. Perhaps a small removable plate in each of the wheel pants could provide this access to the tire valves.

Some popular aircraft now feature neat little access doors built into the speed fairings. They are rectangular in shape and are hinged with piano hinges. Opening and closing of these mini-doors is by means of pushbutton latches. The periodic ritual of removing the speed fairings simply to air the tires is not fun . . . . ask anybody.

Wheel pants add a dash of class to any type of aircraft.

FUEL SYSTEMS

Gravity Flow Fuel Systems

More than one builder has asked me to detail engine installation and hook up methods and to point out problem areas to be avoided. Here is a look at one of the more important hook up jobs, the fuel system.

The gravity flow system is very effective because no pumps, relief valves, or other mechanical units are needed. Because these components are not there, they cannot fail. Their absence and the resulting minimum of connections needed assures you of the lightest possible installation. Figures 1 and 2 illustrate the simplicity of the fuel system.

There's no doubt about it, the gravity flow fuel system is the simplest and most practical fuel system for the typical low-powered amateur-built aircraft. Gravity never fails, but fuel pumps ...... that's another matter.

To utilize a gravity flow system in your bird, you must be able to install your fuel tank at a level higher than the carburetor inlet — the higher the better.

There will be sufficient fuel at the carburetor only if the tank is high enough and the fuel lines are large enough to provide a fuel flow rate of about 1.2 pounds per hour for each takeoff horsepower, or 150 per cent of the actual takeoff fuel consumption (whichever is greatest).

Some mechanics are quite vocal in their belief that a gravity flow system should only be used on high-wing jobs. Their reasoning is that the pressure generated by a gravity flow system is only about 1 psi for each 40 inches head of fuel, and only in a high-wing aircraft can you get the tank higher than 40 inches above the carburetor. (Gravity flow systems are said to operate best at a fuel head pressure of 1½ to 2 psi.)

Well, the gravity flow fuel system is a very good installation for high-wing monoplanes and equally simple to install in the upper wings of biplanes, but it is still being used successfully in one heck of a lot of low-wing jobs too. In low-wing applications, the tank is usually mounted between the instrument panel and the firewall and as far forward and at the highest level possible between the upper longerons. This means, usually, that the tank is not very much higher than the carburetor, and greater care must be

taken to ensure a working installation. (Figure 2)

THE FUEL TANK . . . . WHAT CAPACITY?

Tank size is determined by the size of your engine, its fuel flow requirements, and the space available. The range you want to achieve also enters into the problem of determining tank capacity. One common rule is that the minimum fuel requirements are figured on the basis of allowing .15 gallons of fuel for each horsepower developed at maximum cruise rpm. I maintain this is not enough. An airplane that cannot remain aloft at least three hours without refueling is too limited in its usefulness. Good range is a factor which could affect your future well being. Not all airports carry fuel you know.

WING TANKS

There are some disadvantages to installing wing tanks. Because of space limitations within the wing structure, these tanks must be rather thin . . . . a very inefficient shape. Because the wing is usually small, at least two tanks are needed to provide the necessary capacity. (Figure 1) Quite often builders will install a fuselage tank to supplement the scant supply of wing fuel. If you go this route, be prepared to build two or three gas tanks. On the other hand, look on the bright side. Who ever heard of two or three tanks springing a leak at the same time? In that respect, at least, there is a safety factor in numbers.

Wing tanks are difficult to fill if the wing is very high off the ground. They are likely to induce the development of careless preflight attitudes in the pilot too, as they are very hard to check visually. Each of these factors should be mulled over before you decide on the fuel tank installation for your own aircraft. In fact, there are plenty of things to think out before you start on your tank.

FILLER NECKS

Carefully determine where to locate the filler neck. If the neck is poorly located, you may not be able to fill the tank to its full capacity. Place the filler neck so that when the aircraft is in its normal attitude (3-point), an expansion space is automatically created, even though the tank may be filled to the

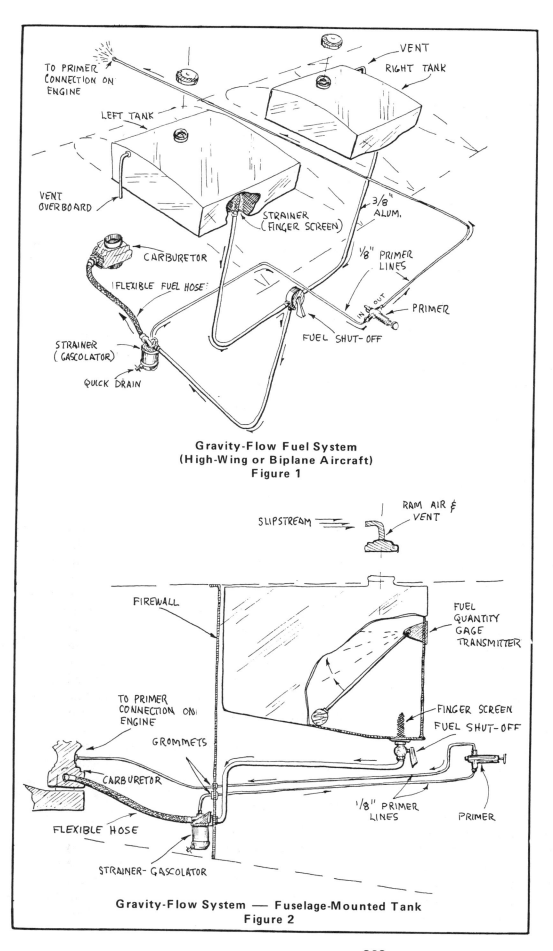

TO PRIMER
CONNECTION ON
ENGINE

VENT
RIGHT TANK

LEFT TANK

VENT
OVERBOARD

STRAINER
(FINGER SCREEN)

3/8"
ALUM.

1/8" PRIMER
LINES

CARBURETOR

(FLEXIBLE FUEL HOSE)

IN OUT

PRIMER

STRAINER
(GASCOLATOR)

FUEL SHUT-OFF

QUICK DRAIN

**Gravity-Flow Fuel System
(High-Wing or Biplane Aircraft)
Figure 1**

SLIPSTREAM

RAM AIR &
VENT

FIREWALL

FUEL
QUANTITY
GAGE
TRANSMITTER

TO PRIMER
CONNECTION ON
ENGINE

GROMMETS

FINGER SCREEN

FUEL SHUT-OFF

CARBURETOR

FLEXIBLE HOSE

1/8" PRIMER
LINES

PRIMER

STRAINER- GASCOLATOR

**Gravity-Flow System — Fuselage-Mounted Tank
Figure 2**

top of the filler neck. (Figure 3)

If streamlining is your game, you can reduce drag by recessing the filler neck into a well on top of the tank. The well should be sealed from the aircraft structure so that any overflowing fuel will not enter the fuselage. This well serves as a scupper with an overboard drain opening located in it to ensure that this area will drain properly. Filler openings are normally marked FUEL . . . . and they show the tank capacity and the type of fuel to be used. Good idea to paint your filler cap red while you're at it! (Fuel caps red and oil caps yellow).

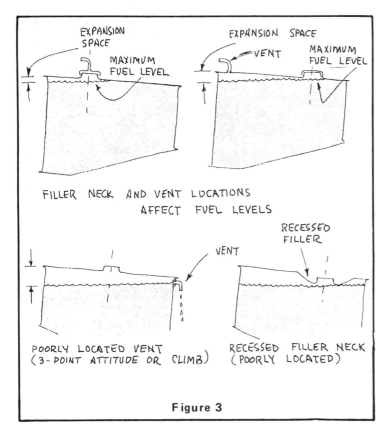

FILLER NECK AND VENT LOCATIONS AFFECT FUEL LEVELS

POORLY LOCATED VENT (3-POINT ATTITUDE OR CLIMB)

RECESSED FILLER NECK (POORLY LOCATED)

Figure 3

VENTS AND OVERBOARD DRAINS

We know that fuel expands considerably on hot days, and it is quite common to see an airplane parked in the sun with fuel dripping on the ground. If the aircraft has an overflow drain in the filler neck or some area near the top of the tank, the fuel will be routed overboard without messing up or staining the aircraft's paint job. However, the problem of a fuel tank leaking excess fuel can be eliminated or minimized if expansion space is provided in the tank. About 2 to 3 per cent of the tank's capacity should be sufficient for the expansion space. More important than the drip, drip, drip of a little fuel though, is the fact that unless the tank is properly vented, fuel will not flow as desired.

While most gas caps are vented in their natural state, almost all builders using gravity flow fuselage tanks will modify the gas cap to serve as a vent and to "pressurize" the tank with the help of the slip-stream. Make sure that the lineman puts this type of cap on properly after refueling your aircraft, if you don't care for surprise performances. (Figure 4)

Often you will see both the fuel quantity indicator and pressure vent built into the same cap.

Sometimes, for greater peace of mind, an alternate vent is built into the tank. Bugs can plug up a vent, so a spare is nice.

Where two wing tanks are used, instead of venting each tank separately, you can interconnect them with a cross-over vent between the two tanks.

It is important to keep overflow fuel out of the aircraft. Vent your line overboard and be on your guard against trapped vapors in low compartmental areas. Fuel vapors are heavier than air, and always settle to the lowest portion of an enclosed area. This makes a perfect set up for an explosion.

FUEL QUANTITY INDICATORS

A fuel gage is mandatory. You have considerable latitude in the choice. The old J-3 Cub variety with a piece of 1/8-inch piano wire connected to a large cork is still the most popular arrangement. You can hardly improve on a positive visual check. Nice thing about this type of fuel quantity indicator is that there is no drain on the battery. (Figure 4)

An electric gage can be installed similar to those found in automobiles and store-bought aircraft. To use one of these requires an electrical source and the

A VFR panel featuring a vertical plastic tube as a constant reading gas gage.

270

implanting of a float and transmitter within the tank. There are also mechanical type direct-reading gages that can be inserted in the tank but these can be used only where you can view the tank. This kind of gage unit is rare and not very practical.

Another type of gage gaining in popularity is the direct-viewing clear glass or plastic tube. A tube is located vertically withing the pilot's span of vision in the cockpit area. One end of this tube is connected to the plumbing at the bottom of the tank and the other to the top of the tank. The fuel will seek its own level within the tube so you have a continuous reading of the remaining fuel. Some pilots don't care for this type installation as it introduces fuel into the cockpit area and can be a source of fuel leaks. No matter what kind of fuel quantity indicator you use, be sure that you establish the FULL and EMPTY positions accurately. (Figure 4)

TANK SUMPS AND FINGER SCREENS

Tanks are being built with and without a sump or depression in the bottom. If you provide a sump, it is standard practice not to draw the fuel from the bottom of the sump, as this is where water, if present, accumulates. Usually, a short standpipe attached to a

finger screen is installed to avoid taking of the fuel from the very bottom of the tank. If such a standpipe is used, it will be impossible to drain off any impurities which might accumulate unless a separate drain plug is built into the lowest portion of the tank's sump. This plug can then be removed periodically to check for accumulation of water, etc., before it becomes excessive and causes engine operation difficulties.

Each fuel tank must have a removable finger screen strainer installed. This comparatively coarse finger screen is made so that it can be installed through the bottom fitting of your fuel tank. Its primary function is to filter out foreign matter and keep it from entering the system lines. It happens that no matter how careful a builder may be, he can somehow fail to completely cleanse a tank. Then we read of another forced landing on a test flight, or not many hours thereafter. At least the finger screen will keep the bigger stuff out of the system. (Figure 5)

A finger screen can be made of a piece of galvanized or (better) brass screen rolled and shaped around a pencil or dowel. Crimp one open end and solder along the seam and the end. A brass tank fitting can be counterbored a bit to receive either a 3/8-inch

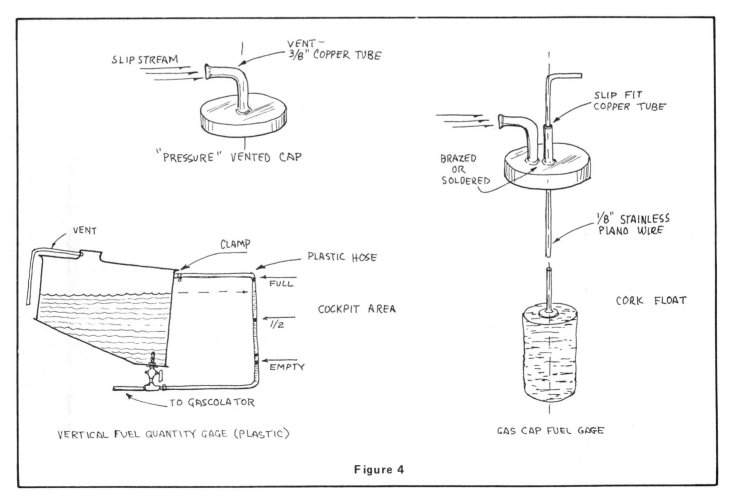

Figure 4

271

standpipe or the screen finger strainer for soldering into place permanently.

FUEL SHUTOFF

Where a fuel tank is installed just forward of the instrument panel, it is often possible to screw the shutoff valve directly into the bottom fuel tank fitting. You should not do this however, unless the shutoff valve can be reached by the pilot. If the valve is beyond easy reach, it is often possible to rig up an extension handle to the cockpit area. Screwing the valve directly into the tank reduces the number of fittings necessary and achieves the same results as when the valve is located further downstream in the system. Always keep the number of connections to a minimum. The fewer such points, the less the likelihood that you will develop fuel seepage or leaks.

Incidentally, if you cannot reach your fuel shutoff valve in flight or on the ground, you may have a serious problem. If, for example, your magneto "P" lead becomes disconnected for any reason, your magnetos will stay hot and refuse to be shut off. Then how would you stop the engine?

PLAN FOR FUEL TANK REMOVAL

Some builders build future problems for themselves when they do not provide for the easy removal of their gas tanks. Tanks have been known to seep fuel and even to leak like a sieve. If you can't remove the tank for repair without tearing up part of the airplane, you are taking a big chance. On second thought, you should plan your entire fuel system so that the whole thing can be removed or replaced without great difficulty.

FUEL LINES

Tubing size is determined by fuel flow requirements and the size of the fitting on the carburetor. For the smaller aircraft engines up to 100 hp, a 3/8-inch aluminum line is adequate. The VW mills, on the other hand, do well with 5/16-inch for the main lines

where you can use U.S. standard fittings. Otherwise you should the standard VW steel lines.

The connection from the gascolator to the engine (carburetor) should be by means of a flexible fuel-resistant hose. It is wise to use flexible hose any place where one end of the fuel line would be fastened to a stationary structure and the other to some movable or shock-mounted point.

Don't forget to anchor your fuel lines every 18 inches or so, because tubing that is subjected to considerable flexing is prone to hardening and possible cracking.

FUEL FITTINGS

Standard aircraft (AN) 3-piece solderless, flared tubing union fittings are the ones to use in making up

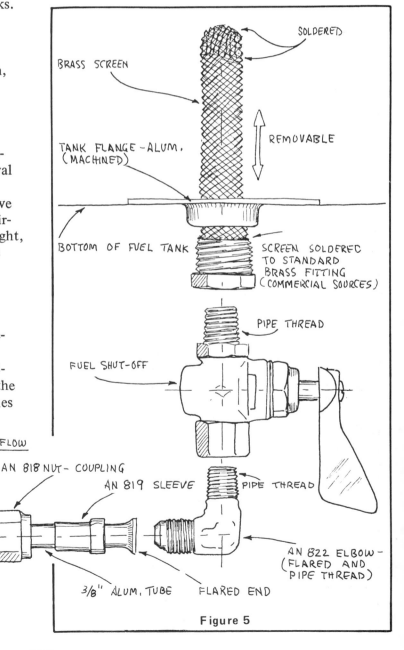

Figure 5

272

Tank shape is dictated by space needed by a couple of instruments and the radio. Cutting tank in half made it easier to install baffle and tunnel for throttle and other controls (left photo). In the next photo, tank is shown joined together with pop rivets through a back-up strip. A layer of glass cloth will be epoxied over rivet line and seams.

fuel lines. Homebuilders are shying away from copper tubing. And why not? Aluminum is lighter and not as apt to harden and crack. The most frequently used type of tubing for fuel, oil, and even medium pressure hydraulic lines, is the 52S0 (5052-0) as it is easily flared and formed. The typical line is fabricated using AN 818 coupling nuts and AN 819 sleeves, coupled to the flared ends of an aluminum tube. You should not use an automotive flaring tool to flare the tubing because its angle is not the same as that used for aircraft fittings.

Be extremely careful to get threads started properly on all fuel line fittings. If you cannot turn the fitting, or nut, with your fingers for the first turn or two, better back off and check things out. It's very easy to get the soft aluminum part cross-threaded, particularly in hard to see locations. Even though you tighten such a boo-boo with a wrench, it is sure to leak. Don't overtorque, the maximum torque in inches for flared tubing fittings is 40-65 inch pounds for ¼-inch diameter tubing, 60-80 i.p. for 5/16-inch tubing, and 75-125 i.p. for 3/8-inch tubing.

CAUTION: After the flaring and forming job is done, check and make sure the tubing is clean inside and does not harbor chips and particles that can cause serious problems later!

By the way, fuel line fittings and connectors may have either straight threads or the standard pipe thread on one end. Components such as carburetors, gascolators and fuel tanks receive a male pipe thread fitting. The tubing, with its flared ends and coupling nut, takes the straight thread. Learn to recognize the difference between the two — **they are not interchangeable!** (Figure 5) Standard pipe thread fittings all have a ¾-inch / foot taper which helps ensure a leakproof connection. Don't try to screw pipe thread fittings in all the way until all threads are engaged.

It can't be done without ruining the fitting or stripping the threads inside the component, and it is not necessary at all.

Another thing, don't use pipe joint compounds to prevent fuel leaks. It is not being done in better aircraft circles. Sometimes, however, a nonhardening thread lubricant (anti-seize compound) is used on the male fitting portion in making the connection. Take care that none of the compound gets into the fitting's opening.

GASCOLATOR

At least one main strainer must be installed between the tank and the carburetor. Locate it in the lowest part of the fuel system to collect foreign matter. Any accumulation of water from condensation and improper handling of fuel will also settle to this point.

This main strainer is normally mounted on the firewall and is often referred to as the gascolator. For safety's sake, especially if yours is a retractable landing gear-equipped bird, mount the gascolator so that it does not protrude below the fuselage. But locate it so you can reach it from outside the aircraft. You can then easily check it on your preflight inspection for the presence of water. As a convenience, most builders install a quick drain in the bottom portion of the gascolator. The only other thing to consider in this respect is to make sure that any fuel, when drawn out through the quick drain, will normally run out on the ground and not some place inside the aircraft structure.

CHECKING FOR LEAKS

There is always a certain amount of suspense the first time you turn on the fuel in a newly hooked up fuel system. If you paid attention to each detail, you

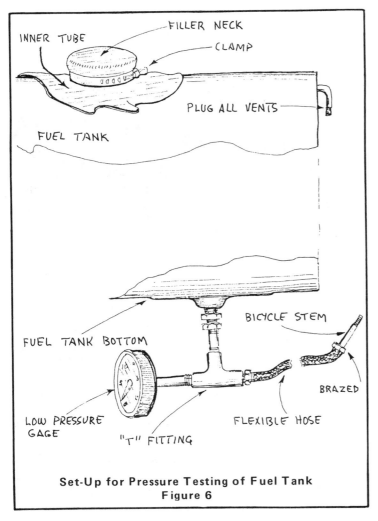

Set-Up for Pressure Testing of Fuel Tank
Figure 6

Labels in figure: INNER TUBE · FILLER NECK · CLAMP · FUEL TANK · PLUG ALL VENTS · FUEL TANK BOTTOM · BICYCLE STEM · BRAZED · LOW PRESSURE GAGE · "T" FITTING · FLEXIBLE HOSE

should have a nice free-flowing system without any leaks. Of course, as already mentioned, fuel line fittings should not be torqued excessively as the threads can easily be stripped.

The main leak source is often a newly constructed tank. A new tank should be pressure tested before installation. It doesn't matter whether the tank is metal or fiberglass, they are checked in the same manner.

First, plug all inlets and outlets. Plugging the filler neck can be difficult. I suggest stretching a hunk of inner tube over the opening and clamping it in place with a large hose clamp. (Figure 6)

The next step is to attach a low pressure gage to a "T" fitting screwed into the bottom of the tank. Then, with a short piece of hose, attach the gage to a bicycle valve stem and a hand pump. Build up about 3½- psi of pressure and see if the tank will hold that pressure for about 30 minutes. If there is a leak, you can locate its source easily by swabbing soapy water

over the outside of the tank. Of course, if you can dip it in a large vat, the results would be as effective and much quicker.

Do not fill fuel tanks with water to check capacity, especially if you have installed Safoam. Water is too hard to drain out completely, and its effect on Safoam, if installed, is not good.

FUEL FLOW TEST

You should make a flow test of the system to assure yourself that the head of pressure will give sufficient fuel flow in a climb attitude, especially if you are working out your own design.

To make a fuel flow test, some builders dig a hole for the tail wheel in order to approximate the maximum climb attitude for the aircraft. It is usually in this more extreme attitude that any fuel starvation problem will manifest itself. The actual test simply consists of disconnecting the line at the carburetor, turning on the fuel, timing the flow, and measuring the amount that comes out of the line over a given period of time. (1.2 pounds per hour for each takeoff horsepower, or 150 per cent of the actual takeoff fuel consumption for your engine is considered a minimum requirement.)

IN RETROSPECT . . . .

By all means make your fuel system installation in accordance with the details shown on your plans.

Unfortunately, some plans are quite vague on such matters and you may have to work out your own details and the best routing of the lines. Keep all tubing as direct and straight as possible, avoiding any vertical humps and bends in the lines where air pockets might form or be trapped. Maintain a constant slope in the fuel lines to the gascolator, and from the gascolator to the carburetor, if you can.

Use standard aluminum tubing and aircraft fittings and connectors. These AN fittings are the familiar blue-colored aircraft items easily obtained through aircraft surplus sales outlets or through any fixed base operator handling parts.

Finally, if you are building your engine up from parts, make sure that your carburetor has the proper parts list number and correct float needle seat for a gravity flow system. For example, with the C-85 engine, the carburetor used with a fuel pump differs in that a smaller float needle seat is required. Normally most of the smaller engines are set up for the gravity flow system.

Evolution of a Fuel System

The fuel system on my Turner was simple until I decided I needed more than just that single gravity-feed 10.5-gallon forward tank.

An aft tank capable of holding 10 gallons was constructed and located behind the pilot's seat bulkhead. It rested on the baggage compartment floor. Initially, it too was gravity-fed, as I intended to use it only in normal cruise level flight. It was tied into the fuel system through a three-way fuel selector which provided a MAIN, an AFT and an OFF position.

In flight I would switch to the aft tank and cruise along blissfully. That is, until I had to make some altitude correction. Suddenly, the engine would indicate its displeasure by sputtering. With a nose-up attitude, there wasn't sufficient head pressure to feed the carburetor from the rear tank for long, relying solely on gravity feed. This problem, of course, got worse as the fuel level got lower. Nothing gets your attention like the spasmodic sputter of an engine experiencing fuel starvation. As if this wasn't nerve wracking enough, there was the constant dread that one day I would forget and attempt to takeoff with the fuel selector in the AFT tank position. The airplane probably wouldn't pick up more than 100 feet of altitude before the engine quit.

A change was made by disconnecting the aft tank from the fuel selector valve. Now all engine operations are from the main tank only. The aft tank is now equipped with an external Bendix electric fuel pump and a toggle switch wired through a green instrument panel light. The fuel line from the aft tank pumps the fuel into an inlet in the top of the main tank.

In operation, any time the main tank gets low, I simply turn on the fuel pump and the aft tank replenishes the main tank. The green light reminds me that the transfer of fuel is going on. The fuel gages, likewise, reveal what is taking place.

In the event I were to ignore the green light, or forget that the transfer of fuel is continuing, the excess fuel would dump harmlessly overboard through the main tank fuel vent. I like this "fool proof" system.

On cross country trips, the first fuel transfer is made when the main tank becomes half empty.

This procedure reduces the remote odds of a fuel pump failure cheating me out of all the reserve supply unexpectedly, when I need it most.

MAKE IT FUEL—PROOF

Fuel systems need more study by all of us. There are so many little things that can go wrong. Things that don't work the way you expected.

For example, I did not want to have the filler cap located in the baggage compartment. A careless line boy could slop a couple of gallons of fuel in on top of the baggage. To avoid this hazard, I made a beautiful little hatch in the side of the fuselage through which the tank could be filled. Unfortunately, this caused the location of the filler neck to be lower in the tank than I wanted. The result, I have a fail-safe filler opening for the tank, but I lost some tank capacity. The 10-gallon tank now holds only 7 gallons of usable fuel.

Other examples. The location of the outlets for the vents and for the hook up of an auxiliary tank are critical. You must visualize the aircraft in a nose-up attitude as well as in a nose-down attitude to determine their effect on the fuel system in flight.

The tank, when it is near full, will overflow through these openings. In the Turner, this was a source of irritation as, during a takeoff with full tanks, fuel flowed back through the system from the main tank, overfilling the rear tank and causing fuel to seep out through the gas cap. This seepage stained the fuselage with that pesky, hard-to-clean-off red dye.

An in-line, one-way fuel check valve was all right during flight maneuvers and climbs, but on the ground after refueling, the fuel — in time — seeped past it. An ineffective valve for my purpose. Perhaps a shut-off valve to the aft tank would be the best solution for this annoyance. But then, this would mean another cockpit procedure, wouldn't it?

Remember, when climbing out, fuel may drain out of a full tank at nose-high attitudes. Are your inlets and outlets positioned to minimize the effects of nose-high and nose-low attitudes? Make a few sketches first and think it out before you make the fuel system installation.

COVERING/PAINTING

12

Fabric Covering....Dacron

Let's explore the finer points of the Dacron covering as practiced by some perfectly rational homebuilders.

The basics for working with Dacron have become rather well known and will not be discussed in this article. However, if you wish to review a few of the informative writings on the basic subject, look up some of the additional material referenced for your convenience at the end of this article. Not to be overlooked as a valuable source of information is the local builder who has already done a Dacron covering job. Seek out this gent and have yourself a nice long discussion on the subject. People do want to be helpful to each other if given a chance to.

Even the most heavy-handed of us can get a good airworthy covering job with Dacron. The objective though, with most of us builders, calls for something more than mere airworthiness. We are interested in aesthetics, too. We are responsive to beauty, and we want our birds to look as nice as possible. Although beauty may only be skin deep, it is a fact that if a builder can achieve a beautiful effect, he must surely be equally capable of turning out airworthy work also. All that may be needed is just a few tips and ideas to motivate him and to get his own ingenious mind and hands to work.

USING FABRIC CEMENTS

For aircraft placarded with a red line, or "never exceed" speed of 150 mph or less, many builders feel that the fabric can be adequately attached by doping it to the structure with a generous overlapping of the seams. Could be, but if you find the need to use something "stickier" than dope, you should get one of the fabric cements known by such names as Poly-tak, Airlac Adhesive, Super Seam Cement, etc.

A lot of people prefer to use nitrate dope or Poly-Brush for attaching fabric and tapes and dislike using the fabric cements because they often end up with rough and ugly seams. However, that problem seems to be one of technique. Where most of us go wrong in the use of the fabric adhesives is in our instinctive and uncontrollable urge to brush across the cemented fabric as though we were using paint or dope. After applying the adhesive, you should not brush over the top surface of the fabric to stick it down better, because you will just generate a mess of curdled little lumps and bumps that will be almost impossible to remove by sanding. It is better to use your fingers to coax the tape or fabric down nice and smooth.

COVERING SEQUENCE. DOES IT MATTER?

Typically, the thing that most affects the appearance of a covering job is the quality of the seams finished with surface tapes. For lapped and doped seams, especially on leading and trailing edges of wings and tail surfaces, you might lap the fabric in the manner indicated in Figures 1 and 2.

A good covering sequence for fuselages is one where you attach the bottom fabric first and then the sides. The top fabric goes on last with its edges trimmed as straight as possible and free from unravelled threads. Of course, if you use the envelope cover technique, or if your project has some unusual design characteristic, the covering sequence for attaching the fabric to various surfaces should be altered to suit your need.

It can be argued that since finishing tapes will cover all seams, the way you lap the fabric is relatively unimportant. True enough in some cases, except that by making the lapped seams as indicated, you are permitted to position your finishing tapes where they are most effective. Also avoided would be those unsightly lumps and lines marking the fabric's ragged edges and lines so often evident beneath the tapes of some fabric coverings. It should result in a better overall finished appearance . . . . besides, no extra work is involved.

POOR MAN'S SPRING CLAMPS

Spring-type clothes pins are valuable aids around anybody's workshop. (Figure 3) In this particular application, you'll find that since Dacron is a rather stiff material, it takes some mighty sticky stuff to make it lie quietly where you want it. This will become very noticeable when the temperature of your work area is a bit on the low side of 70 degrees F.

The clothes pins make mighty effective persuaders in any case, and can be used effectively for

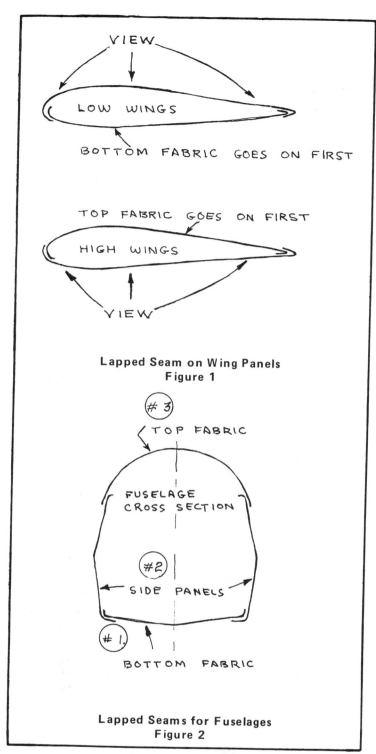

Lapped Seam on Wing Panels
Figure 1

Lapped Seams for Fuselages
Figure 2

CREASING TAPES HELPS

To get your long tapes on straight and with the least amount of difficulty, it is suggested that for most applications you first crease the tapes down the middle. Cut the measured length needed and then fold down the middle. Finish making the crease as shown in the sketch. (Figure 4)

The crease provides an excellent reference for laying down the tape, either along a drawn line, or for the old eyeball alignment check. This crease is especially handy in laying on the long leading or trailing edge tapes on wings. It is also fine for taping the corners on fuselages, as the tape fits better and glues down better. Don't worry about the crease mark showing on the tape. It will disappear when you run the point of a hot electric iron along it after the tape is in place and the adhesive is dry. Be careful! You can make a mess of your tape work if you shrink the tapes carelessly or excessively with the iron. At places where excess or prolonged heat is applied the edges shrink inwardly, narrowing the tape considerably at that point. This gives your tape an hourglass figure at a place where it generates no sex appeal whatsoever. The safest practice with tapes is not to shrink them unless it is really necessary. And even then, try to confine the heat application along the center of the tape.

TAPES.... LAYING THEM ON STRAIGHT

To affix a long piece of tape and to make it look nice calls for this technique. As a starter, stick down about the first 6 inches of one end of the tape. After that dope or adhesive has dried, brush onto the structure a coat of dope along where the tape is to be attached. Then, stretch the tape fairly taut at a shallow angle away from the structure while grasping the free end. With your eyes fixed on the line or mark where you want the free end to wind up, start lowering your end of the tape keeping it taut all the while. You will be pleasantly surprised when that end finally touches the structure. The tape will have aligned itself in a perfect straight line along its entire length, and on target too.

SHRINK DACRON TAPES AROUND CURVES

Unlike cotton tapes, Dacron tapes cannot be stretched to any noticeable degree. Using cotton tapes, it is possible to attach one end and then stretch the tape around a curved wing tip bow, for example, and it will lay down flat. With cotton you can do this consistently, with a high degree of success and a minimum of cutting and lapping. The usual practice with Dacron tape, however, is to cut its edges along

holding your surface tapes snug to the trailing edges of wings or other control surfaces until the dope gets sticky enough to take over. Just slip on a clothes pin every 2 to 4 inches, or at whatever point needed. Try to keep a couple of dozen clothes pins handy to your work area while you are covering. You'll like them because they are so easy to slip on and to take off. Plenty cheap too.

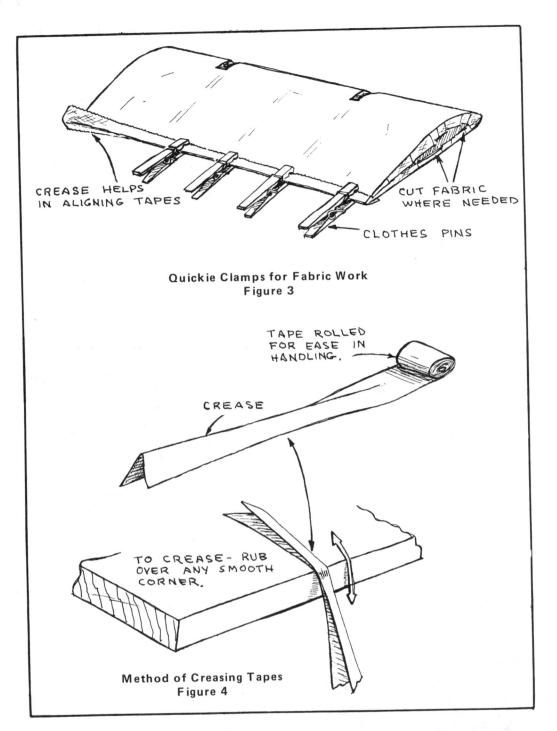

CREASE HELPS IN ALIGNING TAPES

CUT FABRIC WHERE NEEDED

CLOTHES PINS

Quickie Clamps for Fabric Work
Figure 3

TAPE ROLLED FOR EASE IN HANDLING.

CREASE

TO CREASE- RUB OVER ANY SMOOTH CORNER.

Method of Creasing Tapes
Figure 4

sharp corners, lapping them wherever needed, to make it lay down without bulging and to follow the curve neatly.

Two local builder friends of mine hit upon a way to put on Dacron tapes around curved tips without the usual cut, lap and stick technique. In reality, the mechanics are much the same as stretching cotton tapes around a curve, only in reverse. They are shrunk around. (Figure 5) First the Dacron tape is cut to length, then creased to aid in aligning it. Then, using a fabric cement or adhesive, the tape is cemented only at its centerline, all around the wing tip bow. After the adhesive has dried, they start near the wing tip's center with an electric iron and slowly and carefully heat-shrink the tape edges until the tape lays flat and snug against the wing's surface. It is recommended that the procedure be carried out by alternately working both the upper and lower sides of the tape to keep it from being pulled to one side. In the final step, a brush is dipped in dope and the dope worked under the edges of the tape to secure it permanently in place. The results? Most impressive, and with no unsightly overlapped cuts necessary.

Pinked edges are not as common now with

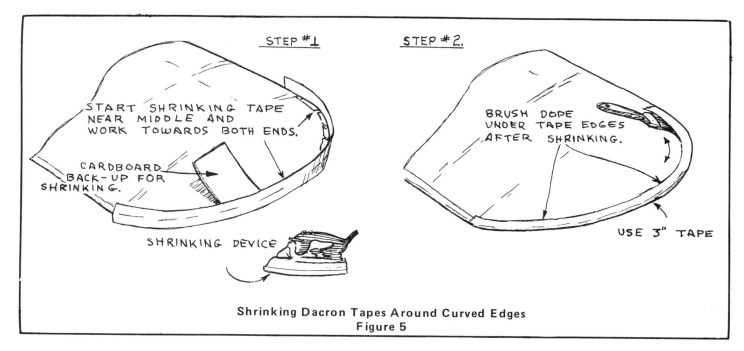

Shrinking Dacron Tapes Around Curved Edges
Figure 5

Dacron tapes as in the past. Quite likely, any tape ordered will come to you without pinked edges. The trend is to use a very lightweight tape with straight edges. Personally, I feel that the artistic finished appearance is not as appealing as the traditional pinked tape job. However, if sufficient silver coats are built up, the thin, straight edge tapes can be made virtually invisible to the eye . . . . and that does look good.

The quickest way to build up the silver dope along the taped edges after you have worked in your prime or base coats is by putting on the first two coats of silver with a brush rather than by spraying them on as is customary. Use a minimum number of brush strokes. The dope dries very quickly and too

much brushing will cause a rough surface. (When you feel the brush dragging, you should have quit two strokes ago.) Just a stroke or two to flow the wet dope on is plenty. Your second coat of silver should be put on with the strokes going crosswise to those for the first coat. A light sanding with No. 320 wet or dry sandpaper, after the second coat, is in order. Use plenty of water and sand until you start to see some clear dope underneath. Dacron doesn't have that fuzzy nap so characteristic of cotton fabric, hence the need for sanding is reduced. Follow up with the usual spray coats of silver, and finish aircraft to suit your fancy.

It's almost sad to think that of all that beautiful construction work you have put into your bird, no-

Covering and doping a one-piece wing in a small workshop is difficult but rewarding.

thing will show except those last few weeks of work spent in your covering and finishing effort.

CLEANING YOUR ELECTRIC IRON

After the heat shrinking exercise on a wing or a couple of other components, you will find the bottom of the electric iron is beginning to pick up burned deposits of dope. If these deposits become heavy enough to cover a considerable portion of the iron's surface, it is necessary to take the time to clean the stuff off. If it is not cleaned off, some of these deposits will be rubbed into and practically fused with your nice, clean doped surfaces.

The iron's aluminum bottom surface is rather hard to clean. Laquer thinner on a rag, rubbed furiously does help somewhat on minor clean ups, but not much. A sharp wood chisel if skillfully manipulated will get quite a bit off too. However, the ironing surface is easy to gouge. My favorite way is to simply hold the bottom of the iron against my trusty disc sander until it is sanded clean. Sanding off a bit of aluminum in the process is acceptable.

Additional Information On Dacron Work

SPORT AVIATION MAGAZINE ISSUES

January 1961 ————— Ceconite 101. . . . New Fabric for Homebuilts, By Joan Trefethen
January 1964 ————— Aircraft Coverings and Their Applications, Part II, By Marty Haedtler
February 1964 ————— More on Non-Standard Fabrics, By Stanley R. Hatfield
January 1969 ————— Aircraft Dacron (Source Information) By B. C. Leach
January 1972 ————— Dacron/Ceconite Fabric (Use Tip) By Tony Bingelis

Other Sources

Stits Aircraft Supplies — Poly-Fiber Aircraft Covering Process — Procedure Manual
C.A.M. 18-FAA Publication now out of print, but reprints available from EAA Headquarters
Aviation Mechanics Journal . . . . Recovering with Ceconite . . . . May-June 1971 issue.

Before You Paint

Kids do it in the elementary schools and grown-ups do it in their garages and on their driveways. I'm talking about painting of course. Magnificent workmanship notwithstanding, nothing affects the appearance of the completed homebuilt as much as its final finish (dope, paint, lacquer, whatever).

Painting, although not difficult, requires the exercise of common sense, observation of basic rules and instructions, and at least an interest in doing a good job. Reasonable weather and working conditions do help, of course.

Unfortunately, as long as we have impatient builders, we will have aircraft with disappointing finishes. Blame it on haste if you will, but techniques of application that are not under complete and absolute control play a key role too.

Nobody has ever learned to paint by reading a book on the subject. You can read (learn) what not to do and what to do, but the "how to do it" part develops only with practice. If you are an observant person, you will quickly learn to control your spray painting applications. Everything else hinges on methodical preparation.

There is no shortage of reading material on the subject. Each paint can has a complete course of instruction detailing how that product should be used.

Furthermore, some of your best friends undoubtedly are experts on the subject and would be only too willing to explain to you in detail how to do it. Or, if you are already in process, tell you why you are doing it wrong . . . . but don't hold that against them, they are only trying to be helpful.

Remember, the painting process is your last chance to turn out a beautiful airplane. So don't get impatient at this late stage of building.

A lot of things have to be considered before you start spraying paint and most of them are not described on the paint can or in any instruction booklet you may have acquired. There are some things that nobody would think of cautioning you about, simply because experienced individuals seem to assume that everybody knows about those pesky little details. Not so.

FIRST THINGS FIRST

The first step in preparing the aircraft for painting entails a close inspection of all of its surfaces for imperfections, proper fit of parts, and smoothness of the skin surfaces.

The complete aircraft should then be cleaned with detergent and water if necessary.

All nooks and crannies should be vacuumed out

Use of fiberglass permits nice compound curves but requires a lot of preparatory sanding before the prime coat and finish can be applied.

to remove dust and other overlooked construction residue. Better not overlook this little detail, for when you do start to spray, the force of the airblast will blow that stuff around and into your paint.

During the initial cleaning process, be sure to remove all marks (pencil, felt pen, chalk, etc.). Otherwise, you might be shocked to see these inoffensive little marks bleed right through the paint.

SURFACE PREPARATIONS

FABRIC SURFACES. These require no special preparation, and are ready for the brush application of clear nitrate dope, or whatever you are using, as soon as they are covered. It is not a good idea to leave fabric-covered components around the shop too long after they are covered before giving them their finish coatings. Keep the fabric-covered surfaces out of the sunlight, as it is harmful to unprotected fabric. Drape the structure with a plastic sheet to keep the dust off.

Dacron will, of course, require heat shrinking before additional finishing efforts are undertaken. Ordinarily no other special surface preparations are required of fabric-covered surfaces.

FIBERGLASS SURFACES. Before any finish is applied to fiberglass surfaces, they should be wiped down with MEK (Methyl Ethyl Ketone — paint stores handle it) and thoroughly sanded to remove all glaze from the surfaces. No matter how smooth the surface may seem to you, you can bet it will not be. After you apply a coat of paint or primer, an unbelievable number of imperfections and pinholes will suddenly appear. Polyester fiberglass is more prone to an outcropping of these surface uglies than epoxy fiberglass.

Cure this condition by spraying a coat of primer surfacer or paint over the pinholes. Wait a bit until the paint begins to set and then, using your finger, smear the still-wet paint over and into the pinholes. Otherwise you will have to spray coat after coat to ultimately hide the pinholes.

Now is it ready to paint? Probably not. The surfaces feel and look smooth, but I'll bet there still are more imperfections, pinholes, lumps, bumps and scratches than there are fleas on a stray dog.

You can prove this. Take the airplane outside where the rising or setting sun shines on it. You will be appalled at the number of ripples and bumps the sunlight and shadows reveal. Back to the sanding block eh?

Except perhaps for fabric, just about any kind of aircraft surface can benefit from at least a light sanding with No. 400 wet-dry sandpaper. Of course, if the surfaces need basic smoothing, you might have

to begin with No. 100 or No. 180 aluminum oxide sandpaper. Don't use that cheap, crummy flint sandpaper! Use the best, the silicon and aluminum oxide sandpapers, and the wet-dry sandpapers.

Always use a sanding block! Regular rubber sanding blocks may be found at paint stores. One should always be used to help maintain level surfaces and flowing contours during sanding.

Has it ever occurred to you that there is a right way to sand a surface to obtain the best finish? There is. Never go around in circles with the sandpaper. Always use that rubber sanding block and sand back and forth whenever possible. A cross-hatch sanding pattern also gives good results. A lot of builders don't realize that the sanding pattern is so important. It can have a marked effect on the finish.

When sanding fiberglass surfaces, an initial fast cut wet sanding with No. 180 paper may be needed to level the surfaces. If so, follow this up with No. 320 grit paper for prepriming finishing.

Here's how to fold wet-dry sandpaper for hand-held sanding. Fold and tear a regular 9-inch x 11-inch sheet of wet-dry paper into 4 pieces. Each piece as it is used should be triple folded, leaving one face toward the surface being sanded, the other toward your hand, and the third portion folded between the two. Use plenty of water and don't be too frugal with the paper. Change it frequently to obtain the quickest sanding results.

PLYWOOD AND WOOD SURFACES. As you may know, plywood is always sanded lightly prior to gluing. This is essential if birch plywood is used as its glaze-like surface — a by-product of the rolling process of manufacture — may also prevent you from obtaining a good paint bond. A light sanding, therefore, is necessary to remove it.

Before applying any finish to wood surfaces, they should be smooth to the touch. Smooth surfaces significantly reduce the amount of varnish that will be required. While you're at it, remove as much of the excess glue from the joints as it practical. Varnishes do not adhere very well to glue joints as they are very smooth and slick. After this treatment, sand with No. 180 and No. 320 sandpaper. Then wipe the surface with a lightly dampened cloth. The surface is now ready for whatever finishing process you want to use.

ALUMINUM SURFACES. Aluminum skin has an oily film over its surface resulting mostly from manufacture. In the process of building, you will have added more oily film in the form of fingerprints. So the first important step before doing any finishing work is to sanitize the metal. Clean it thoroughly, otherwise the paint may not stick uniformly.

What to do? Wipe it with lacquer thinner? Well,

that's not bad, but not too good either. It will help, of course, and is better than nothing. But to be sure, you should wash the surfaces to be painted with a good detergent and follow that with a good rinsing. Don't forget to scrub around the rivet heads . . . . use a firm sponge, stiff brush, or a clean rag.

Next, the highly polished Alclad aluminum surfaces should be dulled or roughened for best adhesion of the paint. Even if you plan to etch the aluminum skin it is still a good idea to precede all of the finishing steps with a light sanding using No. 400 wet-dry sandpaper. Go over the whole aircraft.

Pop rivet holes should be filled as they are natural sources for corrosion. Use a drop of zinc chromate in each of them. Yes, in each of them. This is followed by filling the holes and other imperfections with a glazing putty — Dupont's Lacquer Spot Putty, for example. These fillers are best applied over zinc chromate or a primed surface. Check the instructions.

STEEL SURFACES. Here again, the best adhesion of the prime coat and the finish coat is that obtained on a dull, unpolished metal surface.

For steel tubing and fittings there is nothing like sandblasting to remove rust and scale. This cleaning provides you with virgin metal which requires no further cleaning, as long as a prime coat is immediately applied before any additional handling with bare hands. Brushing steel with a wire brush is acceptable for small parts, but it does a poorer job and doesn't present as good a surface for the primer.

All rust must be neutralized or removed from steel parts before priming and painting. Any rust that remains, however microscopic, will continue to fester and ultimately break through and blister the paint in the areas affected. Sanding steel surfaces will rarely remove all vestiges of rust. Only by chemically neutralizing it are you assured of a long lasting finish. One such easy-to-use neutralizer is OSPHO. It stops rust and prepares rusted surfaces for painting. Other metal conditioners are now on the market and may be found in various discount and hardware stores.

MASKING

Take the time to cover and mask all metal fittings before painting. Cover the wheels and tires and don't forget the tailwheel. Protect the upholstery and control cables from unwanted overspray.

The windshield and windows need special attention and must be completely covered. Remember, certain fumes, when trapped, will cause the plastic to craze. For this reason it is important to remove the protective cover as soon as the painting is completed. Whatever you do, don't let any volatile substances, such as lacquer thinner, get on the plastic windows, as crazing will surely follow at some later date.

For your masking you will need several rolls of fresh masking tape in either the ½-inch or ¾-inch widths. The tape should be no wider than that if it is to be directly affixed to the aircraft skin. Too big a risk is involved in its removal otherwise. As mentioned, the tape must be fresh so forget about putting that old stuff you have on hand next to the fair skin of your bird.

The proper way to mask an area is to first lay the tape along the line to be masked, or along the numbers as the case may be. Then, over that, attach the cover paper. Use a separate piece of masking tape over that which you've already put down. Never try to attach the cover paper directly to the aircraft, as

This cheapskate (the author) is using newspapers to mask his airplane. This is not without its risks.

following nice accurate lines is difficult and the removal of the cover and tapes later would undoubtedly turn out to be a bit traumatic.

Masking is an eyeball exercise. The masked line must look good to the eye, otherwise the painted line will disappoint you. When laying down a long straight line, affix one end of the tape for about 2 or 3 inches and then back off as you unroll the entire length needed, while holding the roll about 8 inches away from the airplane. With your eye affixed to the point where you want your end of the tape to be, slowly lower your end of the tape until it touches. All the while keep a moderate tension on the tape. It will settle in place along a straight line beautifully. You cannot really lay down a straight line if you try to press the tape down a few inches at a time.

Tape needs to be firmly stuck down to keep the paint from leaking under its edges. Minimize this risk by pressing your fingernail (use your thumbnail) against the edge and running the nail the full length of the tape. Any place where two pieces of tape cross, press that juncture point with the sharp edge of your fingernail to insure that there is no gap, however slight, at that crossing of the tapes.

Intricate paint designs like insignias and family crests can often be masked using ¼-inch or 1/8-inch tapes to outline them. An easier way is to use stencils cut from a vinyl self-adhesive decorative paper (contact paper). This decorative paper can be found in the wall paper or household wares sections of discount stores. The stencil is made by drawing the design you want directly on the vinyl paper (select a light plain color or at least some simple pattern). Cut the design out with scissors, peel the paper backing off the vinyl and press the stencil into position. Rub the edges with your fingernail to seal them. After the painting is completed, it can be easily peeled off. A little experimentation should give you a good idea how to best use this handy material for masking and design functions.

You will probably ignore this suggestion, but I am sure you would be much happier if you do not use old newspapers for your masking covers. Use butcher paper or any other kind of roll of cheap, plain paper obtainable from most paper companies.

There are three things wrong with using newspapers for masking covers. Newspaper print comes off, especially on white paint and on paint that isn't completely cured. It will have a propensity for sticking and for transferring its print to your painted surfaces. The second annoyance is that caused by paint spray penetrating through the small puncture marks found along the edges of virtually all newspapers. If you must use newspapers, always make a fold about 6 inches wide along one edge to neutralize this booby trap. Last, but not least, the newspapers are rather short pieces, and you will find yourself working much longer when masking the airplane. Of course, you will also use much more tape. You will soon realize how very nice it would have been to put on long strips of masking cover instead.

A single-edge razor blade is an indispensible tool for cutting the tapes to the proper lengths and angles. The correct way to use the blade is to press it against the tape at the angle you want cut. At the same time pull up on the free end of the tape. It will shear nicely. A cutting, sawing or slicing motion is not recommended, particularly if you have a fabric covering or finger underneath.

These pre-paint preparations take much time, but are critical to the finished product. Remember, the actual painting process takes but a ridiculously short period of time, so don't slight the preparations by rushing things.

A simple paint design is best for small aircraft.

Bold paint schemes are in character with aerobatic aircraft.

Painting the Homebuilt

Paint and finish the airplane before you take it to the airport. I think it is most impractical to fly an unpainted airplane for awhile and then have to pull it in for painting. What a job that would be. The airplane will have acquired dirt (and oil) all over it, and would require a very good degreasing and cleaning before painting. This entails a considerable amount of disassembly work. One more thing, will you have the facilities to paint at the airport, or will you have to haul everything home again?

Because the average builder has never sprayed anything in his life bigger than a birdhouse, he normally approaches this final stage of construction with more apprehension than the situation merits. Typically, he makes his first mistake when he tries to do the job with inadequate equipment. If the proper equipment cannot be borrowed or purchased, it might be wise to get somebody to paint your airplane for you.

You will need a good spray gun, and a compressor large enough to provide a flow of air that stays ahead of the gun's needs. Otherwise, you are in for a difficult time of it.

Sorry, don't even consider painting the airplane with a paint brush .... it will look like it.

Naturally, most of us do not have access to a paint booth large enough to accommodate an airplane, so the garage, the basement, the driveway, or the yard somewhere under the trees becomes our paint shop. The hazards of painting a homebuilt under such conditions are both real and imagined. An explanation is in order.

By hazards, I mean to include bugs, dust, wind, unexpected showers, toxic fumes, newsprint, old masking tape, unstuck masking tape, torn cover paper, runs, too little and too much paint, overspray, lack of ventilation, bleeding paint, telephone calls, visitors, and running out of time, paint and patience.

Painting the airplane in the garage or basement requires ventilation. A generous amount of fresh air must be in constant circulation. Take my word for it before you start. Don't try to paint your airplane in the basement .... not unless you can physically survive the fumes and the ire of a family reacting to the instinct for survival.

Painting in the garage is a lesser evil, as the doors may be left open and a fan used to help move the air. A lot of builders hang a clear plastic curtain all around the scene. This helps control the dust inside the painting area, and it protects your garage and possessions against over-spray. However, you will have a ventilation problem to solve.

Painting the airplane in the yard or driveway introduces still other rusks. Dust and bugs are two of the most common.

It depends somewhat on where you live and the season of the year. But, it seems that some bugs will dive gleefully into newly applied paint, while flapping their wings furiously, apparently bent on self-destruction. Unfortunately, they destroy your beautiful finish as well.

Learn the time of day when bugs are least active in your territory.

Don't spray out of doors when it is windy. You will be wasting your time, and you may find yourself being sued by your neighbor for painting his car an offshade of chartreuse and red.

Even in the absence of wind, dust can damage the overall finish in a manner more devastating than the localized effects of suicidal bugs.

You can help settle some of the dust by watering the surrounding vegetation and wetting down the driveway with a water hose. It would, likewise, be helpful to paint during the early morning hours when the winds are gentle and the air is not rising due to the sun's heating. However, if you are spraying dope, humidity will be a factor to consider during early morning hours.

I believe the finishing of an aircraft can be separated into two categories, (1) Fabric-covered aircraft, and (2) nonfabric-covered aircraft. The nonfabric-covered aircraft category would include those with aluminum skins, plywood covering, fiberglass skins, and similar "hard" surfaces. Essentially, any hard-surface aircraft can be painted with virtually any of the finishes available today

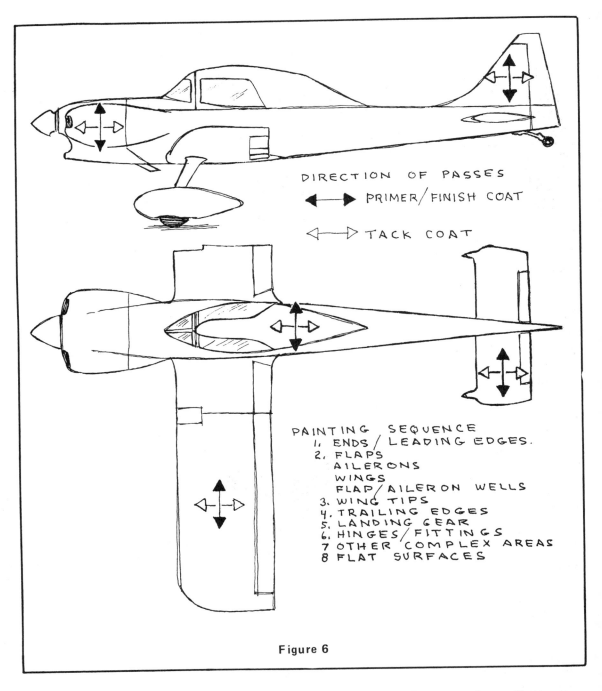

DIRECTION OF PASSES

⬅➡ PRIMER/FINISH COAT

◁▷ TACK COAT

PAINTING SEQUENCE
1. ENDS / LEADING EDGES.
2. FLAPS
   AILERONS
   WINGS
   FLAP/AILERON WELLS
3. WING TIPS
4. TRAILING EDGES
5. LANDING GEAR
6. HINGES/FITTINGS
7 OTHER COMPLEX AREAS
8 FLAT SURFACES

Figure 6

while the options for fabric-covered aircraft are necessarily limited to finishes having a high degree of flexibility.

FABRIC–COVERED AIRCRAFT

No matter how tightly the fabric is stretched (and it shouldn't be excessive), the fabric covering does present a flexible, pliable surface in service. Therefore, any finish applied to the fabric will be constantly flexing and drumming in flight. It is easy to see why the finish used must be flexible enough to withstand the long term effects of such tortures. Until recently, fabric-covered aircraft, almost without exception, were finished with dope . . . . butyrate dope. Butyrate dope is flexible and retains its flexibility very well, with the passage of time. It survives as the most practical finish for fabric-covered aircraft.

Builders dissatisfied with the many-coated and tedious finishing process required with dope have tried painting their planes with enamel.

In the early days of homebuilding, most enamels were rather brittle because of their extremely hard surface. The finish was prone to crack and chip, and the repair or patching of the fabric often meant refinishing a whole panel. Blending a patched area was almost impossible. That is still the case with most enamel finishes.

288

Spot refinishing remains a problem to consider.

Lately, however, some builders are finishing their fabric-covered aircraft with Dupont Dulux enamel and the new polyurethane enamels with considerable success and with good surface longevity. So, now in addition to the traditional butyrate dope finish, you might consider a polyurethane enamel, Dupont's IMRON, for example, along with their Dulux enamel. Of course, other brands of polyurethane may be equally good, and their substitution would be determined more by local availability than anything else.

It takes a heck of a lot of dope to finish an airplane. For this reason, the polyurethane enamels are currently popular with the builders of fabric-covered aircraft. The first Emeraude I constructed is still beautiful in its 11-year-old coat of Dupont Dulux enamel. However, small hairline cracks are beginning to appear along the edges of the fairing strips where the fabric changes direction rather abruptly. The white areas are less affected than are the darker colors. But, I wonder if the same condition would not have developed by now in a butyrate dope finish.

If dope is your choice, you should acquire the use of a pressure pot, since it does take a lot of dope to finish an aircraft. Spraying many coats of dope from a one-quart spray gun is like trying to water the lawn with a squirt gun. It can and is being done, but it takes a long time.

Some airplanes are built with the idea of winning awards and trophies. They receive extra preparation efforts as well as extra coats of dope or paint. Such fabric-covered aircraft look beautiful the first year, but the heavy, thick paint layers tend to develop surface cracks much sooner than the minimum-coat finishes. Completely out of the trophy seeking builder's mind, I am sure, is the fact that there will also be an increased weight penalty for a super deluxe show paint job.

If you are not driven by an intense need to compete for awards, to the exclusion of having a nice, functional airplane, content yourself with the minimum number of coats. When enamel is used, for example, a single full coat will often suffice. By single full coat, I mean a tack or light mist coat that is followed about 10 to 15 minutes later by a full spray top coating.

Heavy coats of paint also affect the balance of control surfaces to the degree that they may no longer be 100 per cent balanced.

It might even be necessary to rebalance your control surfaces after the painting (doping) is completed. Even if your design does not utilize balanced control surfaces, always be wary of adding weight aft of the control hinge axis.

It is important to remember that you cannot successfully put dope over any surface material other than fabric. Dope sprayed on metal will soon peel off, in sheets. This is one of the disadvantages of using dope. As a result, it is necessary to purchase matching enamel for the cowling and other metal or fiberglass parts. (Stay with the same brand for both the dope and the matching enamel.)

There are plenty of good instructions available to builders regarding dope application, finishing and refinishing aircraft. Excellent informational material is put out by Randolph Products Co., P.O. Box 67, Carlstadt, New Jersey 07072. Another good source is Stits Aircraft Coatings, P.O. Box 3084, Riverside, California 92509. An excellent manual entitled Aircraft Painting and Finishing is published by Aviation Maintenance Foundation, Inc., P.O. Box 739, Basin, Wyoming 82410.

No attempt will be made here to repeat the manufacturer's detailed procedures. Rather, let's continue to discuss lesser known little details. After all, who knows better than the manufacturer the best way to use his products? Follow his instructions, and you will have everything going for you in obtaining a good finish.

Don't mix brands. Don't use one brand of paint and another of reducer-thinner, or even two different brands of paint. It might be all right, and then again, it might not work satisfactorily. Why risk a poor finish or one which will break down and peel and/or crack in a few months? A good butyrate or paint job should hold up well for 10 years or longer if the airplane is kept hangared and clean.

NONFABRIC AIRCRAFT

Because aluminum-skinned, fiberglass-skinned, and plywood-covered aircraft do not have flexible surfaces, they can be finished in almost any of the currently available finishes now on the market, with the exception of dope.

Currently the popular finishes include the polyurethane enamels, the acrylic enamels, the Dupont Dulux enamels, and, in some cases, the acrylic laquers. The use of each of these types of finishes is amply covered in the manufacturer's instruction sheets and on some of the labels attached to the containers.

Nonfabric-covered aircraft surfaces will usually benefit from a wash primer coat after the final sanding with No. 320 or No. 400 wet-dry sandpaper. This is true of fiberglass skins and particularly of aluminum skins. A wash primer is one which provides a mild etch to metal surfaces and establishes a good bond for top coats. Acrylic enamel top coats can be

Doping fabric with a small brush is like trying to comb your hair with a toothpick. Use a good 3-inch to 4-inch brush to get the job done properly and fast.

applied directly over the wash primer, but many builders prefer to add a coat of epoxy primer for maximum corrosion protection before application of the top coat finish. Here again, it is best to adhere to the instructions issued by the manufacturer of your finish materials.

My own personal choice for a good, all-around, economical, safe to use finish for nonfabric surfaces is Dupont's Centari Acrylic enamel. It doesn't require a primer and it will adhere to virtually any clean surface. You can paint and repaint as often as you like and it won't wrinkle. You can use it for spot painting and, best of all, it dries fast and rewards you with a beautiful, self-polished shining surface.

PAINTING POTPOURRI

It is probably a universal procedure to shoot the basic color first. In other words, if the airplane is mostly white, spray all the white first. Then mask for the other color(s). There is one big exception. If your basic color is red, put on all other colors first because most red paints/dopes are what is known as "bleeding reds." That is, the pigment of these reds (Tennessee Red, Champion Red, Vermillion, Insignia Red, Stearman Vermillion, Waco Red, etc., etc.) are soluble in solvents and will bleed to the top surface of any color you put over them. I REPEAT, do not try to paint over red with any other color. I'm sure there are some sealers on the market that can seal the red to keep it from bleeding through but these are not commonly known or available in most home towns.

Reds, if used as a trim should be applied after all other colors have been sprayed and are thoroughly dried. A few of the reds are nonbleeding, but you had better make sure of this beforehand.

By the time your project has progressed this far, you probably will have decided on the colors and the basic paint scheme. Perhaps not. A surprising number of builders remain unsure right up to the time they stop in at the paint store.

Here's something to think about. The lighter the color, the lighter the airplane appears to look. White, somehow, makes the aircraft look cool. Furthermore, white reflects light so well that surface imperfections are difficult to discern, and this is good. In hot climates, this is also a very important consideration for another reason. Internal temperatures in the summer can reach close to 200 degrees F in a relatively short period of time. The darker the colors, the higher the internal and surface temperatures. However, on the minus side, white is not a highly visible color in the air.

The smaller the aircraft, the less fussy and cluttered the paint scheme should be. Most aircraft are viewed from a distance. How would your proposed paint scheme look from a distant vantage point? Well, so much for day dreaming. . . .

If you do not have a spraying procedure of your own, you might consider using the general spraying sequence illustrated in Figure 1. Much depends on the aircraft's size, design, and whether it is fully assembled, so feel free to modify the procedure to suit.

Generally, the bottom of the aircraft is sprayed first. If the aircraft is on the gear, the tail may be raised so that the bottom of the fuselage is easily accessible. Some support must be used for the engine when tilted in this manner. At all other times, be careful to weight down the tail so that the airplane will not flip over on its nose unexpectedly while you are working. With wings and tail surfaces removed, and with the engine installed, the tail is very light and requires some restraining weight.

After the initial top coat has been sprayed, particularly on fiberglass surfaces, you might be appalled at the number of tiny little imperfections that appear. If so, a second coat seems advisable. But before putting it on, fill the imperfections using a small, flexible squeegee (artist's spatula) to spread on a thin layer of acrylic spot putty wherever needed. (Remember, read the instructions and follow them to the letter.) After the putty dries overnight, level the treated spots with a small sanding block and No. 100 grit sandpaper (aluminum or zinc oxide grade). Finish the entire part with No. 320 wet-dry paper, using plenty of water while sanding. This will really smooth the surface nicely for the next, and what could be the final coat.

No attempt should be made to hide joints and seams. One example. Do not try to hide the joints between the windows and the aircraft's structure with paint and filler. It will only be a matter of time before the seams crack and look ugly. It might even be better to install the windows and windshield after painting, but this depends upon the means of installation.

WHAT TO DO ABOUT OVERSPRAY

Overspray results when the fine mist beyond the basic spray patterns of the area being sprayed falls on the aircraft surface in a semidry condition. This, in effect, leaves that particular area with a dull granular appearance. The dull appearance of overspray can, however, be minimized or eliminated. Enamel overspray does not ordinarily present the problem that laquers or dopes do since its drying rate is so much slower. The enamel overspray will blend into the finish while it is still wet.

Dried overspray from most paints, other than polyurethanes, can usually be "burned down" by spraying a mixture of one part retarder to two parts thinner on the painted surface while the overspray and base finish are still fresh. The mixture will soften the surface film enough to permit the overspray to sink in and gloss.

It is far better to prevent overspray effects in

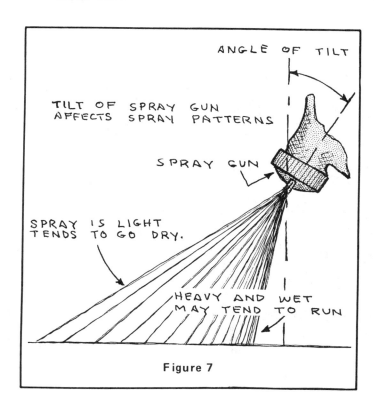

Figure 7

the first place. When spraying, tilt the gun slightly so that the overspray will be ahead of the area being painted, especially when spraying the top of the fuselage and the tops of the wings. The new paint coming out of the gun will wipe out the overspray as you work toward the unpainted area. (Figure 7)

TAPE REMOVAL

Oh boy! Here is where we have differing ideas. If the paint comes off with the tape. . . .you did something wrong and I'll bet it was not in how the tapes were removed.

If you masked the airplane properly, you can easily and quickly pull away the cover paper which should have been attached with separate tapes to the taped outlines. The finesse used to remove the cover tapes is not critical as the tapes are not attached to any of the painted surfaces. After the cover paper is pulled off, however, you would probably prefer to have anyone who has been helping you to go get himself a cup of coffee or go to the movie while you, personally, remove the remaining tapes. They should be removed carefully.

Everybody seems to agree that tapes must not be permitted to remain for long once the spraying has been completed. An hour or so is long enough even for slow-drying enamels. You don't want to allow the new paint to dry to a hard surface before the tape removal, , because the paint line at the tape edges will be forcibly separated in a ragged manner as the tapes are pulled off.

Some say pull the tape away from the painted surface at a shallow angle. Others say pull the tape back over itself at about a 30 degree angle. The method doesn't matter much just as long as the tape is removed while the paint top coat is only partially set and still relatively pliable. It does matter, however, that you proceed with the pulling away of the tape slowly and smoothly. Fear not, you will develop your own personal way of doing it. If it works, you did everything just right.

EAA Aviation Center — Oshkosh, Wisconsin.

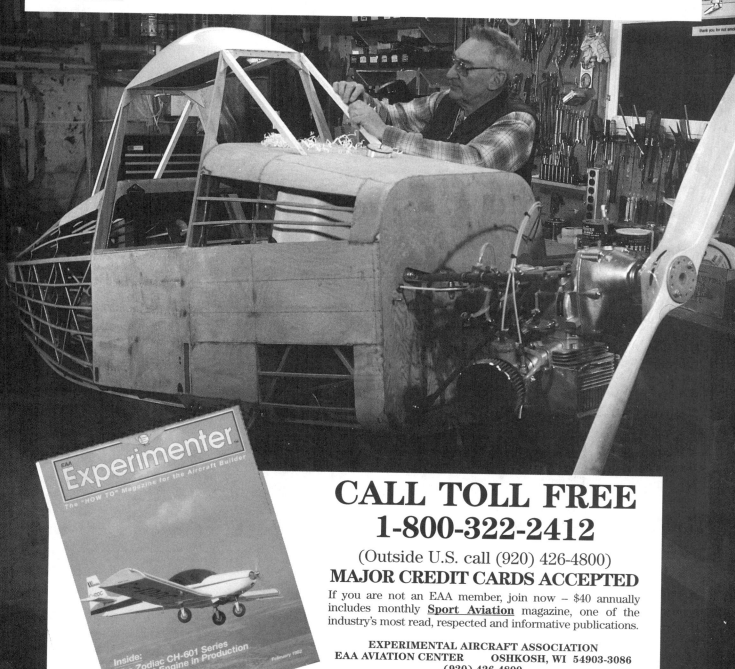

.....AFTER IT'S FINISHED

Weight and Balance

....A Realistic Look

Not only does the FAA require a weight and balance check as part of the permanent aircraft records, but an airplane that is extremely tail-heavy (exceeds c.g. limits) is a potential disaster machine —a set up for a short-lived stall-spin career. So, too, is an airplane so nose-heavy that it can't be flared for a safe landing. Of the two, the nose-heavy condition is the least likely to lead to total disaster, only because you may not be able to get it off the ground.

Whatever you do, don't abandon the idea of weighing your aircraft simply because you cannot find calibrated scales . . . . or any other reason for that matter. You <u>must</u> know what your weight and c.g. situation is before you attempt to fly.

SCALES ARE WHERE YOU FIND THEM

The ease of any weighing effort, naturally, is determined by the equipment used. The scales, ideally should be of a low-platform variety, and accurately calibrated. But, how many of us can really obtain such equipment, even for a once-in-a-lifetime project? Nevertheless, your objective is to get the best scales you can.

Feed stores in many parts of our country have accurate platform scales which often can be borrowed over the weekend for such an outlandish purpose as weighing a homemade airplane. Unfortunately, you can usually only obtain one platform scale at the feed store. You could, perhaps, go to another feed store somewhere and borrow a second scale. It would make your job a lot easier. But, one is better than none.

Here's another lead. The Department of Public Safety in at least one friendly state utilizes special low-profile scales for weighing trucks. These fine folks have been known to drop by when asked and allow the use of their scales in the interest of public safety . . . . and curiosity. Besides, they couldn't permit you to haul that airplane along the public highway if its wheel load were so high it might damage the highway pavement.

Equipment rental shops in larger cities sometimes have scales for rent although the smaller shops are not likely to have anything usable.

Perhaps a university laboratory or an airport maintenance shop can accommodate your needs. Ask someone at your local airport how their weight and balance requirements are handled.

The last common source and last resort, in most cases, are bathroom scales. I'd like to have a dollar for every airplane that has been weighed on bathroom scales.

I don't know which presents the bigger problem, using only a single, accurate platform scale for the weighing, or using five bathroom scales of doubtful performance. Either way you have your work cut out for you.

THE SINGLE SCALE PROBLEM

If you can only obtain a single platform scale, don't be too concerned. You can still do a fairly good job of weighing the aircraft. More work will be involved of course; not only will you have to build a small inclined ramp for each wheel to roll up onto the scale, but you will also need to build a leveling platform for the other main wheel. This ramp platform will have to be built to the same height as the surface of the scale. Remember, the airplane must be level in all directions for weighing. This is particularly important when only one scale is used. That one scale can be used for each of the three weighing points, however, a bathroom scale used under the tail wheel or nose wheel will do much to simplify the problem with little or no sacrifice in accuracy.

THE MULTIPLE BATHROOM SCALE PROBLEM

Bathroom scales are notoriously inaccurate . . . . ask anyone on a diet. Most bathroom scales can only weigh up to approximately 300 pounds. (On second thought, don't ask a dieter.) The range of bathroom scales is usually insufficient to accommodate the weight of a single wheel of a standard-size aircraft. They may work well enough, however, for designs such as the Volksplane I, Teenies II, gyrocopters, Taylor monoplanes, and other light planes with empty weights around 500 pounds (250 pounds or so per wheel).

To weigh lighter aircraft, three scales will do. Larger aircraft also can be weighed with bathroom scales, in a rather primitive fashion, although five scales will be needed. I suggest you solicit all the

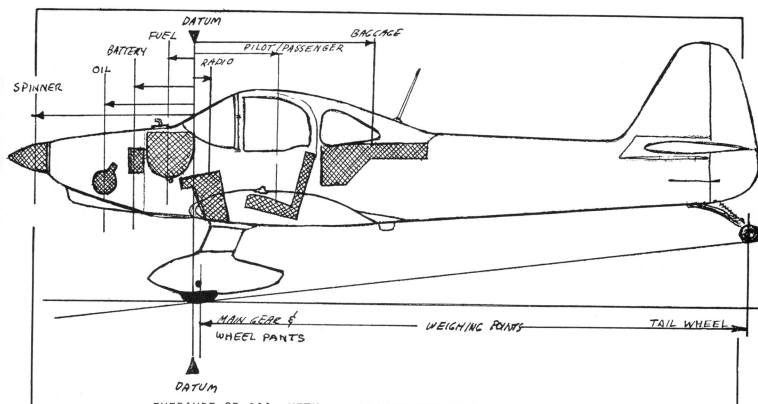

DATUM

EMERAUDE CP 311 N5TX   WEIGHT AND BALANCE DATA

STATIONS	DISTANCE FROM DATUM (ARM)
Baggage	40.0
Battery	-19.75
Gas	-8.50
Landing Gear	3.75
Oil	-27.0
Pilot/Passenger	26.0
Tail Wheel	183.0
Spinner	-51.0
Radio	0.0

DATUM

Datum at leading edge of the wing as measured at rib #3 at 39.7"
from the fuselage axis. (1010 mm.)

LEVEL

Top longeron at the cabin entrance.

Figure 1

C.G. LIMITS

Rear limit is 28% (16.5") or 420 mm from leading edge.
Forward limit is 16% (9.4") or 240 mm from leading edge.

LOAD FACTOR

Estimated at 4.1 G @ 1445 lbs gross
               4.4G @ 1345 lbs gross

Compiled June 3, 1978

WEIGHT AND BALANCE FORM

Aircraft Name __EMERAUDE CP311__   Serial # __TB-5__   Registration # __NT5X__

Owner's Name __TONY BINGELIS__

Address __8509 GREENFLINT LANE__ City __AUSTIN__   State __TX__ Zip __78759__

Datum __WING LEADING EDGE__ Leveling __TOP LONGERON (CABIN)__

EMPTY WEIGHT CALCULATIONS (First subtract oil, if any)

Item	Scale reading	Tare	Net weight	Arm (Inches)	Moment (Inch lbs)
Left Wheel	431.50		431.50	3.75	1618.13
Right Wheel	444.50		444.50	3.75	1666.88
Auxiliary Wheel	30.00	1.50	28.50	183.00	5215.50
Less Oil			− 7.20	− 27.00	194.40
Fixed Ballast					
		Empty Weight	897.30	Total Moment	8694.91

EMPTY WEIGHT C.G. LOCATION: __9.69__ inches.

$$\text{Empty weight c.g.} = \frac{\text{Total moment}}{\text{Empty weight}} = \frac{8694.91}{897.30} = 9.69 \text{ inches}$$

EQUIPMENT INSTALLED AT TIME OF WEIGHING:

EQUIPMENT LIST

Item	Type	Weight	Arm	Moment
Radio				
Wheel Fairings				
Spinner	PITTS	3.50	−36.00	− 126.00
BATTERY	25 AMP/HR	25.00	−19.75	− 493.75

FORWARD AND REARWARD C.G. EXTREMES

Most forward C.G. loading   Most rearward C.G. loading

Item	Weight	Arm	Moment	Weight	Arm	Moment
A/C Empty Weight	897.30	9.69	8694.84	897.30	9.69	8694.84
Oil	10.00	−27.00	− 270.00	5.00	−27.00	− 135.00
Pilot	180.00	26.00	4680.00	180.00	26.00	4680.00
Passenger				200.00	26.00	5200.00
Fuel	126.00	− 8.50	− 1071.00	18.00	− 8.50	− 153.00
Baggage				45.00	40.00	1800.00
Totals	1213.30		12033.84	1345.30		20086.84

Forward C.G. __9.9__ inches   Rearward C.G. __14.93__ inches

$$CG_f = \frac{\text{Total moments}}{\text{Total weight}} = \frac{12033.84}{1213.30} = 9.92''$$ $$CG_r = \frac{\text{Total moments}}{\text{Total weight}} = \frac{20086.84}{1345.30} = 14.93''$$

C.G. LIMITS: Forward limit is __9.4__ inches __16__ % Rearward limit is __16.5__ inches __28__ %

MAXIMUM LOADING:

Pilot & passenger (with chutes)		380.00 lbs.
Baggage, maximum		40.00 lbs.
Fuel, maximum	__21__ gals.	126.00 lbs.
TOTAL:		546.00 lbs.

MAXIMUM ALLOWABLE WEIGHT IS: __1445__ lbs.

COCKPIT PLACARDS: Required only if weight limitations are necessary.

Aircraft weighed by: __Tony Bingelis__

Revised 1-19-87

Date of weighing : __June 3, 1978__

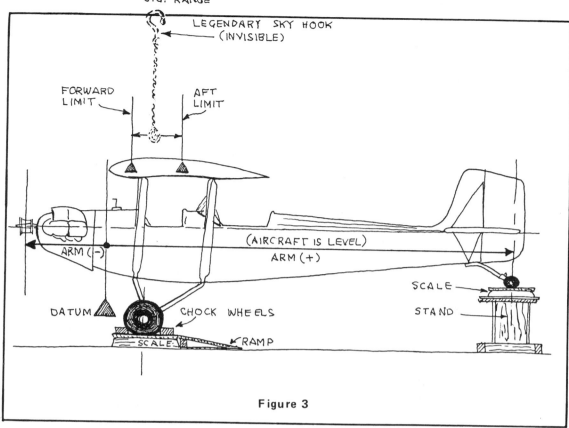

Figure 3

scales you can without built in handles on top. Six or seven will do. By comparing your own, or some known weight on each of them, you can pick the scales that provide the most uniform readings. Don't forget to set each of them to zero before checking.

If your airplane weighs much over 500 pounds, the use of two properly-bridged bathroom scales under a wheel will be required. In other words, the weight of the wheel will be shared by both scales. Each scale will read approximately half of the total weight of the wheel.

Put two of the scales side by side and make sure that they are of uniform height. Bridge across them with a single board to accommodate one wheel. The opposite wheel will need a similar set up. A separate ramp will also be necessary for each main wheel to enable you to push the airplane up onto the platformed scales.

PREPARING THE AIRCRAFT FOR WEIGHING

Remove all the junk, tools, hats, rags, beer cans, etc. from inside the cockpit and baggage compartment. If you haven't done a lot of hangar flying lately, the aircraft may still be clean and orderly. When weighing older aircraft, however, be sure the aircraft is clean (dirt is heavy) and free from mud and mud daubers. Check the wheel pants . . . . they may have accumulated a few pounds of airport mud.

Drain all of the fuel that will come out. If you have been making taxi tests, you will undoubtedly have an unknown quantity of fuel aboard. Also drain whatever oil will run out. Don't bother to run up the engine to warm the oil unless it is wintertime and the oil won't come out of its own accord. Be sure all of the parts are on the aircraft (cowling, windows, propeller, fairings, engine baffles, etc.).

You can either weigh the airplane with the spinner and wheel pants or without. In either instance, they should be listed in the equipment list as should other removable equipment like radios and installed ballast. This will make future calculations of any equipment changes involving weight and balance easier.

GETTING IT ON THE SCALES

Those feed store platform scales you may be using are on wheels. Be sure to chock them before trying to push the airplane up the ramps and onto the scales.

The risk involved in pushing or pulling the airplane up the ramps is in possible abuse to the aircraft. Don't ever permit anyone to pull on the propeller blades. If you do permit anyone to push, be sure to tell him where he can apply the force. One safe way is to muster a couple of helpers whose jobs will be to grasp each tire with both hands and manually rotate the wheels up the ramps. If the aircraft is large and heavy, it would be a good precaution to have somebody with a chock following each wheel.

Actually, getting the plane onto the scales is not a big deal. Simply assure yourself that the aircraft is not being abused and that the push is not so energetic that the plane simply rolls off the opposite end.

Lifting an airplane bodily onto the scales is not recommended if the landing gear is of the slab-spring or tapered-rod type. Those landing gears will flex and exert a springy side force on the scales. This, in most cases, causes improper readings.

Don't forget to chock the wheels immediately. Do not, however, set the brakes, as this can cause scale errors.

LEVELING THE AIRCRAFT

Often, in the process of preparing for the weighing, the builder completely forgets that a tail stand or platform will be needed to hold the tail of the aircraft in a level attitude (tail draggers). This stand should have a large enough surface to support a bathroom scale. It might be difficult to establish exactly how high that platform must be before hand, because you must allow for the height of the scales under the main gear. Don't forget to allow for the height of the scale to be placed under the tail wheel too.

Tricycle-gear aircraft will also require some sort of elevated stand for the nose wheel and scale.

Most aircraft are leveled by using the top longerons as a reference for determining the fore and aft level attitude. Sometimes a large carpenter's square can be laid across the longerons to check the lateral level. At any rate, use whatever level points the designer has identified in the plans.

When you weigh the airplane using a single scale

under one wheel at a time, it is more important than ever to get the airplane level each time the scales are switched to another wheel. Level means level, not almost.

If the aircraft lacks a bit of being level laterally, air can be released from the tire to lower the wing on the high side. To a degree you can take the same corrective action if the nose is slightly high when leveling a tricycle-gear job.

Check everything one more time. Check the levels. Is the airplane all together? The rest is anti-climatic now.

THE DATUM REFERENCE LINE

Before proceeding any further, you must determine the location of the datum. The datum is simply an imaginary vertical reference line from which you make all horizontal measurements for balance purposes. The datum line can be at any easily identified location such as the leading edge of the wing (most commonly used), nose of the aircraft, firewall, or most anywhere you like. A lot of people say a datum line at the nose of the aircraft, or even at some location ahead of the aircraft is best and simplest to use because all of your figures are then positive numbers. I don't think working with a few minus figures is enough of a problem for me to give up the convenience of using the wing's leading edge as an easily located permanent datum. (Figures 1 and 3)

Before removing the aircraft from its level position, you must determine the exact location for certain key elements in the aircraft.

Use a plumb bob to establish centerline marks on the floor between the nose and the tail wheel. Snap a chalk line between these two points, or stretch a string to provide a centerline to work from. Again,

Weighing procedure when you can only get one scale. Note ramp platform under the left wheel.

Aircraft must be level when checking weight at the tail-wheel.

The moment has arrived.

using a plumb bob, mark the location of the datum on the centerline already marked on the floor. The distance (or arm) of the different locations from the datum such as the oil tank, fuel tank, wheels, pilot, passenger, baggage compartment, and installed equipment can now be measured accurately. Record their locations as plus or minus numbers. (Figure 1) Use metric measurements if you like. It will make no difference. Some builders have difficulty in determining the location of the center of gravity of a seated pilot. I understand that is at the belly button (navel, son). No amigo, I don't know if that rule applies equally to boy pilots and girl pilots.

NOW FOR THE NUMBERS

The essential information you have been anxiously awaiting is the empty weight. You arrive at that figure by adding the left and right main wheel weight readings to that of the nose (or tail) wheel reading. Don't forget to subtract the weight of the tare (all of the chock blocks and shim material used on top of the scales). This is your empty weight, like it or not.

.... AND FINALLY THE PAPERWORK

All that remains now is a simple arithmetic problem whereby you obtain certain essential information.

A pocket calculator is very helpful, but so is a junior EAA member who did not flunk his multiplication tables. (Figure 2)

Here is a very rough rule of thumb for determining if your c.g. location is all right. With the airplane loaded for flight, the c.g. should fall somewhere near one-fourth of the total distance back from the leading edge to the trailing edge of the wing. That is a c.g. location at approximately 25 per cent of the wing chord for most airfoils. This is just right. Under no circumstances should it fall further aft than 30 per cent of the chord. If the information is provided in your plans, use those limits as your guide.

Complete a couple of copies of the weight and balance calculations. Give one to the FAA inspector and retain a copy for your aircraft records.

Certification and.....

Annual Condition Inspections

Once upon a time a homebuilt's Airworthiness Certificate automatically expired 12 months to the day after the date of issuance or renewal by the FAA (unless a shorter period was originally prescribed). Unless action was taken to obtain a new Airworthiness Certificate by that date, the old certificate would have become invalid and the homebuilt could no longer be flown legally. But, things do change, and sometimes for the better.

Under the amended provision of FAR Section 21.181 (a)(3), effective September 10, 1979, experimental certificates issued to aircraft for the purpose of exhibition, air racing or operating amateur-built aircraft will have an unlimited duration unless the FAA finds that a specific period should be established. Therefore, recertification inspections on these aircraft by FAA inspectors will no longer be required.

THE ORIGINAL CERTIFICATION PROCESS

AUTHOR'S NOTE:

A book, once published, remains unchanged through the years, governmental regulations, on the other hand, are in a constant state of flux. For this reason, it is impossible to detail the exact procedures necessary to certificate an aircraft, years hence.

The best guidance you can obtain would be from a personal call, or visit, with the FAA office charged with the responsibility of aircraft certification. This is, and probably will remain, the function of your local FAA Manufacturing Inspection District Office (MIDO).

Briefly, you will have to provide the following information about the aircraft:

...Registration No., Model Designation, Serial No., Engine Model, Propeller Make and Model, Number of Seats, Builder's Name/Address, Year of Mfg., Engine Make, Number of Engines, and Registered Owner.

Other requirements you should be familiar with, and evidence or proof you may have to furnish, include:

...an aircraft Log Book containing records of inspections, tests and related findings and means of identifying the areas (photos, etc.) and parts inspected.

...a notorized statement to the effect that the aircraft was fabricated by you (or others) solely for educational or recreational purposes. Federal Aviation Regulation (FAR) Part 21, Section 21.191 (g).

...an AC Form 8050-3 and evidence of compliance with FAR Part 47 (aircraft registration requirements).

...the following placard displayed in full view in the cockpit: PASSENGER WARNING - THIS AIRCRAFT IS AMATEUR-BUILT AND DOES NOT COMPLY WITH FEDERAL SAFETY REGULATIONS FOR STANDARD AIRCRAFT.

........compliance with FAR Part 91, as applicable:
Section 91.33 (instruments and equipment installed).
Section 91.31 (instrument markings/limitations).
Section 91.52 (emergency locator beacon, if needed).
Section 91.31 (aircraft weight and balance).

...assurance that the powerplant has undergone at least one hour of ground operation (idle to full power) and that all systems are operating properly.

...evidence that FAR Part 45 have been complied with (Data Plate and EXPERIMENTAL sign are affixed).

...you must be able to produce invoices or shipping documents to substantiate that the major portion of the aircraft was fabricated by you or individuals.

...the opportunity to indicate your preferred area for the flight test period (usually, a 25 mile radius).

...a signed statement to the effect that:
"I have thoroughly inspected the aircraft and consider that it is eligible for issuance of an Experimental Airworthiness Certificate for the purpose of operating amateur-built aircraft under the provision of FAR 21, Section 21.191"

When you have permanently assembled the aircraft at the airport you should request an airworthiness inspection for the purpose of airworthiness certification of an amateur-built aircraft.

Don't forget to inform the inspector of the location for the inspection, and directions how to get there. Give him your residence and business phone numbers where you can be reached on workdays.

That's the big picture. Good luck.

ANNUAL CONDITION INSPECTIONS ARE REQUIRED

During the aircraft certification procedure, the FAA issues operating limitations, as required by FAR Section 91.43 of FAR Part 91, to ensure an adequate level of safety. Among the limitations imposed is one requiring that the subject aircraft be inspected annually. The requirement will be stated in the following or similarly worded manner:

I certify that this aircraft has been inspected on (insert date) in accordance with the scope and detail of Appendix D of FAR Part 43 and found to be in a condition for safe operation.

Additionally, condition inspections shall be recorded in the aircraft maintenance records showing the following or a similarly worded statement:

No person may operate this aircraft unless within the preceding 12 calendar months it has had a condition inspection performed in accordance with Appendix D of FAR Part 43 and is found to be in a condition for safe operation.

The entry will include the aircraft total time-in-service, the name, signature, and certificate type and number of the person performing the inspection.

WHO MAY MAKE ANNUAL CONDITION INSPECTIONS?

For amateur built and amateur-built exhibition air racing aircraft: Only FAA-certificated repairmen, mechanics holding an airframe and powerplant rating, and appropriately rated repair stations may perform condition inspections in accordance with Appendix D of FAR Part 43.

HOW TO BECOME CERTIFICATED AS A REPAIRMAN FOR YOUR AIRCRAFT

You should make application for a repairman certificate at the time of original aircraft certification. Builders who have had their aircraft certificated prior to the effective date (September 10, 1979) of revised FAR Section 21.181(a)(3) and new 65.104 may make application for repairman certification prior to their next condition inspection due date.

ELIGIBILITY

a. You must be at least 18 years of age and be a U.S. citizen or an individual admitted for permanent residence in the United States.

b. You must be the primary builder of the aircraft. For example, when a school, club or a partnership builds an aircraft, only one individual will be considered for a repairman certificate for each aircraft built, such as the class instructor or designated project leader.

c. Demonstrate to the certificating FAA inspector your ability to perform condition inspection and to determine whether the subject aircraft is in a condition for safe operation.

APPLICATIONS

Applicants may obtain copies of the Airman Certificate and/or Rating Application, FAA Form 8610-2 (OMB 04-R0065), from their local FAA General Aviation District Office or Flight Standards District Office. Applicants must complete this form and submit it to their local FAA office. (See the illustrated example.) The box for "repairman" (at the top of form) must be checked, and underneath in the space for "specify rating" print or type the words "Experimental Aircraft Builder." Also, print or type in the "Type of Work Performed" of Item III the following information relating to the subject amateur-built aircraft:

Aircraft Make _____

Model _____

Serial No. _____

Certification Date _____

When an applicant meets the certificate eligibility requirements, a Temporary Airman Certificate, FAA Form 8060-4, will be issued. Permanent certificates will be mailed to the holder of a Temporary Airman Certificate within 120 days of issuance.

PRIVILEGES AND LIMITATIONS

Holders of repairmen certificates may perform "condition inspection" only on specific aircraft built by the certificate holder. The aircraft will be identified by make, model, and serial number as shown on the repairman certificate.

SURRENDERED CERTIFICATE PROCEDURES

Repairmen certificates should be surrendered whenever the aircraft is destroyed or sold. However, in the latter situation, the repairman may elect to retain the certificate in order to perform condition inspections on the aircraft for the new owner. Surrendered certificates should be forwarded to the Mike Monroney Aeronautical Center, Airmen Certification Branch, AAC-260, P.O. Box 25082, Oklahoma City, Oklahoma 73125, with a brief statement of reasons for surrender.

No certificate may be issued unless a completed application form has been received (14 C.F.R. 65).

Form Approved OMB No. 04-R0085

DEPARTMENT OF TRANSPORTATION – FEDERAL AVIATION ADMINISTRATION

AIRMAN CERTIFICATE AND/OR RATING APPLICATION

☐ MECHANIC   ☒ REPAIRMAN   ☐ PARACHUTE RIGGER
   ☐ AIRFRAME   Experimental Aircraft Builder   ☐ SENIOR   ☐ MASTER
   ☐ POWERPLANT   *(Specify Rating)*   ☐ SEAT   ☐ CHEST
            ☐ BACK   ☐ LAP

APPLICATION FOR: ☒ ORIGINAL ISSUANCE   ☐ ADDED RATING

I. APPLICANT INFORMATION

A. NAME *(First, Middle, Last)*
Charles Mayer

B. SOCIAL SECURITY NO.	C. DOB *(Mo, Day, Yr.)*	D. HEIGHT	E. WEIGHT
134930521	3-21-43	72 IN.	175

F. HAIR	G. EYES	H. SEX	I. NATIONALITY
Black	Brown	M	USA

J. PLACE OF BIRTH:
Donor, Pennsylvania

K. PERMANENT MAILING ADDRESS NUMBER AND STREET, P.O. BOX, ETC.
1000 Beech Street
CITY, STATE, ZIP CODE
Oakton, Virginia 22100
COUNTY
Fairfax

L. HAVE YOU EVER HAD AN AIRMAN CERTIFICATE DENIED, SUSPENDED, OR REVOKED?
☒ NO
☐ YES → If "Yes," explain on an attached sheet keying to appropriate item number

M. DO YOU NOW OR HAVE YOU EVER HELD AN FAA AIRMAN CERTIFICATE?
☒ NO   ☐ YES
SPECIFY TYPE:

N. HAVE YOU EVER BEEN CONVICTED FOR VIOLATION OF ANY FEDERAL OR STATE STATUTES PERTAINING TO NARCOTIC DRUGS, MARIHUANA, AND DEPRESSANT OR STIMULANT DRUGS OR SUBSTANCES?   ☒ NO   ☐ YES →
DATE OF FINAL CONVICTION

II. CERTIFICATE OR RATING APPLIED FOR — ON BASIS OF —

☐ A. CIVIL EXPERIENCE   ☐ B. MILITARY EXPERIENCE   ☐ C. LETTER OF RECOMMENDATION FOR REPAIRMAN *(Attach copy)*

☐ D. GRADUATE OF APPROVED COURSE

(1) NAME AND LOCATION OF SCHOOL			
(2) SCHOOL NO.	(3) CURRICULUM FROM WHICH GRADUATED		(4) DATE

☐ E. STUDENT HAS MADE SATISFACTORY PROGRESS AND IS RECOMMENDED TO TAKE THE ORAL/PRACTICAL TEST (FAR 65.80)

(1) SCHOOL NAME	NO.	(2) SCHOOL OFFICIAL'S SIGNATURE

☐ F. SPECIAL AUTHORIZATION TO TAKE MECHANIC'S ORAL/PRACTICAL TEST (FAR 65.80)

(1) DATE AUTH.	(2) DATE AUTH. EXPIRES	(3) FAA INSPECTOR SIGNATURE	(4) FAA DIST. OFC.

A. MILITARY COMPETENCE OBTAINED IN →

(1) SERVICE	(2) RANK OR PAY LEVEL	(3) MILITARY SPECIALTY CODE

B. APPLICANTS OTHER THAN FAA CERTIFICATED SCHOOL GRADUATES, LIST EXPERIENCE RELATING TO CERTIFICATE AND RATING APPLIED FOR. *(Continue on separate sheet if more space is needed)*

III. RECORD OF EXPERIENCE

DATES—MONTH AND YEAR		EMPLOYER AND LOCATION	TYPE WORK PERFORMED
FROM	TO		
			Make - Mayer's Special
			Model - M-1
			Serial No. - No. 1
			Certification Date of Aircraft - December 1, 1978

C. PARACHUTE RIGGER APPLICANTS: INDICATE BY TYPE HOW MANY PARACHUTES PACKED →

SEAT	CHEST	BACK	LAP	FOR MASTER RATING ONLY	PACKED AS A—
					☐ SENIOR RIGGER ☐ MILITARY RIGGER

IV. APPLICANT'S CERTIFICATION

I CERTIFY THAT THE STATEMENTS BY ME ON THIS APPLICATION ARE TRUE

A. SIGNATURE *Charles Mayer*

B. DATE December 1, 1978

FOR FAA USE ONLY

Emp	reg	D.O.	seal	con	iss	Act	lev	TK	s.h.	Srch	e rte	RATING (1)	RATING (2)	RATING (3)	RATING (4)

LIMITATIONS

FAA Form 8610-2 (10-76)   SUPERSEDES FAA FORM 8310-2 AND FAA FORM 8000-30

INSPECTION TIPS — All amateur-built aircraft require an annual condition inspection, but there is this difference. If you built the aircraft, you should obtain a repairman certificate from the FAA. You would then be authorized to perform annual condition inspections for your own aircraft. If you did not build the aircraft, you may continue to perform whatever maintenance is necessary, however, each year you will have to arrange for an annual condition inspection which must be performed by a FAA certificated mechanic holding an airframe and powerplant rating or a FAA certificated and appropriately rated repair station, in accordance with Appendix D of FAR Part 43.

Whether you are authorized to perform your own annual condition inspection or not, you should develop a systematic inspection system to assure yourself that your airplane remains airworthy and in tip-top condition.

Utilizing a progressive maintenance and inspection concept, modified to suit your available time, permits you to give your undivided attention to each component and system in turn. A separate aircraft component or system can be inspected after a flying period without pulling the aircraft out of commission. This reduces the amount of work time you have to put into the effort for any given day and, somehow, the entire inspection seems easier to accomplish. You can, for example, divide the total inspection requirement into the following work sessions.

CLEAN IT FIRST — Begin with a thorough washing and cleaning of the entire aircraft. Even as you are accomplishing this chore, you will find yourself going over every inch of the aircraft visually as well. As you progress with the cleaning and washing, little problems may, on occasion, be noticed that can be adjusted or corrected immediately.

TAIL SURFACES —— Check for structural integrity, security of attachment, and general condition.

LANDING GEAR —— Jack the aircraft up and inspect the gear for play and wear. Repack wheel bearings and check the condition and adjustment of the brakes.

FUSELAGE —— Check its general condition and all attach points and components.

CONTROL SYSTEM — Inspect and trace the entire control system to and from each component. Lubricate bearings and hinges. Check the condition of all safeties.

PROPELLER —— Remove the spinner and retorque prop bolts. Dress out all rough spots and nicks in the blades. Examine the prop for defects.

ENGINE SECTION —— The inspection of the engine compartment is saved for last.

NOTE: Up to this point in the inspection process, you have probably reassured yourself that the wings and the rest of the aircraft will continue to perform as an integral structure during the next 12 months. Since the engine is also quite important in keeping you aloft, it would be well to devote a little extra attention to it.

If you changed oil a few flight hours back, you can skip that exercise. However, you probably planned an oil change to coincide with the inspection. If an oil change is due after that last flight, drain the oil sump while the engine oil temperature is still over 100 degrees F. For the annual, especially, you should remove and inspect the oil screen for excess scrap metal and sludge.

Don't forget to resafety the drain plug and to refill the engine with fresh oil. Don't go away without doing so . . . . you might forget.

Service all systems (battery, hydraulic, smoke, etc.). Clean the engine by removing all dirt and oil from its exterior surfaces. Note all sources of oil seepage and fuel stains. Then, decide if corrective action is necessary.

During this cleaning process, your eyes and hands will reveal much . . . . like leaks, loose brackets or electrical connections, binding controls, worn or cracked exhaust system parts, etc.

A major system deserving separate attention is the carburetor (injector), the air filter, and induction system. Also clean and service the gascolator.

While you're at it, you might run a compression check on all cylinders. In doing so, you can't help checking the spark plugs, can you?

A very important part of your annual engine compartment check should be to remove the cotter pins from the engine mount bolts and test-torque them. Refer to the engine manual for the recommended, detailed inspection requirements. Everybody should have an engine manual for the model installed.

One more thing . . . . Good flying, amigos.

Amateur Inspection Checklist

Aircraft Make_____ Model_____ Serial No._____

EXITS	Yes	No	Date	Inspector
1. Can aircraft be cleared rapidly in case of emergency?				
a. Are special precautions available during test period, such as jettisonable doors or canopy?				
b. If parachute is to be worn, does it clear all controls?				
BAGGAGE COMPARTMENT				
1. Are walls and floors of sufficient strength to withstand flight loads?				
a. Can anything escape from baggage compartment by accident?				
CABIN - COCKPIT				
1. Instruments				
a. Are all instruments functioning and accurate?				
b. Are all instruments marked, max pressures, temperatures, speeds?				
c. Are all vital instruments easily visible to pilot?				
2. Flight - Engine Controls				
a. Are all engine controls marked or easily identifiable?				
b. Are all engine controls smooth in operation, without excessive resistance and easily available to pilot?				
c. Are all flight controls arranged so that jamming by dropped gloves, etc. is impossible?				
3. Fuel Systems				
a. Are all gas valves easily reached by pilot?				
b. Are all gas valves marked ON, OFF, LEFT, RIGHT?				
c. Are all gas valves in such a position that accidental operation is impossible or guarde in such a way that accidental operation is impossible?				
4. Seats				
a. Are seats of sufficient strength for maximum flight loads contemplated?				
b. Does seat "flex" enough at any time to interfere with flight controls?				

CABIN - COCKPIT (Continued)	Yes	No	Date	Inspector
5. Safety Belts and Shoulder Harness				
a. Is installation and attachments of sufficient strength to meet 9G forward load minimums?				
b. Does attachment connect directly to primary structure?				
c. Are belts and harness in top condition?				
d. Is belt of correct size, that is, no long over-tongue?				
e. Is a separate belt and shoulder harness supplied for each occupant?				
6. Heating - Ventilation				
a. Is cabin or cockpit in negative pressure area and liable to suck in exhaust fumes?				
b. Is any provision made for ventilating cabin other than normal leakage?				
7. Windshield - Windows				
a. Are windshield and windows of recognized aeronautical materials?				
b. Is windshield braced against positive or negative pressures in flight, either by design or extra bracing?				

WING - TAIL SURFACES				
1. Fixed Surfaces				
a. Are all interior fastenings secured and/or safetied?				
b. Is interior properly weatherproofed?				
c. Have any mice been inside lately?				
2. Moveable Surfaces				
a. Are stops provided, either at wing or somewhere else in the control system?				
b. Are all hinge pins secured and safetied?				
c. Are all hinges and brackets sound?				
d. Is there any excessive play in hinges?				
e. Is there any excessive play in control cables or tubes?				
3. External Bracing				
a. Is the interior of all struts weather protected?				
b. Are all adjustable fittings locked, secured and safetied?				
c. Are struts undamaged by bends or dents?				

	Yes	No	Date	Inspector
WING - TAIL SURFACES (Continued)				
d. Are all wires serviceable with proper end fittings?				
4. Attach Fittings				
a. Are bolts of proper size installed?				
b. Are all bolts secured and safetied?				
c. Have all bolts been examined for wear?				
5. Flight Control Mechanism				
a. All cables and tubes unbroken or unbent & with proper end fittings?				
b. All control attachments secured and safetied?				
c. All pulleys free from interference & guarded?				
d. All torque tubes and bell cranks in good condition?				
e. No interference with fuselage or wing structure throughout full control travel?				
6. Fuel Tanks (See Fuselage Section Also)				
a. Are drains supplied at low point in tank when aircraft is in normal ground position?				
b. Fuel overflow drains clear of aircraft -no tendency for overflow to soak into aircraft structure?				
7. Landing Gear				
a. Properly lubricated?				
b. Proper oleo inflation?				
c. Shock cords or springs in good condition?				
d. All attach fittings uncracked and sound?				
e. All bolt holes not elongated?				
f. All attach bolts secured and safetied?				
g. Brake lines in good condition?				
h. Brakes operating properly?				
i. Correct hydraulic fluid in lines?				
j. Wheels uncracked?				
k. Tires unworn and properly inflated?				
l. Excessive side play in wheel bearings?				
FUSELAGE - HULL				
1. Structure				
a. All welds sound?				

FUSELAGE - HULL (Continued)	Yes	No	Date	Inspector
b. All tubing straight and uncracked?				
c. No rust or corrosion?				
d. All attach fittings sound, no cracks, elongation of holes or worn threads?				
e. All rivets properly installed?				
f. Inspection openings for all vital areas?				
g. Fuselage properly drained, that is, no built-in moisture traps?				
h. Firewall of proper fireproof material?				
2. Cover				
a. Properly attached?				
b. No tears, distortions, or abrasions?				
c. Any breaks or ruptures properly repaired?				
3. Control System				
a. Properly secured and safetied?				
b. Controls stops provided and adjusted?				
c. All fittings of proper thread and size?				
d. All pulleys of proper diameter for bends, proper size for cable, and guarded?				
e. All cable of proper size (1/8" min.) & condition?				
f. Any parts in system subject to rotation for any reason properly secured and safetied?				
g. Return springs on rudder pedals?				
h. No interference between any control part (cable, tube, or linkage) and any other part of the structure throughout full control movement?				
i. Adequate room for full control throw when aircraft is occupied?				
j. Controls arranged to minimize danger of blocking by foreign objects?				
k. Grip properly secured to control stick or wheel?				
4. Electrical System				
a. All grommets, particularly in firewall, snug fitting and in good condition?				
b. All wires of proper gauge, insulated, and secured?				
c. Wires do not rest on abrasive surfaces?				
d. Battery installation of sufficient strength?				
e. Battery properly ventilated and drained?				
f. No corrosion at or around battery or its vents?				
g. Fuses of adequate amperage?				
5. Fuel System - Tanks				
a. Drains properly located to discharge clear of aircraft?				
b. All outlets properly screened?				

AMATEUR INSPECTION CHECKLIST

FUSELAGE - HULL (Continued)	Yes	No	Date	Inspector
c. Breather inlets clear?				
d. Fuel shut-off valve installed?				
e. Fuel shut-off valve easily reached by pilot?				
f. All fuel lines of proper approved type?				
g. All fuel lines secured against vibration?				
h. Is tank located so that sufficient head is available in maximum climb with minimum fuel?				
i. Has tank sufficient expansion area?				
j. Any tank overflow discharge clear of hazardous areas on aircraft?				
k. Is tank support sufficient to meet strength requirements?				
l. Does tank clear surrounding structure?				
m. Do tank supports minimize strain and chafing?				

ENGINE & ENGINE COMPARTMENT				
1. Fuel System				
a. All lines of approved type?				
b. All strainers clean?				
c. All lines secured against vibration? Gascolator bowl at low point in system when aircaft is in normal ground position?				
d. Fuel drains operative?				
e. All connections properly tightened?				
2. Oil System				
a. All lines of approved type?				
b. All lines secured against vibration?				
c. Oil tank has no cracks or leaks?				
d. Tank properly secured and safetied?				
e. All plugs and strainers cleaned and safetied?				
3. Ignition - Electrical System				
a. All wiring proper type and gauge?				
b. All fastenings secured and safetied?				
c. Magnetos properly grounded?				
d. Spark plugs cleaned and undamaged?				
e. Spark plugs properly torqued?				
f. Engine grounded to airframe?				
g. Starter/generator secured?				
4. Exhaust Manifold				
a. Secured and safetied?				
b. All gaskets in good condition?				
c. All stacks in good condition - no cracks or rusted-out areas?				

ENGINE & ENGINE COMPARTMENT (Continued)	Yes	No	Date	Inspector
d. Carb heat and cabin heat muffs removed and manifold inspected?				
5. Controls				
a. All secured and safetied?				
b. No excessive play in any linkages?				
c. No interference between any control and the structure thoughout the full operating range?				
d. Carb heater gate open and close fully?				
6. Mount				
a. Secured and safetied?				
b. All joints inspected for cracks?				
c. Any bends in mount tubes?				
d. Bushings in good condition?				
7. Cowlings				
a. Secured and/or safetied?				
b. All latches or fastenings working properly?				
c. Any cracks properly checked or reinforced?				
d. Cowlings clean?				
8. Power Plant in General				
a. All necessary safeties, palnuts, locknuts, etc. in place?				
b. No fuel or oil leaks?				
c. All accessories secured and safetied?				

PROPELLER	Yes	No	Date	Inspector
1. Blades				
a. Laminations not separated?				
b. Breaks, scratches, nicks, tipping?				
c. Loose rivets in tipping?				
d. Drain holes in tip clear?				
2. Hub				
a. Any cracks or corrosion?				
b. Hub properly seated and safetied?				
3. Control Mechanism				
a. Oil leaks?				
b. Worn bearings?				
c. Secure?				

AMATEUR INSPECTION CHECKLIST

PROPELLER (Continued)	Yes	No	Date	Inspector
4. **Attachment**				
a. All bolt and nut threads undamaged?				
b. All bolts and nuts secured and safetied?				
5. **Spinner**				
a. Cracks?				
b. Properly secured?				
c. Is spinner chafing into prop?				

GENERAL

ALL BOLTS, WHEREVER POSSIBLE, HEAD UP AND FORWARD

1. All exterior fastening visible from cockpit or
    cabin should have safetied end toward pilot, wherever possible.

2. A complete walk-around inspection of the aircraft should be accomplished
    to check that every bolt visible on the exterior is secured and safetied.
    That there is no visible structural damage. That all inspection panels
    and covers are in place and attached. That all parts of the aircraft are
    in proper alignment.

DON'T FORGET TO PUT IN ENOUGH GAS PRIOR TO THAT FIRST FLIGHT - GROUND RUNNING
AND TAXI TESTS CAN USE UP A LOT MORE THAN YOU THINK!

OK - Kick the tires, add another coat of paint and AWAY WE GO.

COMMENT

INDEX

EAA Insurance Programs

EAA Insurance programs offer members aircraft hull insurance and liability coverage that is tailored to each person's needs, budget and the type of flying they do. There are special programs that offer expanded coverage that is available only to EAA members. Special discounts are offered to members who participate in EAA Chapter activities and/or the EAA Technical Counselor programs.

Other insurance programs which are available to EAA Members include Accidental Death and Dismemberment, Group Term Life Insurance and Major Medical Insurance.

For more information on EAA Insurance Programs call:
- EAA Aircraft and Ultralight Insurance Plan **1-800-638-8440**

- EAA Antique/Classic Insurance Plan **1-800-727-3823**

- EAA's International Aerobatic Club Insurance Plan **1-800-536-2011**

- EAA's Group Health, Life and Medical Insurance Plan **1-800-241-6103**

For more information on the EAA Aircraft Finance Program call

EAA Aircraft Finance Program

The EAA Aircraft Finance Program is designed to help EAA Members make their purchase of an aircraft, airplane kit or ultralight easier and more affordable. In addition, this plan can provide excellent refinancing for existing aircraft or financing for upgrades in aircraft equipment. The EAA Aircraft Finance Program is available to individual members, flying clubs, EAA Chapters, flight schools and partnerships.

Attractive interest rates, loan minimums of $10,000 and up to 15 year terms are all special features of the EAA Aircraft Finance Program.

For more information on the EAA Aircraft Finance Program call
1-800-851-1367

Easy to Reach:

The EAA Aviation Center is located off Hwy. 41 at the Hwy. 44 exit Oshkosh, WI — adjacent to Wittman Regional Airport.

Museum Hours:

Open Monday thru Saturday 8:30 a.m. to 5:00 p.m.
Sunday 11:00 a.m. to 5:00 p.m.

Visit the EAA Air Adventure Museum

Visit the world's largest, most modern sport aviation museum. Over 90 full size aircraft on display many rare, historically significant aircraft. Prototypes of some of sport aviation's most successful designs. See World War I fighters, antiques, classics, and business aircraft of the 30s — racers, experimental and aerobatic aircraft, ultralights and more! See exact replicas of the 1903 Wright "Flyer" and Lindbergh's "Spirit of St. Louis". View the impressive art and photo galleries, historical artifacts, audio-visual presentations and four unique theatres. Enjoy the barnstormer era that comes to life seasonally at the Pioneer Airport adjacent to the museum — and visit the new Eagle Hangar that honors the aviators of World War II and displays many of the famous aircraft flown in combat. Great gift shop too!

EAA AIR ADVENTURE MUSEUM™
OSHKOSH, WI

EAA AVIATION FOUNDATION

EAA Aviation Center • Oshkosh, WI 54903-3086 • 920-426-4800

START HERE!

Each month valuable information on a variety of technical subjects about designing, building or flying homebuilts, light aircraft or ultralights. EXPERIMENTER keeps you up to date on what's happening in sport aviation — what others are building — what new designs are being developed — building techniques for composite, wood, metal, tube or fabric structures — performance data — flight safety — and a wealth of regular features you'll find invaluable. Learn the right way from the experts.
Be sure to get EXPERIMENTER every month!

The "How To" Magazine for the Aircraft Builder

EAA MEMBERSHIP

Building on Success

One of the greatest tools that any aircraft builder can have is an EAA membership. EAA was built on the sharing of skills and knowledge. Its network of local area Chapters provides an outlet to meet with others who share the same dream. And EAA's Technical Counselor and Flight Advisor programs are extremely useful to those who are looking for information on airplane construction or restoration projects — along with advice on initial ground and test flights.

Building a better future for you and general aviation

EAA began in 1953 as a local club for homebuilders. Today, the design and construction of airplanes remain at the core of many EAA activities. As an EAA member, you'll have access to authoritative "how to"

technical manuals, videotapes and — most importantly — the invaluable "hands on" instruction offered at the annual EAA "OSHKOSH" Fly-In Convention.

If you're building an airplane, or if you're thinking about building an airplane, EAA is for you!

EAA members receive benefits designed especially for the interests and activities of aviation enthusiasts like you. Among a growing number of those benefits: 12 issues of *Sport Aviation* magazine, EAA's flagship publication; Low member rates to attend EAA Oshkosh and EAA Sun 'N Fun Fly-Ins; Free EAA local area Chapter directory (arrives with March *Sport Aviation* magazine); A "Voice in Washington" where EAA is the recognized leader in sport aviation issues, working to keep aviation accessible; Special EAA aircraft finance and insurance plans and much more!

Join EAA® - the Leader in Sport Aviation
We put the FUN in flying!